A HISTORY OF
AGRICULTURE
IN EUROPE AND AMERICA

A
HISTORY
OF
AGRICULTURE
IN EUROPE AND AMERICA

BY

NORMAN SCOTT BRIEN GRAS

Professor of Economic History
University of Minnesota

F. S. Crofts & Co., Publishers

New York

1925

Copyright, 1925,
F. S. CROFTS & CO., INC.

PRINTED IN U. S. A.

THE VAIL-BALLOU PRESS
BINGHAMTON AND NEW YORK

To

WILLIAM FERGUSON TAMBLYN

Teacher and Friend

PREFACE

This book is not a detailed outline of things discoverable in the history of agriculture. It is meant only to describe for general and collegiate use some of the more important developments in the history of rural life in Europe and in America. It aims at both historical and genetic treatment, that is, a description of the phenomena and a statement of the general evolutionary changes.

The survey of agriculture here presented is based on some direct observations, not a little research in the primary literary sources, and the study of secondary works. Although there is no book covering the same field from which this one could derive either inspiration or guidance, there are nevertheless a host of treatises and a great many scholars, young and old, without whose assistance, of course, this book could never have been written. From Professor Edwin F. Gay of Harvard University I received my earliest academic interest in the subject of agricultural history. In the collection of data and for the verification of references I am indebted to two research assistants, Miss Dorothy Fewell and especially Mrs. Helen P. Mudgett. Miss Henrietta Larson has kindly loaned me many of her notes on Minnesota agricultural history, taken from original sources. Mr. Herbert Kellar has been most generous in supplying journals and books from the McCormick agricultural library. Mr. F. K. Walter, and Miss Ina Firkins, and others of the Library of the University of Minnesota have been most helpful. I have had advice and information from such specialists in the general field of agriculture as Professor Andrew Boss, Professor W. H. Peters, Professor C. H. Eckles, and Professor J. D. Black, of the College of Agriculture, University of Minnesota. To Professor F. J. Alway, Professor W. F. Tamblyn, Professor A. C. Krey, Professor H. L. Gray, and Dr. Mildred L. Hartsough, I am greatly indebted for the reading of various sections or chapters of the manuscript. To

PREFACE

Professor Guy Stanton Ford, Dean of the Graduate School, University of Minnesota, I owe a special debt of gratitude for having read virtually all of the manuscript and for having made invaluable suggestions, both critical and constructive. To my wife, as often before, I owe the early appearance and present form of the book, which are due to her constant assistance in the preparation and revision of the manuscript.

N. S. B. G.

TABLE OF CONTENTS

PART I

EARLY AGRICULTURE

PART II

LATER AGRICULTURE IN EUROPE

PART III

AMERICAN AGRICULTURE

CONTENTS

CHAPTER I

GENERAL STAGES OF ECONOMIC DEVELOPMENT

CHAPTER II

THE EARLY STAGES OF AGRICULTURE

CONTENTS

CHAPTER III

ROMAN AGRARIAN HISTORY

xii

CONTENTS

CONTENTS

CHAPTER V

PEASANT REVOLTS

CONTENTS

CHAPTER VI

METROPOLITAN AND NATIONAL ECONOMY IN ENGLAND: THE ECONOMICS AND THE POLITICS OF MODERN AGRICULTURE

CONTENTS

CHAPTER VII

ENCLOSURES, CHIEFLY IN ENGLAND

CONTENTS

CHAPTER VIII

LATER STAGES OF AGRICULTURE AND THE PROBLEM OF SUBSISTENCE

CONTENTS

CHAPTER IX

THE AGRICULTURAL REVOLUTION, CHIEFLY IN ENGLAND

CONTENTS

CHAPTER X

THE PHYSIOCRATS
AGRICULTURE ENTHRONED IN FRANCE

CONTENTS

CHAPTER XI

HISTORY OF PROPERTY IN LAND

CONTENTS

CHAPTER XII

STAGES IN AMERICAN AGRICULTURE

CONTENTS

CHAPTER XIII
ANIMAL HUSBANDRY IN AMERICA

CHAPTER XIV
RURAL TYPES HISTORICALLY CONSIDERED

xxii

CONTENTS

CHAPTER XV

FACTORS IN AGRICULTURAL DEVELOPMENT

CONTENTS

CHAPTER XVI

RESULTS OF AGRICULTURAL DEVELOPMENT

xxiv

CONTENTS

ILLUSTRATIONS

A HISTORY OF
AGRICULTURE

CHAPTER I

GENERAL STAGES OF ECONOMIC DEVELOPMENT

1. COLLECTIONAL ECONOMY.[1] We are accustomed to think of agriculture as a basic form of production, indispensable to other economic activities and developing very early. There is no question, of course, about the fundamental position that agriculture occupies in our present existence, but at the same time there is no doubt that agriculture is relatively recent in its development. Historically, it is as old as Babylonian and Egyptian civilization, but genetically, or from the standpoint of evolution, it is a late arrival. We think of the first man, Adam, as a cultivator in the Garden of Eden. Scientific researches, however, indicate that long before the soil was cultivated, men obtained a living by simply collecting or seizing the things they needed.

Agriculture basic but recent

Like the lower animals, whom in many respects they resembled, early men hunted and fished, gathered fruits, moss, and tubers, seized eagerly upon such small animals as snakes and lizards, and even ate the insects that crawled beneath their feet. While much of the business of getting a living was simple, some of it, especially the trapping and killing of wild beasts, required great skill and ingenuity. Since the various operations involved the appropriation of what nature had provided, we may call the men of this early stage collectors, and their general system collectional economy.

Early man's means of livelihood

Because this primitive mode of production was relatively unorganized and unplanned, some scholars would deny that there was any economy at all. Economy means management, originally just house management. In its earliest forms it was simple, to be sure, but very real. That it was effective is indicated by the fact that it carried primitive man through a longer span of time and a wider space of growth and change

Economy

than any other system of which we now have knowledge. There is really no doubt, therefore, that we are justified in using the term collectional economy when speaking of the earliest economic stage, the one in which men collected the gifts of the world of nature and utilized them in their own crude way.

Man reflects nature

In these early days, of which we speak, man reflected nature, was indeed a part of nature to a much greater extent than at the present time. Man accepted her gifts, followed her laws. Yesterday he was full, to-day empty. In sunshine he was merry, in storm wretched and afraid. Life bore a terrible immediacy for him, with little thought of the future and none of the past. In the childhood of the human race the mind of man was fixed on the present. The individual was careless in the use of his time, destructive of material goods, and fearful of the dark and all that moved at night.

Examples of collectors

In our study of the history of the past and in the descriptions of nature-folk surviving at the present (or until recent years), we find many illustrations of collectional economy. At about the time of Christ and not far from the field of His activities, lived the locust-eaters. We are told by a contemporary that they were short in stature and in the span of life. To secure their favorite food, they built smudges in the ravines; and the smoke, mounting high, blinded the locusts as they flew, causing them to fall headlong into the ravine. There they were collected, pounded together with salt, and made into cakes ready to be eaten. About a century later, one German tribe was in the collectional stage, while others had passed upward in the scale of economic achievement. With herbs and game for food, skins for clothing, the earth for a bed, and arrows their supreme possession, they refused to delve or plow the soil. The wild Veddahs of Ceylon, now almost extinct, had no houses, finding shelter beneath a rock or the branches of a friendly tree. Of course, they never stopped to till the land. They lived on game, wild honey, and whatever else lay at hand. The Eskimos hunt, fish, and gather moss, berries, and roots. Their main reliance is the seal in the water and the reindeer on the land. These provide them with food and clothing, tents and weapons. Many of the North American Indians have been collectors, notably the fishing tribes of the Pacific Coast.

2. CULTURAL NOMADIC ECONOMY. When the collector began to cultivate plants and tend to animals, he took a step away from the old economy in the direction of the new. He had formerly just appropriated what nature had provided; in the new stage he undertook to improve upon her by cultivating her gifts systematically. Thus did he insure himself against the irregularities and the uncertainties of unplanned growth. The collector now becomes a herder and a gardener. Caring for flocks and herds and cultivating small plots of ground are the earliest economic cultures. Both of these activities are, of course, the distant progenitors of our modern agriculture. **First economic cultures**

Man's economic and social progress has always come through a conquest over nature. In the stage of collectional economy, man had used fire to improve on nature's gifts. He had cooked some of his food to make it more palatable and (unconsciously) more sanitary. Man had stored some of his food from season to season as an insurance against a time of poor hunting and fishing. He had fashioned himself weapons and tools to secure mastery in field and forest. In the new stage of cultural nomadic economy, he took up the rôle of cultivator. He learned to direct the lives of animals in order to derive more benefit from their existence, driving them hither and thither to good pastures and safe retreats, and guarding them both day and night from devouring beasts and plundering neighbors. Plant growth he came to guide, somewhat as does the farmer of the present day. He undertook to prepare the soil, place the plant where it would grow best, and fight its battles against the encroachment of rival growth and destructive birds. At such a time, weeds were born into man's life, as plants that give trouble and serve no useful purpose. **Man's conquest over nature**

In the earlier stage of collectional economy man had been nomadic, searching here and there for food and other supplies, and occasionally changing his abode as the fortunes of the chase or of war dictated. In the new stage of cultural nomadic economy man moved about from place to place in order to secure fresher and richer pastures or better patches of **Wandering** ground in which to plant his grain or vegetables. Fear also drove him from his old-time haunts. Sometimes it was fear of a powerful neighboring tribe or clan; sometimes it was sickness or vermin; and sometimes the dread of evil spirits. Whole groups of families moved with all their belongings to visit some sacred spot or village.

Old and new pursuits combined

Men of the cultural nomadic stage retained their fondness for hunting and fishing and still found it necessary to gather wild honey, berries, and herbs. At times food secured in this way was indispensable to their very existence. The cultural nomads, then, are distinguished by a combination of three major practices, collecting nature's gifts as before, moving about as in the earlier stage, and the new habit of cultivating systematically a large part of the things they needed.

Pastoral nomads

Apparently most peoples of the world have cultivated animals before plants. Some of the North African peoples recorded in history became herders of cattle and swine and keepers of sheep and goats. Thus did they provide milk, cheese, and flesh. From the hides of their animals they obtained leather and wool for clothing and tents. By means of oxen, cultural nomads dragged their carts and wagons over the plains. Sometimes horses, probably the last of important animals to be domesticated, swift-footed horses, bore the herders to the pastures and the warriors to the field of battle. So important was the horse for the nomad that its possession constituted a superclass, the mounted nomads of history. The simple nomad with no horse to enable him to sweep across the plains and then disappear as swiftly as he had come, plays little or no rôle in recorded history. The mounted nomad, however, has made for himself a place in the annals of more advanced peoples by the fierceness of his raids upon the borders and the persistency with which he has knocked at the very gates of the highest civilization of olden times.

Movements of pastoral nomads

More important than the plundering expeditions of these nomads are their movements in the pursuit of green pastures. Sometimes they locate on the mountain-sides which are rich in verdure while the valleys below are parched by a burning sun. Sometimes it is on the edge of a desert in which there is somewhere to be found a little pasture, not enough to last long but sufficient for a wandering flock or herd. Sometimes it is on the plains or steppes where pasture is plentiful and where there are no forests and few devastating beasts. Although the environment has been favorable, Australia and America have produced no purely pastoral peoples. In America were the llama, the vicuna, the guanaco, and the alpaca, all allied to the camel tribe. And there was also the peccary or wild pig. Some of these were indeed used in Central and South America, but on the wide plains of North America before the arrival of the white man, only the dog had been domesticated and it was rarely used for food. Men have speculated whether the bison of the plains would not have been herded and yoked in the new world as his kinsman, the buffalo, has been in the old.

While some pastoral nomads go merely up and down the mountains to secure satisfactory pasture for all seasons, others have to march long distances. Such have been the mounted nomads famous in the history of Asia, Europe, and North Africa, who with their horses or camels could cover vast stretches of territory, fishing, hunting, and plundering as they moved. The Kirghiz of southern Russia were accustomed to go a thousand miles northward to their summer pastures and as far back to their winter home. **Seasonal movements**

Pastoral nomads tended flocks and herds and cultivated the soil, but their work was not of a high order. The animals, small hardy beasts, were more ready for a long journey than for inspection on the market place. The cow gave enough milk to suckle her young. This might be used by man, but while good in quality was a miserable showing when compared with that of the better cattle of to-day. The male cattle were strong and tough, prized for their strength rather than the tenderness of their flesh. The life of the nomad little lent itself to careful feeding or selective breeding. Left to themselves, the animals developed those habits that enabled them to march long distances and reproduce their kind. Plant cultivation was similar to animal cultivation. The ground was scratched or dug, seeds were thrown into the soil, and then the **Quality of cultivation** crop was left to grow as best it might. While the people were roaming about, weeds and birds were active. That the yield was not large is, of course, to be expected. Perhaps there was compensation in the excellence of flavor which the better cultivated crops of to-day have at times lost. About the distribution of emphasis upon animals and plants we have but little information. Some peoples engaged in animal culture almost exclusively, but there was a tendency to develop some plant culture as the herdsmen found that they could supplement their other supplies by using their women and such slaves as they could capture to produce grain and gourds, pulse and vegetables.

Examples About 1600 years before the birth of Christ the Jews were pastoral nomads and about 1600 years after the time of Christ many North American Indians were found in that stage. Canadian Indians cultivated maize, but they could not be persuaded to tend their crops when tempted by the profit and the lure of fishing or hunting. It is significant, however, that the Indian did progress so far as to cultivate the soil. Such a fact is indicative of his capacity to advance, though his movement upward would doubtless be at the snail's pace. The Australian aborigine made a beginning at agriculture when in digging yams he returned the heads to the soil. At first this was doubtless by accident but later by plan, to produce another crop. Such planting, however, was followed by no hoeing, weeding, or tending of any kind. It was not agriculture as we know it, but a promise of agriculture.

General cultural attainments Food in the cultural nomadic stage, though not much, or perhaps any, more varied than at an earlier time, was more dependable. The grain grown and the cattle and sheep tended, were normally available for food, and the livestock provided the hides and wool used in the manufacture of clothing, tents, harness, and shields. Storage in this stage was an auxiliary to further production, in so far as seed was kept for the next season's crop and enough animals, even in direst need, were kept (that is, in effect, stored) for the annual breeding. The nomad was a great trader. He sold slaves, wool, hides, and some commodities made by hand. While the pastoral nomad might steal men to sell, the planting nomad would be glad to get extra women, as well as slaves, to do the drudgery of cultivating the soil.

3. SETTLED VILLAGE ECONOMY. The cultural nomads reluctantly settled upon the soil. A large clan or kinship group probably occupied several villages. A small one would make up but a single village. Thus from the first in at least a great many villages there was a strong kinship feeling and relationship.

Kinship settlement

The settled village was not a mere collection of houses. It was a group of persons closely knit together by blood relation, social intercourse, and economic co-operation. But the village was also an area of land, the use of which varied according to proximity of the houses and nature of the soil. Here was a meadow, there an arable field; here was the common pasture, there the waste land.

Village group and area

The process of settling down has been long drawn out. It has occupied, we may safely infer, at least ten thousand years of human effort, and is not yet complete. All tradition and such fragments of early history as we have, indicate that the earliest settlements of historic peoples took place in Egypt, Babylonia, and China, several thousands of years, B. C. The Greeks had already settled when the *Iliad* was composed, perhaps 1000, B. C. The traditional founding of the village which later became Rome was in 753, B. C. The Kelts (progenitors of the Britons, Welsh, and Irish) settled in about the fourth or fifth century, B. C., and from that time on to this, hardly a century has elapsed that has not witnessed the settlement of at least one important people. The illustration of most prominence in history is the prolonged wandering of the various German tribes in search of suitable lands, and their final residence in the territory now roughly bounded by Germany and some adjoining states. After the settlement of the Germans, came the wandering and finally the permanent location of the Slavic peoples—in Czecho-Slovakia, the Balkans, Poland, and Russia.

Process of settlement

In Asia and Africa nomadic peoples are still settling down. During the last two generations the Algerian nomads have

Settlement in Algeria

9

HISTORY OF AGRICULTURE

been gradually undertaking permanent occupation. The tent is giving way to the house. At first the house was simply a winter residence. During the summer the bulk of the nomads, or "Arabs," would go off in search of good pastures, leaving a few agricultural laborers to till the soil. Then slowly and reluctantly the whole people would settle down in a village with their houses clustering around their most valued possessions, their livestock.

Why Nomads settle down
The loss of livestock through disease or disaster is probably the most striking cause of settlement. Those groups that are deprived of their capital, that is, their sheep or cattle, have no alternative except to steal those of others or to adjust themselves to a humdrum agricultural existence which stands out in marked contrast to the ever changing life of the nomad. In other instances settlement may have come about through the failure of crops that were planted but not tended. Even early peoples could learn that a field carefully tended would feed more mouths than one neglected, or yield a larger amount of food than the same amount of land used as pasture.

Form of the village
Sometimes the village had a compact (nucleated) group of houses at or near the center of the village area. This compact form was convenient for defence and for animal culture. It facilitated co-operation in certain kinds of public works such as the banking up of the village nucleus in Egypt to keep back the flood waters of the Nile. Where defence was not an issue, and where plant culture was all important, however, we often find scattered villages. Sometimes the houses were strung along a single street, sometimes grouped in hamlets of a few households. Where there was only a small patch of usable land in this valley or in that, there were no villages at all, just scattered homesteads, as in parts of Scandinavia.

Phases of village economy
In the first phase of village economy men were free. No lord—nobleman, bishop, monastery, or temple—held a village as exclusive property. There were political chiefs who claimed and received allegiance and gifts or taxes, but there was in this phase no feudal nobility, no class of landed aristocracy collecting rents and demanding services from a whole village. In the second phase, however, such aristocracy did

10

exist, and, indeed, when the second phase was well developed there was no land, whether in village or hamlet, without a lord. The village in Europe became the manor and the population submerged in a social system which men later came to associate with degradation and from which they sought emancipation in revolts and revolutions.

In the first phase, that is, in the free village, the normal villagers were freemen. Some of these might own more land or cattle than their neighbors and be more skillful in war and be surrounded by a more numerous progeny and military band than the others. These might be called "nobles" or "barons," that is, men *par excellence,* but they belonged to the same class as the poorer freemen. Below the freemen, far below them in fact, were the slaves, not great in number, but still standing as visible evidence of what social and legal distinctions really were. The village as such was free, free from a lord, but some of the villagers were legally the property of the free villagers. Slaves had existed in the cultural nomadic stage, but were of much greater use in village economy because of the aversion of freemen to the continuous labor which settled agriculture involved. Some of the slaves had been captured in war, some won in gambling, some bought from nomadic slave owners, and some born as the children of slaves. While some of these slaves were attached to the person or household of their owners, others were left to cultivate land, partly for themselves and partly for their lords. Some slaves won their freedom and these *freedmen,* constituting a kind of third class, stood as clear proof of the possibility of changing one's status, as did those freshly enslaved by war or games of chance. It is easy to overemphasize slaves and freedmen. It was after all the freeman who was the typical citizen, gave color to village life, made the laws, and fought the battles.

Both the freemen of the village and the cultivation which they carried on in the early period of settlement reflected conditions of the earlier stage of cultural nomadism. Animal culture was still important, though plant culture came to occupy a larger and larger place in the life and work of the people. These two had developed separately in the nomadic stage, and

Freemen and slaves in the village

Animal and plant culture in the free village

11

they remained largely separate for a while in the first phase of village economy, but in time they were to be woven together into one series of integrated activities. While men were engaged in herding livestock and in carrying on war, women were busy cultivating the fields with more continuous labor than had been required of them in the nomadic stage. Sometimes indeed the men cut or burned down the trees on a plot of ground, leaving the actual cultivation solely to the women. Sometimes they aided the women in planting and harvesting also, but not in the care of the crops. Plant cultivation was primarily woman's occupation, unless it was perchance done by slaves, or by freemen who had lost all their cattle and consequently had no choice but to till the ground.

Probable system of cultivation

That part of the village area which was marked off for tillage was probably divided into compact family holdings. The share of each family would be little more than a garden, small in size, cultivated with a hoe or spade and not manured. The crops would vary with the soil and climate. There would be barley, rye, wheat, millet, beans, peas, and root crops, such as manioc and sweet potatoes in the warmer regions. There could be little thought of conserving the fertility of the soil so long as land was plentiful. When one section of the village area had been worked out or fouled with weeds, it was abandoned to the livestock or left entirely waste, and another part was set aside for the purposes of tillage. All in all, the practices of the settled village at first showed but little advance over the methods of the cultural nomadic stage, apart from the more continuous cultivation already considered.

Examples of early settled villages

Many peoples illustrate this first phase of village economy. The Kelts of Gaul at the time of Christ are a case in point. The women had been the agricultural laborers, but they were giving up field work to the men who were released from the duties of military service by the peace that Rome had imposed upon them. Much later (1190) their kinsmen in Wales are described as cultivating oats but depending largely on animal products, notably milk, cheese, butter, and flesh. Since the men were frequently engaged in conflicts, we may assume that much of the agricultural labor was performed by women.

12

Teutonic peoples, such as the Franks, Lombards, and Anglo-Saxons, also illustrate the first phase of village economy. Some of the North American Indians lived in settled villages. In this condition both the French and the English found them in the early years of settlement around the Great Lakes and in New England.

Doubtless immediately after settling down in permanent villages, sanitary conditions were very bad. The nomad had moved away from accumulations of filth which the settled villager could not flee from. In one way or another probably unconsciously, habits of more sanitary living were learned so that villages could increase in population, as in China to-day, without suffering much from their situation. **Health**

Some villages had peace, because nobody sought their infertile lands. Others came to enjoy peace through the very conquest that deprived them of their political independence. The conquerors of the villages protected them against further molestation. To be sure, this was near the close of the first phase of village economy, when the free village was giving way to the unfree or manorial village. **Peace**

The net result of better health and more peace was an increase in population. This left more men free to engage in tillage. The increase in peace left the male members of the community with less excuse for avoiding the cultivation of the soil. Thus did circumstances influence the course of agricultural history. The males of the village continued to tend the livestock and now they took over the labor in the field as well. This meant that the two operations would be integrated more than formerly. Cattle would be used to plow the soil, and perhaps to tramp in the seed, or to harrow the land. It was a long time, however, before land used for tillage was converted into pasture fields or meadows as a regular or systematic part of agriculture. **A higher type of agriculture**

All who have possessions are called upon at times to defend them. The collector has to fight for his hunting and fishing preserves and the cultural nomad for his pastures and cultivated fields. The settled villager is called upon to protect his house and fields as well as his livestock. To be dispossessed **The village and war** of his holding means to begin life over again. Unlike the collector or the cultural nomad, he cannot shift his area without great loss. The fact that he has improved the soil by more or less carefully preparing it leaves him vulnerable to a marked degree. Moreover, the villages are isolated and communication not convenient nor much practiced. Accordingly mobilization to resist attack is difficult. It is a matter of historical record that men in the first phase of village economy are open to easy conquest.

Conquest

When the village had been conquered, the victors generally, sooner or later, developed into a class of overlords. As such they protected and exploited the subjugated villagers. Where conquest by an alien people was avoided, it was usually by evolving an internal system of defence which usually resulted in the establishment of an aristocratic system of landlordism comparable to that imposed by foreign conquerors. It was, doubtless somewhat more palatable for the Germans to evolve their own aristocracy than for the English to be conquered by the Normans and the Irish by the Anglo-Normans.

Manor

The result of the forces at work was the manor or unfree village. With its birth the first phase of village economy was over. The formerly free villagers, to a greater or less extent according to circumstances which varied not a little, lost their freedom, not only as persons but as communities. They were no longer free to move about as they wished. They were compelled to attend the lord's court for justice in place of the old tribunals or resort to adjudication in case of dispute. The details of the organization of the manor and the story of its development will be dealt with elsewhere.[2]

Storage

The incoming of settled village economy meant much for production, for agriculture as we have seen and also for the storage of goods. The nomads had possessed little more than they could conveniently take with them. They had preserved meat by drying and smoking; and, of course, by herding their livestock they kept a supply of fresh meat always at hand. Their grain supplies, however, had to be hidden while they moved about. In the village stage the storage of grain, vegetables, and other commodities was relatively easy, because there was no movement. Granaries, high, dry, and commodious, could be erected—not for a season but for many years. The flesh of animals could be pickled in brine, which had been impossible at an earlier time because of the difficulty of carrying casks or other containers. The very settlement in one place had made much of this pickling necessary, because the restricted amount of pasture and winter fodder forced the villager to slaughter most of his animals, in fact all not needed for labor or for breeding.

The settled village was the scene of many kinds of productive activities. The collective pursuits continued as the fishing, berrying, and hunting seasons came around. The economic cultures, both plant and animal, were practiced and developed. Manufacture was carried over from the earlier stages. Women (and sometimes men) were skilled in making cloth and clothing; men in tanning hides and making shoes, shields, and other leather wares, as well as in the mining, smelting, and beating of metals. Either sex might engage in the fashioning of pots and pitchers out of clay. Specialization in industrial employments increased considerably. House building required carpenters, masons, and thatchers, who, while still cultivators, served their fellows as their particular aptitudes and experiences permitted.

Village industries

As we have seen, the nomad had been a trader. Probably settlement, bringing less mobility and greater isolation, was immediately accompanied by some decline in the exchange of goods. Gradually, however, a new type of trade in market places developed, which has never died out, though it has now declined in relative importance. Sacred spots were set aside for trade, it might be on the village boundaries, or in the village center. Some villages came to be known for their markets to which neighbors went for the exchange of goods. Gods were invented to protect the markets. Special peace was bestowed upon them, and those going to buy or sell were given a peculiar status. Original producer met original producer; and grain was exchanged for cattle, seed grain for seed grain, or manufactured goods for raw products. In pure village economy there were probably no merchants, that is, no persons

Village trade

making a living exclusively by trade. On the whole, village economy was more characterized by the lack of trade than by such measure of it as did exist.

Lack of individualism In settled village economy, we must note in conclusion, the individual was submerged in the group. Cultivation was carried on in accordance with the decision of the group. The restricted area of the village hemmed the individual in, while previous stages had provided ample space and opportunity for him to be alone, to get away, if only for a short time. Of course, the lack of individualism was an objective reality. The villager probably was not conscious of what he had never enjoyed. The village was his world of operations and of ideas, of work and play, of economic and social existence. In such a village co-operative agriculture was easy and natural. The individualism found in the make-up of the modern English, French, and American farmer had not yet been born.

Village and town contrasted 4. TOWN ECONOMY. While co-operation characterized production in village economy, individualism gradually developed in the economic and cultural activities of the town. While the village was largely unfortified, the town practically always had some effective means of defence. While the village was primarily agricultural, the town was primarily commercial.

Village and town trade In the village, trade had been carried on between peasant and peasant, that is, between original producer and original producer. In the town, on the other hand, there were specialized traders who gained their livelihood almost solely from the exchange of goods. The town was born when stores were established. The village had possessed a market place; the town had its market or markets but also its stores. Trade took place not one day a week but every day, except on festal occasions.

Location of towns Since the town found its existence in trade, it had to be favorably located for transportation and communication, while the village in the days of settled village economy was more concerned with soil fertility than with convenience of location. If the town was very well situated, it grew large and prosperous. If on a river, it might be at the head of navigation,

16

like Basel, at a good landing place, like London, or at the confluence of two rivers, like Coblenz, the town was likely to grow large and wealthy. A town situated on the sea shore and having a good riding for ships, especially if located at the mouth of a river stretching far inland, had great advantages. Examples come from every age and continent. Among them are Carthage and Rome, Lisbon and Dantzig, Shanghai and New York.

Every town, large or small, had as its tributary area the surrounding territory, large in one case small in another. A common area of influence would have a diameter of about ten or twenty miles, in which a score or more of villages (or hundreds of scattered homesteads) would be located. The relationship between the town and the neighboring villages was one of mutual dependence. Each village sold to the town its grain and livestock, its manufactures such as beer, butter, coarse cloth, and wooden utensils. The town sold to the villages wares from other villages and from towns both near and far, and, as time went on, some of its own goods of finer craftsmanship than was usually found in the country. Thus it is evident that town economy is an organization of producers and consumers who supply their needs through the agency of the town. *The town's tributary area*

In social evolution, as distinct from history, there are no dates. Towns arose when some villages developed merchants with stores. In other words, when conditions were ripe, village economy gave way to town economy. The story is, however, not so simple or straightforward as this, for towns could in turn slip back into villages in individual cases and over vast areas. Indeed thousands of years of human history have been occupied with such a see-saw. As towns have arisen, history has recorded a dawning civilization; as they have declined, history has recorded a general social decay or has itself disappeared. And so we have layer after layer of civilization in the distant past, that is, eras of town economy, interspersed with eras of unrecorded village economy. *Time of town beginnings*

The village might become a town while still free or after it had become a manor. The older the town the more likely it *Which villages became towns* was to grow out of a free village. Freedom was necessary to town prosperity, but it mattered little whether it came from a community that had never lost its liberty or one newly enfranchised by a manorial lord. The lord, whether he was bishop or abbot, count or king, granted charters of freedom to villages that were developing into towns, because of the financial advantage that accrued to him. He did this partly because of the price paid for the charter, partly because of the greater yearly fee paid to him, and partly from the greater general prosperity that arose out of the new economic activities.

Town agriculture
The early town was commercial and the later town both commercial and industrial. But all the time, the town retained some agriculture which it had inherited from the village, out of which it had sprung. Beyond the town walls lay the town pastures and arable fields. It is clear that the townsmen supplied themselves with some part of their foodstuffs and other raw products. Some of the houses had cow stalls, granaries, and wine presses. The town as a whole often had its shepherd. In late medieval towns we find laws against the practice of allowing pigs to wander about the street. In one English town exception was made in favor of a sow with her young. The small agricultural holdings of townsmen, the fish ponds, the family cow tended by the common cowherd, the sty of pigs, and the doorstep chickens all did their part to support the citizens. And yet there would be plenty of supplies that the town would have to secure from the country.

Mutual dependence
One of the outstanding features of town economy is the mutual dependence of town and countryside. Neither could do without the other. If there was no country, the town would disappear. If the town decayed, town economy would revert to village economy. In the first phase of town economy, the town was prepared to furnish the rural district with raw materials from distant parts or with manufactured goods secured from other lands. The country stood ready to supply raw materials such as wool, hides, flax, lumber and a few manufactured goods, such as charcoal, yarn, turpentine, and wooden utensils, and food in great plenty such as grain, wine, olive oil, cheese, butter, and beer. In the second phase of

town economy, the town continued to buy from the country as before, but supplied one additional kind of commodity. It sold to the country industrial products of its own manufacture, as we have noted above.

From the first the country has been a place of manufacture, though in our time this kind of production is fast waning in some nations. During the first phase of town economy, when the town was a commercial center, the country was the chief seat of industry. When the town developed industrial skill in the second phase of its history, however, the country looked to the town for the finer products of manufacture. This was to be expected, because townsmen specialized while countrymen did not. The urban artisan did little besides practise his craft, whether the weaving of cloth or the making of shoes. His craft gild set up high standards of workmanship that elevated the whole trade. And these standards were enforced by gild officials. So severe did the gild restrictions bear upon the ambitious artisan-employer, that he found it profitable to move into the country where gilds and regulations had no existence, and also where wages were lower. Accordingly we find a new industrial movement of great import. Townsmen not only purchased the rougher manufactured products of the country, but employed peasants to make goods as they wished the goods to be made—of finer quality than countrymen themselves demanded and of a size and weight suitable for prospective customers. This was probably of great economic and therefore social advantage, especially to the poorer peasants who had little or no land. It enabled the country to support a larger population with a greater measure of well-being. To us of the twentieth century a similar development may be profitable and even necessary.

The same advantage that Europe enjoyed in town economy was early perceived in America. Towns provided an exchange of goods and services that enabled many persons to specialize as their aptitudes indicated they should. European settlers in America had left towns in the old world and quickly felt the need of them in the new. Sometimes scholars speak of independent domestic economy, an organization based on

Rural industries

Towns in America

the household, as prevailing in America. For a short time this was doubtless true, especially in frontier days, whether east or west of the Alleghanies. Nevertheless, soon a town sprang up in almost every neighborhood, a town that performed essentially the same services as towns in Europe and elsewhere. Some of them had walls and fortresses; a few even had gilds—notably Boston and Philadelphia in early days, and restrictive trade regulations too, such as the English towns had imposed. In time these combined to build highways, canals, and railroads which benefited towns in general but which put an end to town economy. The new alignment involved the dominance of one thriving town or city over the others, and the incoming of a new economic system. In short, metropolitan (or large-city) economy came to supplant town economy in the new world as in the old.[3]

Cultural attainments of the town Civilization is often identified with the town. Within its walls were sheltered artists and philosophers, teachers and orators, men of letters and men of science. Religion became somewhat more rational. Individualism was displayed in art and in business, in thought and in action; but it was accompanied by worldliness which the countryman, indeed, identifies with the town. Although elaborate means of sanitation were perfected, dreadful diseases were engendered in spite of all precautions. Organized charities existed in the town, but their capacity was taxed by the numerous poor. In short, the material and higher culture of the town was progressive, as was the agriculture which made it possible, but the greater attainments of modern times had to wait for a later stage, metropolitan economy, which will be separately considered elsewhere.

5. SUGGESTIONS FOR FURTHER STUDY

1. Why was agriculture not the first kind of production undertaken by man? Does agriculture involve any initial difficulties, physical and psychological?

2. What are the essential differences between agriculture and collectional economic pursuits?

3. What examples of collectional economy do we find to-day in the general business of farming?

4. Which cultural nomads cultivated the soil, which did not?

5. Why was the cultivation of the soil at the hands of cultural nomads not very successful?

6. Do you know of any instances of cultural nomadism among the whites of the United States? Consider especially the ranges of the west a few years ago.

7. Why were the people who settled down in permanent villages more favorably situated for making progress in agriculture?

8. Do you identify the rise of systematic agriculture in the third stage with the incoming of hard slavish work?

9. Was the villager engaged in agriculture to the exclusion of manufacture?

10. Could the town have developed without an agricultural background?

11. Which probably had the greater effect upon agriculture, the growth of the manor or the rise of town economy?

12. What effect did the rise of towns have upon the psychology of the cultivator? Consider the plan of Michael Gaismayr, a reformer in the Peasant Revolt in Germany, 1524–1525, that henceforth there should be no towns, just villages, so that in the future no man should think himself any better than his neighbor.

13. Is it true that "the first farmer was the first man, and [that] all historic nobility rests on the possession and use of land," as Emerson says in his essay on *Farming* (1858)?

For further suggestions, see the notes below.

6. NOTES TO CHAPTER I

1. Practically all of this chapter is based upon the author's book called *An Introduction to Economic History* (1922), chs. I–IV.

2. See below, ch. III, sect. 69, p. 26; ch. IV, sects. 24–30, pp. 78–96.

3. See below, ch. VI, sect. 41, pp. 130–145; and ch. XV, sect. 108, pp. 369–373.

CHAPTER II

THE EARLY STAGES OF AGRICULTURE

Optimism 7. TWO ATTITUDES TOWARD AGRICULTURE. Having outlined general economic development roughly down to the Modern Period, we may now note the chief changes in agricultural methods. Many people have no interest in the technique of cultivation or even the life of the farmer; on the other hand, some individuals, less numerous, have been enthusiastic. Kings and poets, generals and philosophers, statesmen and scholars have written about agriculture, and, writing with warmth and enthusiasm, have bred contagion until there has come to be a literary glamor about the business of the cultivator. And no wonder, for there is independence in his life, health in his work, and satisfaction in accumulating a harvest of plenty. The gods of heaven above, the sprites of the woods, and mother earth herself are the helpers of the tiller of the fields.[1] We may well pardon the zeal that lauds the producer of man's necessities and that is inspired by the idyllic beauty of rural life with its expanse of skies, evening shades, and fresh morning dew, but fairness to facts bids us see the other side.

Pessimism By some it is thought that he whose lonely steps follow the monotonous plow, who sleeps on a pallet of straw, who may in long periods of years face starvation through the ravages of war or the unkindness of weather, is really no happy figure, for his hands are hard, his back bent, his mind furrowed by each day's toil.

> "Bowed by the weight of centuries he leans
>   Upon his hoe and gazes on the ground,
> The emptiness of ages in his face,
>   And on his back the burden of the world."[2]

22

His life is a continuous fight against relentless enemies. The worm has taken part of the crop; the hippopotamus has helped himself; mice have swarmed into the fields; locusts have descended from heaven; and the sparrows have had their fill. Such was the complaint made long ago by the cultivator in the fertile land of Egypt.[3] These two attitudes toward rural existence are both true, in time and place. We might analyse conditions and find them fair in America, black in China, promising in Canada, discouraging in France. But our concern is with the changes in rural methods throughout the ages. This leads us, not into minute studies of a past century's special problems, but into a consideration of the general steps that the cultivator has taken upward in the march of progress.[4]

8. NATURAL HUSBANDRY. In the halting course of agricultural progress, we may discern six stages.[5] The first three of these, natural husbandry, the fallow system, and legume rotation, will be dealt with here; the last three (field-grass husbandry, scientific rotation, and specialized intensive) are reserved for later treatment. In natural husbandry, the earliest of all, man just sows and reaps, performs a minimum of operations, and is content with a scanty yield. He gives no thought to the effect on land. The nomad in his wandering **Nomadic** throws seed upon the half-worked soil, and late returning in the year reaps a meagre harvest. When he finds his reward too scant, he chooses a new plot, and so goes on cropping till chance or want leads him elsewhere.[6] And the settled villager **In the set-** does but little better, except more thoroughly to exhaust the **tled village** fertility of the soil. At first he keeps plant culture quite separate from animal culture. While woman plants, tends, and harvests the crops, unaided by beasts of burden, man hunts, fishes, and cares for flocks and herds. When man takes over most of both plant and animal culture, there is at least a partial combination of the two. He uses his oxen to tread in the grain, or to drag a plow. And when the grain is harvested, the animals are turned upon the stubble to graze—and also to manure the land for the next crop.[7]

From the first stage to the last, the problem of the cultivator is fertility, how to obtain new fertile lands or how to keep

23

old lands productive. In this stage nature is substantially the only provider of fertility. The abandonment of the soil to nature is the universal practice of the primitive agriculturist. There is no thought of an efficient rotation of crops, no idea of alternating tillage with carefully prepared pastures, and no **Nature's** notion of a naked-fallow system.[8] To an extent not found in **part** any subsequent type, nature is the determining factor. For nature not only maintains a continuous supply of heat and moisture during the growing season, but provides the elements of which artless man has robbed the soil.

Among the In one form or another this first stage of agriculture is **early Ger-** found among early peoples and in modern nations of backward **mans** habits. Shortly after the time of Christ, it prevailed among

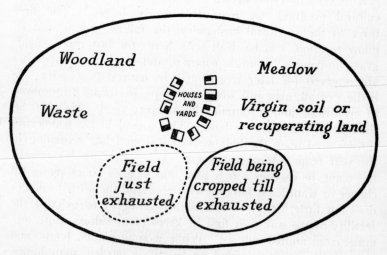

SIMPLIFIED PLAN OF A GERMAN VILLAGE SHOWING THE SYSTEM OF NATURAL HUSBANDRY, ABOUT A. D., 98.

the Germans,[9] as late as the eighteenth century it was found in Scotland, in the nineteenth century in Ireland,[10] and in the twentieth in America.[11]

Scotland In Scotland the land was divided into infield and outfield, one near the village group of houses and the other at a greater distance. The infield was used year after year for barley or oats.[12] On the outfield one-half of the land was cropped for about three years, usually under oats, and then left to rest for the same period. During the time of rest, it might be used somewhat as pasture, but the rank growth of weeds made this far from profitable. The only advance over the early German system to be found on the Scottish outfield was that abandonment took place after a shorter period of cultivation and more regularly.[13] Indeed we may regard such a type as transitional, showing advance over the early irregular abandonment, and yet falling short of the more effective method of dealing with the idle land, found in the following stage.

18th century

9. NAKED-FALLOW STAGE. To offset the evils of natural husbandry, a system of naked fallow was adopted.[14] Every year, according to a plan that finally became quite definite, some part of the soil was given special treatment. On this part no seed was planted. The stubble and weeds might be allowed to grow for a few months, and used for a while especially as sheep pasture, but in due time they were plowed under and the land dragged or harrowed. The advantages of such a system were numerous. The land would be cleared of many weeds which for one year at least would not be allowed to come to seed. The soil would likewise be rid of some parasites which had fed upon the main crops. Heavy lands would be put into good tilth, that is, the large clods would be broken up, thus allowing the more complete decay of old plants and the growth of new ones. Lighter and unfertile soils would be grateful for the addition of vegetable matter, which came from the plowing in of stubble and weeds. And lands suffering from inadequate rainfall would rejoice at the greater moisture, for the accumulations of two years instead of only one would be available for the next crop. This was made possible chiefly by curtailing transpiration (evaporation through plants), and to some extent by the checking of capillary attraction which takes place on hard uncultivated lands, but which is prevented by the formation of a veneer of loose earth, through which the water passes with difficulty on the way to the surface.[15]

Advantages of fallowing

25

Fallow system in the settled village

The naked-fallow system generally arises in settled village economy.[16]   After a people have fouled or exhausted part of the best soil and especially the land nearest to their dwellings, they try the naked-fallow system.   The impending danger of an exhausted food supply would be hastened by an increase in population within the village itself and by the establishment of new villages on the borders of the old ones.   Setting aside such a large part of the available land for tillage as was involved in the fallow system, probably indicated a greater dependence upon grain and less on livestock and birds and beasts of the chase.   How the discovery of the fallow system was made, we do not know.   Probably it was a social contribution made more or less by the group wherever the demand for food was increasing and the supply was threatened.

Fallowing among the Ancients

Naked fallowing is not to be confused with the mere resting of the land, which was found in the preceding stage of agriculture.   It is not clear whether the sabbatical year of the Old Testament refers to a genuine fallowing system, or, as seems more likely, merely to a religious observance involving freedom from agricultural labor.   Certainly among the Hebrews it was decreed that every seventh year was to be a period of rest for grain and vines.   There was to be no planting and no pruning, only the gathering of the spontaneous growth.[17] This was clearly not the resting of one-seventh of the land each year, but the resting of all the land every seventh year, a very uneconomical and hazardous procedure.   It is not now possible to discover how common the naked-fallow system was among the ancients.   It may have existed in Greece,[18] and it probably occurred in Italy in the days of village economy and early town economy.   When Roman literature affords us detailed information about conditions in Italy, however, agriculture had already developed into the next stage, the one associated, as we shall see,[19] with later town economy and with Rome at its height.

In Germany

The outstanding historic example of the naked-fallow system is found among the Teutonic peoples at least from the eighth century [20] onwards, in some places till the end of the middle ages [21] and elsewhere until the nineteenth century.[22]

26

And in Russia the system still exists. The land of the German village was divided ordinarily into three large sections called fields. One was devoted to winter grain, a second to spring grain, and the third to fallow. And these were annually rotated so that normally all of the arable land was fallowed every third year. For centuries the fallow land seems to have been plowed but once as fallow, and then again, of course, when the year of fallowing was over as a preparation for the winter crops of wheat or rye. In the thirteenth century the fallow, at least in parts of Germany and in England, was plowed a second time in the summer. In other words, the fallow was given three plowings in all.

It happens that we have considerable information about the **In England** fallow system of medieval England. Probably arising in the free village, it was clearly evident in the later unfree or manorial village. About the manorial village, or manor,[23] we know a good deal [24] because of the existence of special treatises on the subject,[25] and because of the numerous surveys describing the resources of the manor, and the accounts showing its actual operation. We know about its houses and how they were usually huddled together. We know about the social classes, free and servile groups, the courts for settling disputes and recording transfers of land, the officials from the bailiff of the manor to the humble swineherd, the lord's special properties, his manor house and grange, his fish-pond, mill, and demesne lands. Our main interest at this point, however, lies in the division of the lands and the uses to which they were put.

Each cottage had attached to it a garden, which was used **Separate** as the cottager thought fit. It was removed entirely from the **lands** general management of village agriculture. The arable fields lay on every hand and constituted, with the meadow, the most valuable part of the land. The permanent meadow, belonging to the village jointly, often lay along a stream or river, where the spring overflow both watered and fertilized the ground. The permanent pastures were variously located as soil and topography served. Usually near the confines were the waste lands, from which supplies of wood for building and heating were secured, in which pigs were commonly pastured, and out

27

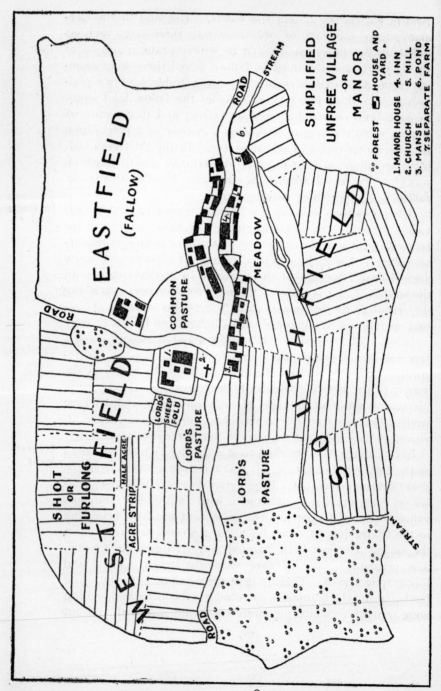

SIMPLIFIED
UNFREE VILLAGE
OR
MANOR

°° FOREST ▣ HOUSE AND YARD ▪

1. MANOR HOUSE   4. INN
2. CHURCH   5. MILL
3. MANSE   6. POND
                 7. SEPARATE FARM

EASTFIELD
(FALLOW)

SOUTH FIELD

WEST FIELD

SHOT OR FURLONG

HALE ACRE

ACRE STRIP

LORDS SHEEP FOLD

LORD'S PASTURE

LORD'S PASTURE

COMMON PASTURE

MEADOW

ROAD

STREAM

ROAD

ROAD

STREAM

of which were occasionally carved new holdings for various special purposes. On one English manor the number of acres of arable was about 1,600, meadow 109, and pasture only 33.[26] 1086 Of course extra winter pasture, such as it was, was available on the stubble of the arable and meadow lands. The most noteworthy feature is that all these divisions, garden, arable, meadow, pastures, and waste, were normally permanently separated. The arable land, for instance, did not cease to be arable in order to become meadow or pasture. Thus the system was rigid where it should have been flexible, permanent where at times it should have been changeable.

The arable land was divided into two large fields or sections in the two-field system, and into three in the three-field system. Each was divided into "shots" of from 12 to 20 acres, more or less, and each shot was made up of acre or half-acre strips belonging to the villagers, or villagers and lord. Each of the village families possessed, say, thirty of these strips divided more or less equally among the two or three fields,[27] and widely scattered over each field. Accordingly, each had land that was of all kinds, good, bad, and indifferent.

Divisions of arable land

In the case of the two-field system, one half of the land was left fallow, while the other half was planted with winter and spring grain. In the three-field system, as noted above, one field was fallow, the second planted with winter grain (wheat or rye), and the third with a spring crop (barley, oats, beans, peas, vetches). We know little about the relation between the two- and three-field systems, whether in most countries they existed side by side, or whether the one tended to supplant the other. No doubt the two- and three-field systems, however, were found together in England.[28] The two-field system would be better on heavy soils and in districts of restricted rainfall; the three-field system more adapted to light lands and to areas of greater moisture. In certain districts, however, it was doubtless of little moment, as far as the soil was concerned, which system prevailed. In such cases we cannot help noting that the three-field system was superior or seemed to be superior from the standpoint of cultivation. The two-field system with its larger amount of fallow twice-plowed, required

Two- and three-field types of fallow

more labor than the three-field system with a smaller percentage of fallow also to be plowed twice.[29]

Distribution of labor

The fallow system, whether of the two- or three-field type, provided for a fairly equitable distribution of labor through at least a part of the year. The spring-grain field was plowed in April. In June the fallow was given its first plowing, and in July a second. About September, after the harvest was over, the field for winter grain was plowed, harrowed, and sown. Then in October or November, according to some local practices, the field to be sown next year to spring grain, was given a preliminary plowing.

Equality and co-operation

The particular type of fallowing here described, the two- and three-field systems, had the further advantages of maintaining a feeling of equality among the villagers and of providing for the co-operation of the cultivators. All concerned, either directly in primary assemblies or indirectly in the meeting of elders, probably helped to decide when and how the land was to be used, when plowed, and when harvested. And they assisted each other by providing, one a horse, one a plow, another so much labor in working the lord's land, or in cultivating the holdings of an unfortunate fellow villager.

Defects

But these same two- and three-field systems had serious defects. The community regulations left little initiative to the single cultivator, who, it must be admitted, probably was capable of very little initiative. They caused daily losses in labor by forcing the cultivator to go long distances to work. The practice of allowing livestock to pasture on the stubble of the arable land prevented the cultivation of root crops in the fields, for these do not ripen until after the beginning of pasturing on the open fields. These root crops, long grown, of course, in the garden, would have helped provide a more efficient rotation of crops than existed. And when new crops were planned, such as flax, hemp, madder, saffron, and later, potatoes, they had to be cultivated somewhat apart from the other crops, so rigid was the old system. And yet the old system actually could be adapted, for these new crops did gradually creep in. The fallow system in itself, whether of the two- or three-field type or some other variety, was wasteful of good land, for this fallow land was left to recuperate instead of being re-vitalized by a profitable crop carefully planned and rotated with other crops. In other words, the system involved a rotation that turned on fallow instead of on restorative crops. The livestock were half starved, only slightly housed, and often lost sight of for weeks. Few were maintained at any time, and largely because of lack of hay and roots still fewer could be kept over winter. Accordingly there was a minimum of animal manure. And what did exist was deposited for the most part on the permanent pastures where it was not so much needed and where it was in some cases harmful. The gross yield under this system was slight (about six or eight bushels of wheat per acre in medieval England) and for centuries showed no change.

10. LEGUME-ROTATION STAGE: ILLUSTRATED CHIEFLY BY ROMAN AGRICULTURE. The naked fallow gives way to the legume-rotation system.[30] Instead of maintaining the fertility of the soil by the old fallowing device, a fertilizing crop is used, not casually on a few acres, as beans, peas, vetches, lupine, and alfalfa (lucerne). These crops are rotated with the non-leguminous wheat, rye, barley, and oats. The legume is a nitrogen producer; the non-legume is a nitrogen consumer. Hence one supplements the other in a very satisfactory manner. *Fertilizing crop*

There are two types of legume rotation. One is the partial and the other the complete legume rotation. In the former only part of the old fallow is replaced by legumes. In the latter all the fallow is supplanted by legume. One is but the logical extension of the other: The partial legume rotation, as the term indicates, is made up, not only of the usual cereals and the old fallow (at least in part), but of a legume crop in addition and on a par with the other units. The resulting rotation would be somewhat as follows: fallow, wheat, beans, oats. Or it may be expressed more generally as naked fallow, winter grain, *legume,* and spring grain. It is obvious that, since the amount of fallow or unplanted land was less than formerly, and since a leguminous restorative crop occupied an important place, considerable advance was made. *Two types of legume rotation*

Arises in
advanced
town econ-
omy
Legume rotation is found developing in those lands where town economy has already made some progress, that is, where severe demands have already been put upon the land, notably near the towns themselves. We have two illustrations of this development. One occurs in the ancient world when, long be-
Ancient
world
fore the time of Christ, legumes came into common use,[31] in Greece and in Italy, and probably continued for a few centuries. Then with the decline of the power of Rome and the
4th cent. f.
retrogression of society from town to village economy, there was probably, in the Western Empire at least, a general return to the naked-fallow system. As village economy in turn gradually gave way to town economy, however, the naked-fallow system was found increasingly inadequate, and finally when town economy had again been well developed and when the pressure of town demands had been felt by the soil, the
Modern
world
legume rotation was again introduced—in Germany and England,[32] and elsewhere, as a kind of four-field system of
16th cent.
husbandry.

We may very well illustrate the legume rotation from the history of Roman agriculture, but before proceeding to the details of cultivation, let us provide ourselves with a general
Signifi-
cance of
Roman ag-
riculture
background for such a subject. Roman agriculture was not so unique an attainment as Roman law, but it is of the greatest interest in the field of ancient economic history. Rome developed the stage of legume rotation, as we shall see in detail. Rome managed to evolve a complexity of agrarian problems as difficult for us to unravel as for contemporaries to solve.[33] Almost the earliest literary enterprise of the Romans was the composition of agricultural treatises, a fact which in itself indicates the importance of land cultivation in their economic life.

234-149,
B. C.
The earliest of the Roman compilers was Cato the Censor. Although he seems to have had no Roman prototype to furnish information, he made not a little use of earlier Greeks.
Roman ag-
ricultural
writers
He was a lawyer, soldier, administrator, and cultivator. Vigorous in mind and active in body, he sat down at ripe old age to record the agricultural situation of his day.[34] Although his Latin is inelegant, his attitude oracular, and his arrange-

ment erratic, he leaves impressions that are clear cut. To
Cato, farmers are the best citizens and soldiers. The farmer
should have first-hand knowledge of his estates, even though
he leave the actual control in the hands of bailiff and slaves.
The farmer's business, he thought, was to sell the maximum
and buy the minimum. Olive oil, wine, cattle, sheep, and
worthless slaves who were sick and old, were to be disposed
of at the best price obtainable. He gives advice as to the
cultivation of the soil and the care of livestock. About a
century after Cato's brief treatise was written, Varro composed a much longer commentary. Scholar, statesman, gen- **About 50,**
tleman farmer, and friend of Cæsar, at the age of eighty-four **B. C.**
he had to his credit almost as many books as years. For writ- **116–27,**
ing on agriculture he had prepared himself by actual experi- **B. C.**
ence, by a study of the past, and by considerable travel. The
first part of his treatise deals with the tillage of grain, legumes, olive trees, and grapevines. The second is devoted to
the raising of the larger stock, such as cattle, sheep, goats,
pigs, asses, and horses. The third includes the smaller animals, peacocks, pigeons, geese, ducks, rabbits, snails, bees, and
fish.[35] It seemed to Varro that Italian agriculture was a great
success, though not without its faults. Whether that was
strictly true of the agriculture of his day, it certainly was true
of his own commentary. In style, arrangement, and fullness,
it is a great improvement over Cato. After Varro, came
Columella with his twelve books on agriculture,[36] bulking **A. D., first**
much larger than Varro's but on the whole less valuable. La- **century**
ter still Palladius put together fourteen books on the same subject. He was but one of several who wrote on agriculture **Perhaps A.**
by copying or paraphrasing those who had gone before.[37] **D., 4th cen-**
There were other commentators writing in Latin, perhaps **tury**
many others, whose works are either lost or unimportant.

The Romans grew wheat, spelt, and barley, but not rye at **Roman ag-**
all, and not oats till late in their history. They used milk and **ricultural**
the cheese made from it, but they ate no butter and little beef. **products**
Of small animals, such as rabbits, and of fowl generally, they
were very fond. Grapes were not widely grown in the early
period, but after they came into favor for the making of wine, **2nd cen-**
tury, B. C.

vineyards multiplied very rapidly. Rice and Indian corn were introduced in modern times. Of the larger kind of livestock there were about all the varieties known to us today. Oxen were valued for plowing and asses for carriage and use in the mills. Fodder of various kinds and apparently of excellent quality, was grown for the livestock.

We cannot discover the precise effectiveness of Roman agriculture. The best cultivators used animal manure and later marl as well. Two or three plowings were thought to be worth while, also the burning of the stubble and cross-plowing. The instruments of husbandry, such as the harrow and the plow, were very crude. Labor-saving devices, such as the header or reaper, had appeared in Gaul but not in Italy. The result was that in Italy the yield was commonly as low as four times the seed planted, but in certain districts much higher, over eight times in Sicily and over ten in Tuscany.[38]

Although the relatively poor results of Roman agriculture may have come from such divers sources as the use of slaves, negligence in applying manure, clumsy machinery, and neglect of seed, nevertheless, much is to be ascribed to bad rotations. The first three stages were probably all in existence at about the time of Christ. Natural husbandry, or continuous cropping, is found, though not in a very serious form,[39] or in particularly rich districts, such as Campania.[40] The naked-fallow system probably was used by the backward cultivators, especially by those in the more out-of-the-way districts of Italy. The Roman agricultural writers, doubtless describing the more advanced practices, clearly indicate the existence of the third stage, legume rotation.

The emphasis on the legumes in Varro, Pliny, and Columella, is significant. A typical rotation, probably the most common, was made up of fallow, grain, and legume.[41] This is the well-known Virgilian system of cultivation described in the *Georgics* of Rome's most esteemed poet, whose works were never lost and presumably never ceased to be read. The influence of such a work was doubtless great. Virgilian agriculture may be best presented as the poet describes it, nevertheless paraphrased and abbreviated. After harvest, let the

Quality of cultivation

Crop management

Both types of legume rotation in Roman Italy

Partial legume

30, B. C.

34

fallow fields (*novales*) lie at rest in succeeding years (*alternis*), and let the resting land harden with mould. Then, where you have reaped the legume with shaking pod, the vetch and the lupine, sow your wheat (or spelt, *far*). Flax, oats, and poppies burn the land. Labor is made easy by rotation (*alternis*), but that fact should not deter you from scattering manure upon dry soil and ashes on exhausted fields. It is profitable to burn the stubble on barren soils, to break the clods with rakes (or mattocks, *rastri*), to harrow the land, and to plow a second time right across the first furrows. Seed is treated with nitre and lees of oil, and specially chosen too, but without success, unless selected by hand.[42]

It is to be expected that the Romans would take the obvious step of eliminating the fallow altogether. In introducing the legume as a field crop, they encroached on the fallow. To substitute legume for the whole of it was to be expected. In other words, this involved the cultivation and planting of the whole of the hitherto naked fallow, so that legumes and cereals would alternate. We find this system set forth in Pliny, though not with much emphasis. He tells us of the alternation of spelt and beans.[43] This addition to the amount of leguminous crops is explained by the increasing usefulness which men found in legumes. They might be simply plowed into the soil while green, regenerating the land by adding to its humus, by building up its nitrogen content, and by increasing the number of bacteria favorable to plant growth in the following year. Sometimes the seed of the legume was used as food for man or fodder for livestock, while the rest of the plant was plowed into the soil.[44]

Complete legume type

In the Middle Ages legumes such as beans, peas, and vetches were planted in the fields and fed to man or beast. The amount, however, was slight. I have found instances in English villages of lords using some of their separate fields in this way, while their tenants were still cultivating according to the old naked-fallow system. Whether legumes gradually grew in importance during the Middle Ages is difficult to determine, though the amount of beans and peas, entering into foreign and domestic trade as the Middle Ages drew to a close

Legume rotation in the Middle Ages

16th cent.

35

and the early Modern Period began, seems to have increased, at least in England. It is safe to say that, as far as medieval Europe as a whole is concerned, the highest step of progress was a partial legume rotation, though here and there, as in Flanders,[45] special investigation might unearth a more complete utilization of legumes as a substitute for fallow.

Literary tradition

One of the attainments of Roman agriculture, apart from the rotation of crops, was a literary tradition. Just as Latin prose literature took its beginning in agricultural commentary, so did it occupy itself at a late date and even to the end with that subject.[46] The extent to which such treatises were influential is indicated by the number of manuscripts that existed in the Middle Ages, by the copying of passages by medieval writers, such as Petrus Crescentius,[47] by the early printed editions (1472–1549), and the numerous translations into modern European languages. The influence of the literary tradition seems to have been felt in three different parts, in Italy itself, in the Saracenic lands, and in north and western Europe.[48] To what extent it actually influenced the development of agriculture in medieval and modern Europe is a question not likely to be solved. One may plausibly argue that the influence was slight, because in the Middle Ages the agricultural system was less advanced than the Roman, and in the early Modern Period, when progress was made, it was not in accordance with any well-developed Roman prototype.

1230–1307

Brief description

11. FIELD-GRASS HUSBANDRY, CHIEFLY IN THE EARLY MODERN PERIOD. In field-grass husbandry [49] all kinds of land (arable, pasture, meadow, waste) were at last thrown together for common treatment. A fixed idea has up to this time run through the systems of cultivation, that the different kinds of fields should be kept separate. This notion seems to reflect the piecemeal development of agriculture. But all that is at last over and forgotten. There is but one use now and that is the alternation of cereals and field grass, a dry and a green crop. This system is sometimes called convertible husbandry because of this very conversion or alternation of uses. Of course, it is not to be assumed that a field sown one year with field grass was sown the very next with a cereal. A crop such as rye

grass or other artificial grass would ordinarily stand for two or three years, it might be for six or seven or more, though the danger of a rank growth in the latter case would be great.

The kind of agriculture found in this stage is called field-grass husbandry because of the important position of field grass in the system of cultivation. In so far as the field grass is leguminous, it resembles the previous stage of legume rotation. But some of the grasses are not legumes at all, as is indicated in the following convenient analysis of crops.

Kinds of crops

LEGUMES AND NON-LEGUMES

Legumes:
1. Pulse crops: beans, peas, vetches, cowpea, chick-peas
2. Field grass (artificial grass): alfalfa, trefoil, clover

Non-Legumes:
1. Dry crops (true grasses): wheat, rye, barley, oats, maize
2. Field grass (green crops, artificial grass): rye grass, fescue, timothy

Thus it is obvious that this stage is more than a mere extension of legume rotation. The integral crop of field grass may not be a legume at all, and, as has been seen, the new system calls for a merging of arable and non-arable land. In such a system the fallow either disappears or is used more sparingly than previously.[50]

To a large extent the Romans kept plant and animal cultivation separate.[51] The pastures and meadows were meant to be permanent, that is, they were not alternated with the ordinary tilled crops. Still we find a significant exception. A field of lucerne was expected to yield from four to six crops of hay a year and to last for ten years.[52] This seems to imply that at the end of the tenth year, the meadow would be plowed up for other purposes. It was said by one Roman writer that if a meadow could not be put into good condition by the scattering of fresh seed and the application of ashes on the mossy spots, then and only then, was it to be plowed up and other crops planted for a few years. As an emergency measure, hay or grass on the one hand was to be alternated with turnips

Field-grass husbandry appears in the ancient world

(or beans), grain, and tares on the other hand. Then the field was to be ready for use again as a meadow.[53] If this had become a common practice, the Romans, that is, the ancient Italians, would have anticipated modern Europe by about sixteen centuries.

Medieval retrogression

The Italians of ancient days apparently commonly practised the naked-fallow system, made some headway in legume rotation, and adopted the field-grass system as a mere emergency measure. It seems that all that they attained in the stage of legume rotation was lost when Rome declined and town economy reverted to the more primitive organization of village economy. With town economy went legume rotation and in their places we have village economy and the naked-fallow system. The details of such a change in technique are not known to us. Later, when the Middle Ages were well along, towns were re-born and in due time, they attained proportions and cultural heights known in the days of ancient Rome. Then the system of legume rotation began to develop again but soon gave way to field-grass husbandry, doubtless partly in answer to the same need of replenishing a soil hard put to it to maintain its fertility in the face of urban demands.

The historic occurrence of field-grass husbandry is relatively late in history. It is found developing in England in the sixteenth century or earlier,[54] in central and northern German lands somewhat later,[55] and in northwestern France. It is specially applicable to moist temperate climates where the growth of sward is quick though not excessive.

Enclosures and field-grass husbandry

This new kind of agriculture could most easily be introduced by persons holding definite blocks of land. It was difficult to apply it on lands divided into strips, as under the two- or three-field system. Accordingly, there was a tendency to consolidate and to enclose scattered acres so that a cultivator might use the new system of field-grass husbandry. The enclosure movement in sixteenth century England helped somewhat to prepare the way for this kind of cultivation.[56]

Advantages of field-grass husbandry

The advantages of the new agriculture were far-reaching. As has been noted, the fallow entirely disappeared, except on the heaviest and poorest soils. All the crops were used for

	1st. Field	2nd. Field	3rd. Field	4th. Field	5th. Field
First year	Pasture (Field + grass)	Meadow	Oats	Wheat	Barley

	1st. Field	2nd. Field	3rd. Field	4th. Field	5th. Field
Second year	Barley	Pasture (Field + grass)	Meadow	Oats	Wheat

	1st. Field	2nd. Field	3rd. Field	4th. Field	5th. Field
Third year	Wheat	Barley	Pasture (Field + grass)	Meadow	Oats

SIMPLIFIED DIAGRAM SHOWING A TYPE OF FIELD-GRASS HUSBANDRY ON ENCLOSED HOLDINGS (FIVE FIELDS IN YEARLY ROTATION, TWO IN FIELD GRASS AND THREE IN CEREALS. ONLY THREE YEARS OF THE FIVE-YEAR CYCLE SHOWN).

food or fodder, none just plowed in as a concession to a disordered and hungry soil. More animals were provided for than in previous systems, both in summer and in winter. Accordingly there was an unprecedented supply of wool and hides for the growing industries, and an unwonted abundance of meat, so that the poor were no longer restricted to pork but could enjoy, more or less frequently, the luxury of beef and mutton. While formerly much manure had been lost by grazing livestock on permanent pastures, now this was all made available for the cereal crops that followed the grass and hay. Of course it is true that cattle had been turned on to the stubble of arable lands and meadows in earlier systems, both to feed and to fertilize the ground, still this was but for a short period (in the winter chiefly) and, because of the scant pick-ings, the practice yielded but little manure for the soil. Greatest among the contributions of this system, then, are the restoration and partial maintenance of the fertility of the land by alternate cropping and pasturing.

Maintaining soil fertility

Keeping the land fit has been a difficult task. Egypt has succeeded throughout the ages, largely by means of the continued bounty of the Nile. Campania, in southern Italy, was a land of plenty in ancient times [57] and has remained so up to this day. But just to the north, Latium, the cradle of the Latin race, once a fertile land of small farmers, later a stretch of large plantations, is now an arid waste. Sicily, Sardinia, and the Carthaginian district of North Africa, were once world-famed granaries, but what are they now? The causes of soil depletion are complicated and require special consideration; but in this connection we may stress the question of a proper system of conservation of fertility. Simkhovitch has put it very pointedly in his essay on "Hay and History.[58] According to his theory, hay might have restored the soils of the ancient world, might have prevented the surface deposits from being thinned and washed away into the rivers and streams, and accordingly might have preserved the forest and the farm. Of course, along side of hay should be put pasture, and the whole issue should be broadened to include the legumes in general. If the nations of the ancient world, threatened with soil depletion under the naked-fallow system, had adopted legume and field-grass cultivation, they might have been saved, according to the theory. The general idea is a good one, the application somewhat uncertain.

China

China presents a case of great interest to the historian of agriculture. We may well fear to generalize about a land having such diversity of soil and climate, but the parts have much in common. There are no pasture lands in China proper, no milk, butter, or cheese worth speaking of. The only animals of importance are the pig, the water buffalo used for plowing, and fowl. This is very curious in a land, the inhabitants of which were once probably cultural nomads. After a period of natural husbandry, the Chinese probably adopted a naked-fallow system [59] and reached the stage of legume rotation.[60]   And the rank and file of small farmers never got beyond this type, though the larger holders did, if they followed the advice of a wise agricultural writer of about the time of Christ.[61]   Doubtless the great growth of population in periods of peace would have finally exhausted the soil, had it not been for the intensive cultivation adopted under the system of legume rotation.   The Chinese farmer labors long and hard; he gets two or three crops a year, where the climate is favorable; he uses irrigation and drainage on a large scale; he puts upon the soil every ounce of manure, vegetable, animal, and human, that he can procure; he cultivates two or more crops together; and he packs his fields so tightly that his farm resembles the scales of a fish.[62]   It is not hay that has kept the soil from depletion, for there is little of it in China.   It is not legumes alone, but the intelligent intensive system of cultivation that has kept that country from exhaustion.   Unfortunately these have not saved her from famine, but that is another matter—chiefly of inclement weather.

The legume rotation supplanted or threatened to supplant the naked-fallow system, in China and elsewhere, when demand put pressure on supply.   A similar pressure made legume rotation give way to field-grass husbandry.   The increased demand came, not from within the village, as when natural husbandry gave way to the naked fallow, but from the outside as village economy gave way to town economy.   The commercial town demanded foodstuffs from the village; and later the industrial town required raw materials for its manufactures.   Accordingly the villagers were compelled to produce a larger surplus than before and at the same time maintain the fertility of the soil.   This was accomplished by the invention and adoption of the legume rotation.   Other things being equal, it took place first in those villages near rivers and seacoasts or otherwise within easy reach of town markets.   In many places it came not rapidly but slowly.   If the adjustments had been more rapid and complete, indeed, much greater rural progress would have resulted.   Catering to the town market meant a money income, a larger share of worldly goods, more luxuries, and greater opportunity to pur-

Legume rotation and then field-grass husbandry arise in town economy

chase freedom from serfdom where it existed, and a better tenure of land, usually the substitution of money rents for services.[63]

Economic accomplishments

12. EARLY RURAL PROGRESS. In these early stages of agricultural development, all the way from natural husbandry to the field-grass system, man learned to construct implements which, though clumsy, were fairly effective. Instead of the hoe, he came to use the plow. Instead of a limb of a tree, he learned to use a wooden harrow with iron teeth. The husbandman came to know the value of barnyard manure and other fertilizers, though we cannot tell how far he actually made use of them. He was aware that seed should be procured from other estates than his own, and that he should select the largest and finest specimens for planting. Gradually the countryman learned to survey his holdings with a fair degree of accuracy, or to employ persons specially trained to do that work, the *agrimensores* of Roman days and the surveyors of sixteenth century England. Accounts came to be kept by the larger holders of land, those employing bailiffs and laborers to do the work. As we have seen, improvements were made in the management of crops by more complete and continuous use of the soil and by a better rotation. In a sense, the climax of economic advance was reached in the rise of a town marketing system. A surplus of products was available to feed the men of the town. In this way those who lived within walled centers were able to engage in non-agricultural pursuits, such as trade, manufacture, arts, and sciences. With the income from his products sold in the town, the farmer could buy the services of townsmen. We can appreciate the significance of all this when we remember that there had been a time, before the town was born, when the farmer had to turn aside from his fields to make whatever manufactured wares he needed, and had in most cases to be his own family physician and surgeon as well as veterinary. But now an agriculturist could command the time and skill of a town carpenter, fuller, or physician.[64]

Other material accomplishments

Most of the material advance of the peasant was on the economic side. Along with homemade shoes and homespun

42

clothes, there were the finer wares of town manufacture, at least among the more prosperous peasants. The occasional purchase of foreign dried fruit or trivial article of adornment gave greater variety to country life. The houses of the poorer tillers of the soil were still wretched enough, but the owners of large estates built homes of elegance and ease. In our modern emphasis on the poor and the downtrodden, we cannot help noting that the pigeon-holes of the Roman slaves sleeping tier on tier and the hovels of the squatters on waste lands were almost equally repulsive.

Work on the soil is hard and exacting. We do not expect it to lead to the highest attainments, but we find some progress. The roads leading to town centers were avenues of relief for those not fitted for agriculture. Sons and brothers living in towns and entertaining country cousins not only gained by the association with simpler minds but themselves imparted gentler ways and more refined tastes which could hardly fail to influence the countryside. Because of the existence of town walls and of lordly castles, it was possible for the peasant to flee before an invading host and save not only some of his belongings but his own life and his wife's honor. For the farmer who had large herds of cattle, sheep, goats, and horses, or for the cultivator with valuable vineyards, olive groves, or fruit orchards, such a refuge was not sufficient. Only a state that was strong enough to keep the enemy away from the boundaries was of any service to such semi-capitalistic enterprisers. For a few, the masters of slaves, the owners of rented estates, or the lords of villages, there was leisure for the higher things of life. Not only was there time and occasion to write treatises on agriculture and the management of estates, but there was opportunity to collect and read books from the town, to buy and enjoy pottery and statuettes from distant lands, and to summon and entertain friends from the town or near-by mansions. This was a selfish enjoyment of the world's delights, but it was also the necessary patronage for higher things. To be a gentleman farmer, an appreciative scholar, and an orthodox worshipper, has values which pass current even in our day. The Roman

Non-material accomplishments

43

senator, the English gentleman and lord, the Teutonic knight, and the Prussian Junker, all derived not only much of their sustenance but most of their character from their rural background.

Short-comings It would have no meaning to condemn the life and accomplishments of the early peasants for not developing a system of education. It is a fact, however, that opportunities of formal instruction were confined to rural temples and monasteries or to urban institutions. The application of capital and skilled management was not extensive during the early stages. The rich man might spend enormous sums on stocking cattle ranches and the powerful lord might employ many officials to supervise his rural enterprise and collect his land rents, but the amount of capital and of management that went into an acre of ground was comparatively slight. Inequality of possession and opportunity was the price a people often had to pay for security and culture, but the frequent upheavals of rural society show that it was not always willingly paid. Dependence on the town for a market and for cultural inspiration was as promising as warm rains and gentle showers; but when the town weakened and decayed, the country had no avenue of escape from the disaster involved. This is, however, as much a criticism of town economy as it is a statement of rural weakness. Many of these shortcomings will appear in the study of both Roman and medieval agrarian history, dealt with in the following chapters.

13. Suggestions for Further Study

1. See the articles, Agriculture in the *Encyclopædia Britannica* (11th ed.) and *Landwirtschaft* in *Wörterbuch der Volkswirtschaft*.
2. For single-volume histories of English agriculture, see R. E. Prothero's *English Farming, Past and Present* (1912, 1922), and W. H. R. Curtler's *A Short History of English Agriculture* (1909).
3. What economic cultures are there besides agriculture?
4. Enumerate the advantages and disadvantages of each stage.
5. Determine as far as possible the time and the circumstances of the introduction of each stage in some one European country.

6. With which stage do you identify the agriculture of early North American Indians?

7. If you were a farmer, what method of cultivation would you adopt? Why?

8. What is the method of cultivation with which you are most familiar in your district? Does it fit into one of the stages or types here set forth?

9. Are the three-field system, the naked-fallow system, and manorial agriculture the same?

10. Which is the most appropriate term, open-field system, two- (or three-) field system, or naked fallow? Keep in mind the use of fallow in countries where the above-mentioned field systems did not prevail.

11. Some regard the permanent separation of arable and non-arable (meadow and pasture) as the distinguishing mark of the agriculture found on the manor (our naked-fallow system). Others emphasise the combination of the arable and the non-arable through the pasturing of cattle on the stubble. Compare these views with the one embodied in the term naked-fallow system.

12. Compare the use of permanent pastures and meadows with collectional economy. Compare also natural husbandry with collectional economy as to exhaustion.

13. What is the difference between (a) permanent and alternating pastures, (b) meadow and pasture, (c) pasturing and soiling, and (d) naked and cultivated fallows?

14. Compile statistics of fallow for England, France, and Rumania. Ready reference may be made to the *Stateman's Year-Book*. In France the amount of fallow in 1789 has been placed at 10,000,000 hectares, about 100 years later at 3,644,000. L. Schöne, *Histoire de la Population Française* (1893), p. 405.

15. Describe and appraise the following types of fallow: (a) naked, black, or bare (whether neglected or clean), (b) green, and (c) cultivated or bastard. What are the respective advantages of summer, autumn, and winter fallows? Consult agricultural dictionaries or technical treatises.

16. For some of the most significant parts of Cato's treatise, see *Roman Farm Management* by a Virginia Farmer (New York, 1913), pp. 19–47.

17. A scholarly translation is available in *Varro on Farming* by L. Storr-Best (1912). Read especially pp. 1–59, 63–69, 81–83, 92–106, 119–120, 121–125, 239–257.

18. For Virgilian agriculture, see the *Georgics* of Virgil (trans. by T. C. Williams, 1915). Virgilian agriculture is regarded as a fallow system, but is it really a naked fallow or a partial legume?

19. Columella's treatise on agriculture has been translated into

English (e. g. as *Husbandry,* 1745). See especially, bks. I and II.

20. C. Daubeny's *Lectures on Roman Husbandry* (1857) are still worth while reading. It is a paraphrase of Cato, Varro, and Columella.

21. Parts of Pliny's *Natural History* may be read with profit, for example, bk. XVIII, chs. 1–43, 47–55 (in the trans. by J. Bostock and H. T. Riley, vol. IV, 1856, pp. 1–54, 60–72).

22. See T. Mommsen, *The History of Rome* (trans. by W. P. Dickson, 1891), vol. I, pp. 139–140; 246–258; vol. II, pp. 430–448.

23. Correlate the development of legume rotation with the growth of towns and improved methods of transportation.

24. Which was the more intensive the two-field or the three-field system? Explain.

25. Was the naked-fallow system (for example, the three-field type), intensive or extensive agriculture? Which from the stand-point of labor, management, and capital combined?

For further references, see the notes below.

14. Notes to Chapter II

1. Cf. Varro in *Roman Farm Management* (1913), p. 53.
2. Edwin Markham, *The Man with the Hoe* (1899), p. 15.
3. A. Erman, *Life in Ancient Egypt* (1885, 1894), p. 445.
4. Such an outline sketch of the development of agriculture as is found in this chapter is no substitute for the careful study of local conditions at different times. Variations will be found in great plenty and perhaps so many that some features of the outline will have to be changed.
5. The six stages in the history of agriculture are based largely on the work of Hanssen, Roscher, Hahn, Mucke, Meitzen, and Von Inama-Sternegg. Further study, however, has pointed the way to changes both in emphasis and in terminology, primarily in order to increase the scope of application. What these stages are will be apparent from the text. Those of Roscher (*Nationalökonomik des Ackerbaues,* 1859, 1903, pp. 32–33, 106 f.) may be set forth at this point:

   a. Hoe culture (*Hackbau*)
   b. Burning husbandry (*Brennwirtschaft*) Wild field-grass husbandry (*wilde Feldgraswirt-schaft*) } Our natural husbandry
   c. Two- and three-field system (*Zwei-und Dreifeldersystem*) (Open-field system)
   d. Field-grass husbandry (*Feldgraswirtschaft*)
   e. Rotation of crops (*Fruchtwechselwirtschaft*)
   f. Garden culture (*Gartenbau*)

6. See above, ch. I, sect. 2, pp. 5 f.

7. See below, ch. IV, sect. 27, p. 90.

8. See below, ch. II, sect. 9.

9. C. Tacitus, *Germania* (98, A. D., ch. 26); G. Hanssen, *Agrarhistorische Abhandlungen* (1880), vol. I, pp. 125–131.

10. See below, ch. VIII, sect. 54, pp. 185–186.

11. See below, ch. XII, sect. 85, pp. 285 f.

12. The infield was treated in this way, usually without any alleviating crop, such as peas or clover. The wonder is that after a long period of continuous cultivation, there was any yield at all. Perhaps there would have been none, had it not been for frequent manurings and the practice of leaving a long stubble to be yearly plowed into the soil as fertilizer. Both of these practices were condemned as favorable to the growth of weeds. In the case of this infield, as we find it in the eighteenth century, there was a slight tendency in the direction of intensive agriculture, in so far as manure was used. But there is no evidence of a general intensive system, in which large doses of labor, capital, and management were applied to small units.

13. See *An Essay on Ways and Means for Inclosing, Fallowing, Planting, . . . , Scotland* (1729), p. 62; *The Scots Farmer*, vol. I (1773), pp. 21, 66, 182–183, 400.

14. E. g. *Zwei-und-Dreifelder-system,* and *Körnerwirtschaft.* T. von der Goltz, *Agrarwesen und Agrarpolitik* (1904), p. 26; G Hanssen, *Agrarhistorische Abhandlungen* (1880), vol. I, pp. 152 f.

15. From the standpoint of accumulated moisture it was doubtful practice to use the fallow system in England and other lands of considerable precipitation. In the dry sections of America, fallowing with frequent plowing is a device to conserve the moisture.

16. See above, ch. I, sect. 3, pp. 9 f.

17. Bible, Leviticus, ch. XXV.

18. Cf. Theophrastus, *Enquiry into Plants* (trans. by Sir A. Hort, 1916), vol. II, p. 179; The Economist in *The Works of Xenophon* (trans. by H. G. Dakyns, 1897), p. 281.

19. See below, ch. II, sect. 10. p. 32.

20. The earliest evidence of a three-field system seems to be from Upper Germany, 771, A. D. See A. Meitzen, *Siedelung und Agrarwesen,* vol. I (1895), pp. 461–462; K. T. von Inama-Sternegg, *Deutsche Wirtschaftsgeschichte,* vol. I (1879), pp. 401 f.

21. G. von Below, *Probleme der Wirtschaftsgeschichte* (1920), p. 71.

22. In Prussia until about the time of the edict of 1821 providing for the separation or enclosure of holdings.

23. See below, ch. I, sect. 3, p. 14.

24. See above, ch. IV.

25. See the treatises published by E. Lamond along with Walter of Henley's *Husbandry* (1890).

26. W. H. R. Curtler, *The Enclosure and Redistribution of our Land* (1920), pp. 30–31.

27. See the map above, p. 28.

28. H. L. Gray, *English Field Systems* (1915), ch. II and app. II.

29. See Walter of Henley's *Husbandry* (ed. by E. Lamond, 1890), pp. XXVIII, 9. Let us compare the two systems on a manor containing 1800 acres of arable land. In the two-field system, we would have

900 acres (arable plowed once)	. . . .	900
900 " (fallow " twice)	. . .	1800

Total acres of plowing 2700

In the three-field system we would have

600 acres (winter grain plowed once)	. .	600
600 " (spring " " ")	. .	600
600 " (fallow " twice)	. .	1200

Total acres of plowing 2400

Thus in the two-field system we get only 900 acres of crops for 2700 acres of plowing, whilst in the three-field system we get 1200 acres of crops for 2400 acres of plowing.

30. The term "legume rotation" is my own. It is obviously imperfect but indicative of the main idea of a rotation in which a legume plays a vital part.

31. Cf. Theophrastus, *Enquiry into Plants* (ed. Sir A. Hort), vol. II (1916), p. 185.

32. See G. Hanssen, *Agrarhistorische Abhandlungen,* vol. I (1880), pp. 184–190.

33. See below, ch. III.

34. *De Agri Cultura* in 170 brief chapters (ed. by H. Keil, Leipzic, 1882), partly translated in *Roman Farm Management* by A Virginia Farmer (New York, 1913).

35. *Rerum Rusticarum Libri Tres* (ed. by H. Keil, Leipzic, 1884). Translation as *Varro on Farming* by L. Storr-Best (London, 1912).

36. *De Re Rustica* (ed. and trans. into French by Nisard, *Les Agronomes Latin,* 1877, pp. 165–517. A translation into English was made anonymously (London, 1745).

37. *De Re Rustica, ibid.,* pp. 519–650. A metrical translation in English was made in the 15th century (*Early English Text Society,* ed. by B. Lodge, 1873 and 1879).

38. Cf. G. Salvioli, *Le Capitalisme dans le Monde Antique* (trans. by A. Bonnet, 1906), p. 182; J. Carcopino, Le Sicile Agricole au dernier Siècle de la République Romaine, *Vierteljahrschrift für Social-und Wirtschaftsgeschichte,* vol. IV (1906), p. 135.

39. Columella, *Husbandry* (1745), pp. 82, 87; *De Re Rustica* (ed. of Nisard, 1877), pp. 210, 213.

40. Pliny, *Natural History* (trans. by J. Bostock and H. T. Riley), vol. IV (1856), p. 68.

41. We should not think of this rotation as a naked-fallow system, as has commonly been done, but as a fallow-legume rotation. Fallow was there along with the grain but also the ameliorating legume. Virgilian agriculture and fallow legume are synonymous.

42. Virgil, *Georgics,* bk. I, lines 70–99, 191–198.

43. Pliny, *Natural History* (trans. by J. Bostock and H. T. Riley), vol. IV (1856), p. 68.

44. On this general subject, see the following: F. H. King, *Farmers of Forty Centuries* (1912), p. 10; *Theophrastus, Enquiry into Plants* (trans. by Sir A. Hort, 1916), vol. II, p. 199; *Les Agronomes Latins* (ed. by Nisard, 1877), Cato, p. 16; Varro, pp. 82–83; Columella, p. 214; and Palladius, p. 595; *Le Livre de l'Agriculture d'Ibn-al Awam* (ed. by J.—J. Clément-Mullet, 1866), vol. II, pt. I, pp. 13–15; G. von Below, *Probleme der Wirtschaftsgeschichte* (1920), p. 71.

45. For instance in West Flanders about 1328, a certain Jehan de Saint-Nicholay had 24 mesures of land, 8 of which were in wheat, 8 in oats, and 8 in beans. He had also 2 mesures of [separate?] pasture. H. Pirenne, *Le Soulèvement de la Flandre Maritime de 1323–1328, Academie Royale de Belgique* (1900), pp. VII n. 1, 208.

46. See the article Geoponici in the *Encyclopædia Britannica* (11th ed.), and in classical dictionaries.

47. Pietro Crescenzi of Bologna (1230–1307) wrote a treatise (*Opus Ruralium Commodorum libri XII*) that was frequently printed (1471 f.) and often translated (into French, 1373, 1486; into German, 1493; into Italian, 1478).

48. As late as 1725, R. Bradley, Professor of Botany at Cambridge, published *A Survey of the Ancient Husbandry and Gardening collected from Cato, Varro, Columella, Virgil* [etc.], indicating the value of ancient ideas and practices in contemporary agriculture in England.

49. This is substantially the German term *neuere Feldgraswirtschaft.* Cunningham, Ashley, and Gray use the phrase convertible husbandry which, however, was sometimes employed to describe the scientific rotation stage.

49

50. Of course, the fallow did not entirely disappear, especially on wet and heavy clay lands, and has not up to our time. About 1914, fallow amounted to approximately 3% of the corn and green crops of England and 10% in Rumania.

51. *Varro on Farming* (trans. by L. Storr-Best, 1912), p. 15.

52. Columella, *Husbandry* (1745), p. 81.

53. *Ibid.*, p. 96.

54. See for example John, or Sir Anthony, Fitzherbert, *Surveyinge* (1523, 1767), ch. XL; W. Blith, *The English Improver Improved* (3rd ed., 1652), pp. 107, 132; W. Marshall, *The Rural Economy of the Midland Counties,* vol. I (1790), p. 187.

Some English bailiff's accounts from about 1300 onward show the lord of the manor renting out consolidated fields one year for pasture and another year for tillage; or in case there was no renter, they show the lord using these fields for pasturing his own stock or for tillage on his own account.

55. W. Roscher, *Nationalökonomik des Ackerbaues* (1859, 1903), pp. 118–120.

56. See below, ch. VII, sect. 46, p. 159, and sect. 50, pp. 171–2.

57. See Strabo, *Geography* (Bohn's Classical Library), vol. I, pp. 360–361.

58. *Political Science Quarterly,* vol. XXVIII (1913), pp. 400–401. See also A. P. Usher, Soil Fertility, Soil Exhaustion, and their Historical Significance, *Quarterly Journal of Economics,* vol. XXXVII (1923), pp. 385–411.

59. M. P.-H. Lee, *The Economic History of China with Special Reference to Agriculture* (1921), pp. 38, 43, 45–46, 69, 132–133, 229.

60. *Ibid.*, pp. 66, 150.

61. *Ibid.*, p. 150.

62. Cf. *ibid.*, pp. 264–265.

63. Of course, the question of agricultural advance, like that of rural progress generally, cannot be written wholly in terms of marketing conditions. In France, before the Revolution and since, even to the present moment, the existence of small holdings has meant a backward agriculture. Fallow still exists, as does the open-field system in modified form. Machinery is introduced but slowly and co-operation makes no certain advance.

In Germany, on the other hand, a highly developed science of agricultural chemistry, taught by schools easily accessible in various parts of the country, has aided the cultivator, in fact stimulated him, though most successfully where the size of holdings was large or medium and where marketing conditions were favorable.

64. Varro, *Rerum Rusticarum Libri Tres,* I, 16, 4 (ed. of H. Keil, 1889), p. 33.

CHAPTER III

ROMAN AGRARIAN HISTORY

15. THE POSITION OF AGRICULTURE IN ANCIENT ITALY. **Agriculture the chief form of production** Roman agriculture is the earliest about which we have much information. In the ancient period Italy was overwhelmingly an agricultural country. Most people lived in rural parts and obtained a living by tilling the soil or by animal husbandry. The rich put their capital, or a large part of it, into land either for gain or display. Although there were some towns well along in industrial development, generally speaking they were not advanced in manufacturing. Many of the industrial activities were but one degree removed from agriculture, for instance, the making of olive oil and wine, the pressing and firing of clay bricks, and the cutting of wood and timber. Goods requiring a great deal of labor were, of course, made then as now, but many of them were manufactured in the households, both in town and country. Accordingly, apart from foreign luxuries, expensive cloth and jewelry, there was but little traffic in fine wares. The articles of trade were relatively few in number and of the nature of necessities. The Italian peoples had no large amount of capital locked up in transportation systems, no mercantile marine doing the carrying trade of the Mediterranean world, and of course no railroads. The highways were generally unpaved, with some notable exceptions. Throughout the history of the Roman period, trade was local and interurban. There never was any marked commercial concentration in Italy, not even in Rome. It is, of course, true that many wares from distant and neighboring lands went to Rome, but they were for use in Rome, often really provincial tribute. They were not in any sense made up into finer wares or traded for other goods. Rome was not so much a market as a commercial sink.

Agriculture and the Roman state

The largest single group of producers in Italy was agricultural. The chief taxes fell upon the land. The most important legislation was agrarian. And upon agriculture depended the success or failure of the provinces in Italy and overseas. With agriculture the fate of Rome was closely and inseparably bound up. In short, agriculture and the Roman Empire were united in their destinies.

The general situation

16. THE SMALL CULTIVATOR: FIRST PERIOD (up to about 200, B. C.). The beginnings of Roman agrarian history lie beyond the reach of our knowledge. We can reconstruct, we can infer from analogy, but we can probably never really know what the start was like. Probably the basic institution was the free village community of men cultivating the soil and herding the cattle co-operatively. It is not unlikely that this freedom was disturbed by conquerors who not only dominated in a political way but economically as well. In Rome itself such a duality is represented by the plebeians and the patricians. The plebeians seem to have been the original settlers. They were the subject people, the small land holders, always in debt. The patricians seem to have been new-comers. They were the ruling class, the ones in whom was vested the right to newly conquered lands, and the creditors of the plebeians. When the plebeians were vocal, they were found chafing under their political subordination, impatient with their small share in the public lands, and restless in their bondage of debt. The plebeians were the growing class, the one upon which the future of Rome so largely depended, both in peace and war, in agriculture and in politics. For many generations, however, leadership lay with the patricians, as did all the advantages that go with leadership.

Small size of estates

Estates in the earliest part of this first period were very small. Both the early records and the later commentaries agree as to this. The hereditary estate was in early times called a garden (*hortus*) [1] rather than a farm (*fundus*). At

Romulus

Servius Tullius

first it seems normally to have consisted of a little over an acre (two *jugera*), and later of a little over four acres (seven *jugera*). Indeed it was said that any one not content with four acres was a dangerous citizen.[2] Other units which we find mentioned are eight acres (fourteen *jugera*) and fifteen acres (twenty *jugera*). No matter what minor changes may have taken place in the size, the unit was small, from one to fifteen acres. To explain how a family could subsist on so small a holding, we must suppose one of two situations. It may be, as some think, that the cultivation was very intensive, as far as labor was concerned, the hoe and spade being the chief instruments. Or, as seems from analogy much more likely, the estate always referred to was the hereditary part of the family holding and included only the arable and meadow. The family might lease other lands, especially those belonging to the state. And it might possess in common with other members of the village, rights in the common pastures and woods. In other words the effective holding of the early Roman cultivator (*colonus*) was probably many times the dimensions indicated.[3]

4th century, B. C.

As conquests were made the Roman state found itself possessed of new lands, at first in Italy and later beyond. The policy was (1) to rent this public land to the former holders, (2) to plant new colonies on it, (3) to lease it to Roman citizens, (4) to sell it to Romans who might in turn sell or devise it (the land still to pay a rent to the state), or (5) if unassigned, to use the land for pasture. Many were the abuses to which this system was subject. The patricians profited at the expense of the plebeians, as the latter thought. The patricians obtained large shares and evaded payment of rent to the state. The agrarian laws, or many of them, were designed to remedy these conditions. An early law provided for the assignment of part of the public lands to the plebeians in full ownership, and also for the renting of part of it to them. Certain concessions to patricians, according to this law, were to be revoked, that is, concessions that had been made subject to withdrawal by the state. How far the law was enforced we do not know, but its provisions indicate the nature of the land situation. A later law limited the land held by the patricians to 300 acres (500 *jugera*). Probaby this applied to the amount of public land held by the patricians, not to their total holdings of private and public land. It is

Agrarian laws

486, B. C.

367, B. C.

53

thought that this law was enforced for about two centuries.[4]

One of the most interesting questions concerning the period with which we are dealing, is whether the agriculture was intensive or extensive. It has been held that the cultivation was excellent and intensive,[5] and that finally the soil was exhausted.[6] Another view is that it was intensive only near Rome itself, where there is unquestionable evidence of soil exhaustion and agricultural ruin.[7] Let us see what the arguments are on both sides. Firstly, on the one hand, there is the view that the early holding was from one to four acres in extent; on the other hand, the interpretation of this given above,[8] is that the total family estate was much larger. Secondly, there is the fact that the plebeians were perennially in debt to the patricians, a situation that may have arisen out of the difficulty that the plebeians had in tilling small estates. But in the absence of specific information we may equally well argue that the indebtedness was due to something else, exhaustion through war, through dues levied by the patricians on the plebeians as their clients, or through heavy interest on loans made by the patricians to the plebeians. Thirdly, the plebeians were demanding more land, thereby indicating that they had worked out what they possessed. But they may have demanded more land, not so much because they needed it as because it was available and was being unfairly occupied by the patricians. Fourthly, there is the undoubted case of exhaustion in Latium (the district just southeast of Rome). But this may have been due as much to vicious methods of cropping a shallow soil, as to intensity of cultivation. At any rate, Latium is likely the most exceptional case of all, from which no general argument can be obtained. Fifthly, the relatively intensive agricultural system of modern China and Japan is thought to be an analogy for that of ancient Rome. But it is hardly fair to apply the analogy of a relatively advanced people living under a highly developed form of town economy to a relatively youthful people struggling in the first phase of town economy. And sixthly, it is argued that much labor was spent on the land with spade and mattock, rather than plow and harrow. At best this would be labor intensity, leaving out of account intensity of application of capital and management. But even the labor intensity is questionable in the face of the following established facts. The cultivators were frequently away from home, fighting the battles of Rome. During their absence the cultivation of the fields was left chiefly to slaves, whose general incompetence and carelessness, especially on small estates without overseers, are well known. There is some positive evidence that early labor was not only not intensive but very inefficient. The story of one early cultivator illustrates this point. He was a freedman (emancipated slave) who had such good crops, while his neighbors had poor returns, that he was accused of enticing the crops of others by his sorcery. On the day of trial he had brought into the market place a great deal of his equipment. His servants were robust, in good health, and well-clad. His tools were stout and strong. His oxen were in fine condition. "Here," he said, "are my implements of magic." He was, of course, acquitted by the shame-faced multitude.[9]

C. Furius Chresinus

It seems that the agriculture of the Roman state and the Italian provinces generally was extensive during this period, but that it was more intensive nearer the towns than at a distance. Probably the methods were inferior in this period as at a later time. There were large stretches of mountain and waste land, good only for pasture, which were gradually being used by the patricians. It was the inequality of holding, the injustice of land distribution, and not the exhaustion of the soil generally, that constituted the greatest problem connected with the land. In other words, the issue was agrarian rather than agricultural. Wars were putting an increasing burden on the farmer, offering him tempting alternatives, leading him off to the towns, inducing him to become a professional soldier or driving him into the ranks of the proletariat. Well under way in this, the first period of Rome's agrarian history, these developments, nevertheless, reached full fruition only in later times.

Agrarian or agricultural distress?

17. THE SLAVE PLANTATION: SECOND PERIOD (about 200, B. C., to the time of Christ). The distinctively new development of this period was the slave plantation (*lati-*

Novelty of the slave plantation

55

fundium). This does not mean that there had been no plantations before, but that now they were regarded as sufficiently numerous to be characteristic. There is, of course, no thought that the small (and medium) holdings of the past disappeared as the plantations increased in number and size. The plantation was a danger and a threat to the farm as an institution, that is all. The slaves on the plantations did not constitute a wholly new group. Slaves had been used before but they had been Italian, not barbarian, and there had been probably only a few on each small holding, while now they worked in gangs and constituted a new and disturbing agrarian element.

Slave plantation described

The slave plantation was an estate of hundreds or thousands of acres. Almost all of the labor was performed by slaves, except during harvest when free laborers were hired. The owner often possessed several of these plantations in different parts. In many cases he was necessarily an absentee landlord. Probably in all but a few instances, the owner employed a bailiff or overseer (*villicus*) to supervise the work, keep accounts, and be generally responsible for results.

Products of plantations

There is wide difference of opinion as to what the slave plantations produced. Some think they were chiefly for the growth of olives and grapes. Others hold them to have been largely for animal husbandry. And still others with greater right see wide variation according to the nature of the soil and the distance from the nearest town market. In Sicily the slave plantation was commonly devoted to the raising of wheat. In the mountain districts of the mainland, especially along the east coast, it was most adapted to the raising of horses, asses, mules, sheep, and goats.[10] Near towns it was given over to the production of a wide variety of commodities saleable in the local market.

Twofold origin of plantation

The plantation seems to have come from two sources. Generally it was carved out of the public land, notably in the case of the livestock plantations. But to some extent, and especially south of Rome in Latium, the plantation was built on the ruins of small holdings.[11] Because of the social evils resulting, it was this situation which brought the plantation into the notice of the public and caused Pliny to declare that the plantation was ruining Rome and the provinces. It is frequently observed in social history that contemporaries correctly see the direction of developments, but do not rightly estimate their extent. In this case the exaggeration was probably considerable, but how great we cannot now determine.

Senators, knights, and the newly rich generally, were the owners of the large estates. One gentleman farmer,[12] who wished to attract attention to his methods, squandered a large fortune in cultivating the land to the highest degree of perfection. So far had this wasteful expenditure gone that his heir renounced the inheritance. Another rich Roman [13] left 4,116 slaves, 3,600 pairs of oxen, 257,000 heads of other kinds of stock, and a large amount of ready money. We are not told how much land he possessed. **Planta-tion owners 17, B. C.** **8, B. C.**

The slaves on the plantation, unlike the slaves in America, were generally white men but non-Romans. They might be Greeks or Gauls. In many cases they were experienced agriculturists, snatched by the fortunes of war from their own fields and their own firesides. The most worthy and the most fortunate were dealt with tolerably well, but the rank and file were meted out the harshest kind of treatment. The recalcitrant were chained together while at work in the fields, and housed in the notorious slave prisons (*ergastula*), both dark and damp. They were also branded either as a punishment or in order to make escape difficult.[14] If possible, worse conditions were found on the great livestock plantations where the slaves were put out in the open with the stock to get along for themselves as best they might. Here they had to defend themselves against hunger, the elements, and the wild beasts, as well as to protect the cattle and other stock put into their charge. It is small wonder that this period saw frequent slave revolts [15] which could be put down only by well trained Roman armies taking the field against them. The most alarming slave revolt was led by the famous Spartacus, a Thracian slave being trained as a gladiator. The slave bands increased till they constituted an army. Not only was the land laid waste and **The slaves** **73-71, B. C.**

cities plundered, but several Roman armies sent against them were defeated. Rome received a terrible scare but the permanent effect of the revolts is imperceptible.

Legislation of the period
The growth of slave plantations aroused public opinion. There seems to have been no concern about the welfare of the slaves but much about the danger that the state was running from the loss of independent citizens, when a plantation was created out of small farms. Hence important agrarian laws were enacted in this period as in the preceding one. According to one of these laws, for which Tiberius Gracchus was largely responsible, the public lands which had been taken

133, B. C.
without authorization and those held without the payment of taxes, were to be taken back by the state. The lands so recovered were apparently to be divided into lots of thirty acres (fifty *jugera*) for distribution among Roman citizens and Italian allies. Each recipient was to have perpetual enjoyment on condition that he grow grain and that he pay taxes to the Roman treasury. A very significant clause provided that holders of the public land might retain 300 acres (500 *jugera*) for themselves and 150 acres (250 *jugera*) for each of two sons, a maximum of 600 acres (1000 *jugera*). This was generous treatment indeed, especially for those who had illegally occupied and retained public lands, but this part of the law was superseded. Nevertheless it indicates the size of the holdings of individual possessors of public land, when

111, B. C.
they were allowed to retain only 600 acres. Not much time elapsed before the owners of public land legally obtained, were

59, B. C.
given full ownership. Then a law, for which Julius Cæsar was responsible, provided for the purchase of lands from revenues derived from the Asiatic provinces. These lands were distributed to poor families of parents with three or more children. It is said that this law had some success in aiding agriculture but more in helping Cæsar to gain popularity. Long before the end of the period the public lands had ceased to exist in Italy. The poor could no longer obtain estates through legislation. The state could no longer redress the balance of small and large holdings, except by the seizure or forced sale of lands already alienated. To resort to this ex-

pedient was, of course, to threaten the whole institution of private property. In other words the way was now paved for efficient or greedy individuals to go to the logical limit, of arrogating all land to themselves even at the expense of their neighbors. We shall see how this worked out in the later periods.

There remained during the period with which we are now concerned, a great many small and medium-sized holdings.[16] The evidence for this view comes from several sources. There was a periodic establishment of colonies, tending more and more, however, to be beyond the Italian borders, in which the allotments consisted of but a few acres.[17] Inscriptions, too, indicate the existence of small estates. Contemporary writers, not themselves primarily dealing with agriculture, such as Horace in our period and Frontinus, Martial, and Juvenal at a somewhat later date,[18] assume or assert the existence of small holdings. The writings of both Cato and Varro, themselves cultivators and well acquainted with affairs generally, indicate that the small or medium sized estate was common, even normal. Cato speaks of cultivating sixty-six acres (100 *jugera*) of vineyard farmland, only part of which was to be in vines. On such an estate there were to be fifteen regular workers, besides the bailiff.[19] He also speaks of an apparently ideal olive farm as containing 144 acres (240 *jugera*). On such a farm, twelve workers, in addition to the bailiff, were to be regularly employed.[20] Varro thought that a more acceptable size for an olive farm would be 120 acres (200 *jugera*).[21] So it seems that we may safely conclude that, although the slave plantations were threatening in their number, extent, and social danger, the small and medium-sized holdings remained in great numbers. As we have already noted, contemporaries often can be relied upon for evidence as to kind but not degree, as to direction of developments but not as to extent.

Even if we accept the view that small and medium estates existed throughout the period, we still have to account for the growth of the slave plantation. On this subject, as on most others connected with Roman agriculture, opinions differ

Survival of small holdings

About 150, B. C.

About 50, B. C.

Causes of slave plantations

rather radically, but these differences can be noted here only incidentally. Probably the earliest factor giving rise to the slave plantation was simply the opportunity for gain afforded

Rich man's gain

by the public lands which could be secured cheaply or in some cases without any payment at all. This applied particularly to the large pastures and waste lands occupied in the first as in the second period of Roman agricultural history. The means of making large profits were limited—to money lending and

Soil exhaustion

to the exploitation of the land. The exhaustion or sickness of the soil is a second factor of great importance in some places. In Latium, south of Rome, cultivation seems to have been perhaps more intensive during the first period than elsewhere in Italy. Its soil was shallow, and many towns, including Rome, secured their grain from its farms. The result was partial exhaustion. Some of the towns disappeared. Large swamps and malarial districts came to occupy much of the land. Some slave plantations arose to use the land in extensive cultivation, to use it for what it was worth. Here and there in other parts of Italy near the towns, it is not unlikely that soil depletion may also have given rise to a plantation system, especially for animal husbandry or a greater variety of crops. There is, however, no real evidence for exhaustion in Italy as a whole.[22] A rather strong case can

War

be made out for war as a factor. War took the soldier-farmer from his estate, kept him away for long periods at a time, broke his habit of labor, and brought him back with an inclination to live in the town. Neglect of his holding was natural under the circumstances, and ultimately its sale or loss through mismanagement. On the other hand, war gave to the rich and to the leaders large gains from plundered provinces. It provided slaves in plenty for the working of the soil or the tending of flocks and herds. In other words, war caused many small holders to give up their lands and enabled the rich and

Importation of wheat

powerful to buy and operate them. It used to be commonly believed that the importation of Sicilian, Sardinian, North African, and Egyptian wheat ruined the small estates and brought on the slave plantations.[23] It is unquestionable that,

241, B. C.

beginning with the conquest of Sicily, an annual tribute in

60

wheat was exacted from some of the provinces, and that this wheat was sent to Rome for sale at a low price to the people of that city. The only unfavorable effect that this could have on Italian agriculture, however, was to make grain raising unprofitable in the immediate vicinity of Rome. But, as we have seen, the agriculture of the district south of Rome was already declining, and the imports were more likely to have been a result of the decline of the Latin agriculture than a cause of it. There is no evidence that Italian agriculture as a whole was in any way influenced by the annual tribute; and it is indeed unlikely that such was the case, because the trade in grain, except in the case of Rome and perhaps a very few other towns, was purely local.[24] A final cause is ostentation, as the historian Livy pointed out. The rich purchased lands often just for personal satisfaction. They wished to enjoy the feeling of broad acres and to have their friends see the visible evidence of their wealth and power. Often they lost money rather then gained it by such ventures. It was the more the pity because such estates were probably most often made up of the holdings of formerly free peasant proprietors (*coloni*).

Psychic satisfac-tion

18. THE ESTATE WITH FREE TENANTS: THIRD PERIOD (from the time of Christ to about A. D., 200). The characteristically new type of holding is the large estate with tenants entering into a free contract to pay rent and to observe other conditions. The tenants were free men, free in person and in tenure. They could give up one holding to take another. They were free to make the best bargain that the market would afford. The old types were not gone: they were simply no longer new or characteristic of the times. The small holding of the peasant proprietor and the slave plantation [25] were both there, but they tended to give way before or develop into the new institution of tenancy on a large scale. Tenancy, too, had existed before,[26] but it had never been so common as it became in this period.

Novelty of this type

One prominent Roman landowner saw his tenants getting into arrears of rent and planned to change from a money rent to rent in produce, much as he disliked doing so.[27] The same

Illustra-tions

Roman tells of his plan to purchase a large estate which adjoined one he already owned. The price was fairly low, but the land had been run down. It was a naturally rich soil, but damage had been done by bad management. The tenants had been in the habit of getting into debt, and in order to collect the arrears of rent, the owner had sold some of his tenants' stock.[28] The effect of this was unfortunately cumulative. The prospective purchaser saw that he would have to hire laborers to recuperate the land, since he had no slaves on any of his own estates. We are interested in these details because they illustrate the change from slave plantations to estates of free tenants, from large-scale cultivation to small rented farms, from the profits of one's own agriculture to an income in the form of "rent" from tenants.

For further exemplification of the large rented estate we may turn to Columella who wrote a long and well-ordered treatise on agriculture. One section of the work of this author is devoted to the subject of tenancy which is treated somewhat parenthetically, sandwiched in between sections dealing with the rural mansion and slaves. Its existence, however, is significant of the change—gradual but real—from slave plantations to large estates rented out in small holdings to freemen. Columella tells us that in his opinion, the owner of the land should be discriminating. Rents were important but the tenants' husbandry (*opus*) was really more vital. Presumably the author was thinking of the possibility of vicious or careless cultivation which would wreck the estate in the long run. The tenant farmers under consideration were apparently willing and able to work with their own hands. The best ones were those born on the estate, probably the sons of former tenants. The urban tenant coming with his slaves to work the land was a doubtful asset. The author is careful to indicate that, if the soil is fertile and the district healthful and convenient, it would be better for the owner to work it himself by means of a bailiff and slaves. But if these conditions do not prevail, and if the bailiff is indolent or rapacious, it would be better to rent the land to free tenants (*coloni*). The slave system had been tried and found wanting, especially for grain farming. The slaves had a reputation for feeding the oxen badly and for surreptitiously renting the oxen out to strangers to their own profit. They stole when they could, and allowed others to steal. Columella is balancing the old and the new, the slave plantation and the estate with free tenants. He saw both around him and thought each had its advantages and disadvantages, according to circumstances.[29]

The factors that led to the incoming of the system of free tenants, we can infer from circumstances and contemporary comments. In this third period there were fewer wars and accordingly fewer slaves. The price of slaves would rise, and therefore too much capital would have to be invested in slave labor. As we have learned from Columella, Romans saw how inefficient slave labor really was, how wasteful of stock and injurious to land. Equally clear was the difficulty of management. A good bailiff, generally a slave, was hard to find, a man who was at once honest and efficient, a good cultivator and a capable buyer and seller. These are simple factors but in the long run potent and decisive. **Factors**

Christ to about A. D., 200

19. THE RURAL MANSION, OR VILLA. So far we have been thinking of estates and their use. Now we may well stop to consider the life and enjoyment of the owner. About the homestead of the small and medium-sized estate, we know very little. Cato says that the dwelling should be commensurate with the means of the owner. The better the house the more likely the owner is to live on the land instead of in the town. Attached to the rustic villa should be both an orchard and a garden—a garden for flowers as well as vegetables. Columella is most concerned with a good healthful situation, running water, and location on a quiet road. He feared not only the mosquitos (?) and vapors of the swamps but the wayfarers and guests of the main highways. **The rustic homestead**

The rural mansion, as distinct from the humbler house, has the attraction of marble halls, of castles in Spain, of the abodes of luxury, ease, and repose. Pliny the Younger, a gentleman and a scholar, has described in delectable terms the structure of one of his villas and his daily life in another one.[30] His **Pliny's villa**

Laurentine mansion lay some seventeen miles south of Rome, just a pleasant horseback ride. After passing the entrance and arriving at the portico the visitor might turn to either wing of the house. Each wing seemed equipped almost as completely as the other, so that if an earthquake ruined one half, the owner could exist in the other. When the author and owner describes the various chambers, drawing-rooms, dining rooms, library, sitting rooms, and gymnasium, he points out their suitability from the standpoint of view over the sea or distant hills, warmth obtained from the sun's rays, or height of the ceiling for coolness in summer and warmth in winter. Some of the rooms were heated both from under the floor and from pipes in the walls. The baths were well equipped. There was a cooling room, two tubs, an anointing room, two little bath rooms, and a swimming pool with warm water. If the eye of the languid bather should tire of the exquisite artistry near at hand, it could find rest in the waters of the sea in front of the villa. The kitchen garden was well stocked, but the eye sought out the terrace with the perfumed violets. Storerooms there were, but the shaded walk and the tennis court appeal to us more strongly. Fish could be procured from the sea nearby, and fuel and milk from the estate. If anything else was needed, the servants could be hurried off to the town and port of Ostia, a short distance away. The ordinary Roman would be well content with such a villa, but Pliny was not. He had built specially for his own use a garden apartment, off from the main villa, and overlooking the sea. Here he was alone, secluded from the world; here he could shut himself off from the noise of the ocean and the chatter of servants, from the flash of the lightning and the bright rays of the sun. Here was the inner shrine of study and contemplation.

How the master spent the day

In his Tuscan villa Pliny's life was much the same. He rose with the sun, as did others who were driven early to bed by the lack of adequate lighting devices. Here in seclusion he thought out the substance and the form of what he wished to write. Then calling his secretary he dictated with the shutters open and the light streaming in. Then for a change he went to the terrace for further dictation. A chariot ride followed by a walk prepares him for the reading of some Greek or Latin oration. Again he walks in the open, is anointed, takes some further exercises, and has a bath. At supper some one reads aloud, if his wife or friends are with him; after supper, a comedy or some music; then a walk with his servants, some of whom are learned men. Thus fades the day into evening, and thus faded the strength of Rome in the enjoyment of life. The rich Roman secured much of his fortune, many of his slaves, and most of his art in conquered lands. A people may safely enjoy the works of its own hands, but it cannot indefinitely live on borrowed culture or the profits of power.

20. THE ESTATE WITH SERVILE TENANTS: FOURTH PERIOD (about A. D., 200–400). In this period the estate is large, becoming larger in fact, and the tenants are losing their freedom. They are serfs, bound to the soil that they cultivate.[31] The typical unit is a large estate with many serfs, each living with his family on a small holding and each paying the lord rent in money or in kind. As the period proceeds, serfdom increases in extent and intensity. Alongside of the new institution, the estate with servile tenants, especially in the first part of the period, are the survivals of past times, the small independent cultivator, the slave plantation, and the estate with free tenants. But these are all going into the pot together, to be fused into the one new type, which will ultimately become the manor.

The new type and old survivals

The unfree tenants, or serfs, probably came from three different groups. Most commonly in Italy they were the free tenant class of our third period.[32] The free barbarians who were settled on various estates in the empire, constituted for some provinces an important element.[33] Slaves make up the third class.[34] The first two groups were numerous and formerly free; the third was smaller and formerly quite enslaved. Accordingly, the development for the larger number meant going downward in the social scale, but for the slaves it meant an upward move. The whole process was a social levelling

Serfs from three groups

off, in which the extremes of cultivators met, but there can be no question that, generally speaking, the result was a distinct social loss.

How serf-dom developed

Serfdom developed from two different sources, from above and from below. By the action of their masters, the slaves were treated as serfs, though the process is obscure. This situation was partly recognized by imperial law to the effect that no slave was to be sold off the estate.[35] The lords made the formerly free tenants into serfs by binding contracts, crystallized into custom. The law of Constantine, that a serf should not leave the estate, simply gave established custom a recognized status in law.[36] The settlement of free barbarians upon the private estates of the rich and the strong indicates, at least in part, pressure from above. On the other hand, there was an important relationship known as patronage which shows the rise of serfdom from below. Individuals, sometimes whole villages, commended themselves to the powerful, and by agreement became the men or subjects of their new lords. Sometimes they did this for protection at a period when violence within the empire was increasing. In such cases the central government seems to have had no objection. But when the commendation and patronage were for the evasion of taxes, the state offered strenuous opposition.[37] The laws came rather tardily and could not be continuously enforced. The officials in the provinces were among the chief offenders and could be checked only by removal. Governors, military leaders, and even the church, were the prime factors in the movement. It must always remain an open question to what extent the movement was from below, and to what extent it was really from above though nominally from below. It can also not be determined to what extent the tenants expected to escape taxes through the coercion that their new lords could exert upon the tax officials, and to what extent it was their expectation to escape taxes through the exemption that their masters and their masters' property enjoyed. The taxes were both on the person and on the land and seem to have become specially burdensome as the period drew to a close.

A. D., 367–375

A. D., 332

A. D., 360–534

66

There was a large private estate known as the *saltus,* or **The saltus** ranch,[38] which deserves special attention. It is found chiefly **or ranch** in North Africa, but may have been more or less common in most parts of the empire. Some of the *saltūs* were owned by the emperor, some by senators, and some by the church. They may have been built up in the ways just dealt with. There were two parts to the *saltus,* the tenants' land and perhaps in most cases a small demesne, or home farm, reserved for the owner of the *saltus.* The tenants (*coloni*) were unfree or were on the way to serfdom. They paid their rent probably chiefly in produce, but perhaps commonly in some minor labor services also. The chief tenant or lessee was called the *conductor* who paid a lump sum to the lord, and from whom the other tenants rented their land and to whom they paid their dues. Over the whole estate was a *procurator,* corresponding to the manorial bailiff, the lord's personal representative on the *saltus.*[39]

The explanation of the phenomenon of human debasement, **The causes** becomes an absorbing as well as difficult problem. Why did **of serfdom** men sell their birthright of freedom? What was the mess of pottage? Except where the evasion of taxes was involved, the state was generally in favor of the development of serfdom. The church participated in the movement. Except for Salvian, a Christian-socialist, there were apparently few or no strong voices raised against the loss of freedom. According to one view it was a matter of state action. The government had to step in to save agriculture from the practices of the slave owners. In order to do this, legislation was enacted to force the sale of land along with the slaves and tenants.[40] Another view is that the binding of the tenant to the soil was not a measure to save agricultural technique but to solve the problem of agricultural labor. War had caused depopulation so that the land was threatened with underdevelopment. To remedy this predicament Constantine enacted a rule binding the tenants to the soil, and subsequent clauses **A. D., 332** in the Theodosian Code enforced it.[41] The most likely view, as it seems, is that the development of serfdom in the empire was part of the decline of town economy. It is a plausible theory, which is supported by some evidence,[42] that hard money was drained off to the east to pay for luxuries and spices. Even before the period with which we are now concerned, this phenomenon existed, but during the period in question it was much accentuated. The result of the loss of the gold and silver was a fall in prices, which would discourage trade, and would bring distress to both the government and to tax payers generally. The merchant and manufacturer would buy less and less, expecting a fall in prices. The surplus of agricultural production would be increasingly difficult to dispose of. The distress thus arising in the countryside would in turn lessen the demand for town products. And so the vicious sequence of action and interaction would continue, until the chief economic concern became not a surplus for sale but just enough for subsistence. In such a situation, men thought of security of livelihood and of possession. In return for the protection of a rich or powerful leader, they were willing to give up freedom. In return for a tenantry bound to the soil, and capable of rallying to his support, the strong man, their lord, was willing to accept lower rents. It would seem as though there was a general retrogression from town to village economy, in which not surplus, nor opportunity, nor free contract but subsistence, maintenance, and status counted. The change took place gradually and was at times furthered, at times checked, by a generally impotent government. It was not a change for which the government was fundamentally responsible. It was not a desperate effort to prevent soil exhaustion or to maintain the labor supply. Apparently there was less demand on the soil than before, since only necessities were provided for; and there was less need for labor than ever, since not a surplus but a minimum of production was sought. The trouble seems to have been the constriction of trade, the decay of the urban middle class, the decline of town economy. Without the town and the town market, the countrymen could aspire to nothing higher than security and permanence. There was no longer the prosperous town, the center of economic opportunity, to flee to, if the rural holding was lost. Thus the canker of declining trade was eating the heart out of the old economic order. This was at the very time when the barbarians were knocking at the decaying town gates, behind which men no longer found enough profit to justify the sacrifice of human life and remaining property.

The fifth period in the history of Roman agriculture sees the development of the manor.[43] During this period the lord follows up the advantage he had in serfdom. If his tenants could not legally move from his estate, he might place new burdens upon them. He might increase the amount of rent in kind, but he would be continuously faced with arrears of rent, as misfortune or carelessness brought bad harvests, at a time when just enough for serf and lord was at best expected. A much more certain source of income—and security was the keynote of the age—was to force the tenants, the serfs, to labor each week upon the lord's own land, his home farm or demesne, under the eyes of the lord's personal officials. In such a system, income from tenants depended not upon a yearly payment of rent but upon weekly, almost daily, payment of labor. Accordingly, the whole system of agricultural services, a considerable demesne, and bailiff farming were developed.[44] In the fourth period there had been small demesnes and some service rents in plowing and harvesting times. But now the demesne is considerable and a large part of the income that the lord gets from the tenants, the serfs, is in the form of weekly services. At this point we may speak of the manor as fully developed in all essentials.

There appear to be two more or less distinct sources of manorial growth in the Roman empire. The first is from the private estate, which went successively through the stages of slave plantation, estate with free tenants, and estate with unfree tenants or serfs. This development has already been traced in outline. The other source is the free village which, surviving here and there, commended itself in the fourth period to a Roman patron for protection or freedom from burdensome taxes. It would seem that the first origin, from the private estate of serfs, was more common than the second, from the public village of free men.

Margin notes:

A. D., 400–800

The manor

Operae

Twofold origin of the manor

Private estate of serfs

Public village of free men

Town economy as a factor

21. CAUSES AND RESULTS. It would not be profitable to recount here the numerous causal relationships already noted in this chapter, but there are a few points that may be given special consideration. The rise of town economy, in Rome and other Italian districts, was a factor in early agriculture, the influence of which it is now difficult to appraise. It would seem very probable that the general farms near the towns would take on a more intensive system in order to supply the market right at hand. This would lead to some special cultivation on both large and small estates to provide such commodities as vegetables and flowers for sale in the town. In the more remote parts, lands would be devoted to the production of such commodities as could be transported long distances, notably livestock, fowl, wine, and olive oil. Large estates as well as small could participate in this development; free holdings of small cultivators as well as slave plantations. The trade in these commodities was not only of the local town type, but interurban and even international. But in any case these articles were disposed of in the mechanism of town economy.

War as a result

We have already noted the decay of the agriculture of Latium, just south of Rome. It is a tempting inference that the loss of Rome's local supply of grain induced her to seek the next most accessible fields, Sicily and Sardinia, which belonged to Carthage. Apparently no ancient writer has made any statement to this effect, but historians of the ancient world were not given to explanations along economic lines. It is certainly an interesting fact that many of the prominent conquests of the later republic and the early empire were of rich grain lands, of which Egypt was the most prominent. After Italian slave plantations got well under way, there seems to have been grown a surplus of products over and above the needs of the Italian population. This was particularly the case with wine. It has been maintained that one reason why the leaders of Rome, the owners of slave plantations producing wine, went to war, was to procure new markets for the Italian product. In other words it was not simply to secure foreign wheat but to sell Italian wine that Rome waged war and made conquests.[45] A similar line of reasoning can be followed in the case of slaves, that wars were waged in part at least to procure slaves with whom to work the large plantations. We have already noted that the possession of slaves was conducive to the growth of such plantations.[46]

One of the greatest facts of history is that Rome fell. One of the greatest puzzles is to determine why it fell. We are interested in that problem only in its connection with agriculture, and here the immediate issue is whether Rome fell because agriculture declined[47] or agriculture declined because Rome fell. It seems more likely that the second view is the correct one. A conjunction of two developments, one military the other political, may be regarded as an effective circumstance leading to Rome's ultimate decay. The constant hammering of enemies, persistent barbarian hordes, taxed Rome's supply of men and money. Trade with the Orient seems to have drained off much of the supply of money to the east, as has been seen.[48] Apparently Romans were unable to mine sufficient gold and silver and unable to produce commodities saleable in the east. This lack of money injured trade in general and undermined the town. Since the town, or municipal organization including the town and the surrounding country, was the chief unit of government within the empire, the very existence of the state was threatened when the local town was impaired. As the town suffered economically and therefore disintegrated politically, the rural districts sought safety in withdrawal from urban connections. As we have seen, the village gradually reduced its surplus of products, as the town's buying power was impaired. It also sought to withdraw from the administrative sway of the town, thereby robbing the town of many tax payers and making the town's tax burden the heavier.[49] In other words the village tended to become an economically self-sufficing unit and to seek administrative extraterritoriality.[50] The village group left the town fold both economically and politically. It did this in order to provide security for itself as the Roman empire decayed. In withdrawing from effective economic and political co-operation with the town, the agricultural interests con-

Fall of Rome as a factor

tributed a cause for further decline of empire. Fundamentally, however, it seems that agriculture drew back into a clamlike seclusion, changed from commercial to subsistence agriculture, because the Roman empire was a dying institution.

Parallelism of fortunes of Rome and Roman agriculture

The first of our five periods, is the iron age of Rome. That city conquers Italy and begins to try its strength on other peoples. This is the period of the soldier-cultivators of the small general farms. The second period is the golden age of Rome, when Rome becomes mistress of the Mediterranean world and reaches her greatest cultural heights. At the same time the slave plantation, fed by war, provided its owner with luxury and ease. The third period is the silver age of Rome, when that city reached maturity and put a limit to its ambitions for conquest. In agriculture, the slave plantation owners also drew back, contenting themselves with rents from free men rather than profits from the labor of men driven to work under the lash. The fourth period is one of imperial decline, of division of empire, and local political security or feudalism. In the country districts, too, we find the rent takers seeking economic security rather than large incomes. And finally in the fifth period the empire goes to pieces in the west, dissolves into its integral parts; commercial agriculture gives way to a relatively self-sufficing manorial system. As long as the prevailing unit was town economy, the government could secure resources for both civil and military affairs, because within the towns was mobilized the personal property of the empire. With this at its disposal, the government could pay officials to administer provinces, hold courts, collect taxes. With this it could pay soldiers and provide food and clothing for them. But with the town going or gone, the task was difficult or impossible. Out of the walls of towns had been built the walls of empire. When towns decayed the empire declined. And with them agriculture descended to its lowest depths. Or, perhaps we may say, the wheel had come full circle: the empire went back to the dust from which it had sprung and agriculture went back to a dependent village organization, something like that which prevailed in the days of Roman beginnings, when patricians lorded it over small plebeian cultivators.

22. Suggestions for Further Study

1. Why is this chapter called Roman agrarian, instead of agricultural, history?

2. Enumerate the chief periods in Roman agrarian history. What are the chief characteristics of each?

3. Read as much of W. E. Heitland's *Agricola* (1921) as you have time for, particularly pp. 131 f.

4. See E. Huntington's article, Climatic Change and Agricultural Exhaustion as Elements in the Fall of Rome. *Quarterly Journal of Economics,* vol. XXXI (1917), pp. 173–208.

5. Read *Varro on Farming* (trans. by L. Storr-Best, 1912), pp. 6–24, 46–55, 239–262.

6. Read the following articles in the *Encyclopædia Britannica* (11th ed.), Agrarian Laws, Cato, Gracchus, Latium, Spartacus, Varro.

7. Were the Roman agricultural writers, such as Cato, Varro, Columella, and Palladius, describing exceptional or normal conditions? Are they credible witnesses for the average or for the unusual?

8. Consider the lot of the Roman rustic slaves, under the head of food, clothing, shelter, work, and manumission. Look up the words *columbaria, egastulum,* and *peculium* in some classical dictionary.

9. For slave labor in the Roman state, see A. H. J. Greenidge, *A History of Rome during the later Republic and early Principate,* vol. I (1904), pp. 80–100.

10. Re-state the reasons for the formation of slave plantations.

11. For an account of the Gracchan land reform, see A. H. J. Greenidge, *A History of Rome during the later Republic and Early Principate,* vol. I (1904), pp. 101–144.

12. What is the argument that the importation of Sicilian wheat was a result rather than a cause of Roman agricultural developments?

13. Why did the Romans not make more progress in agriculture, industry, and commerce? Did too much war and the luxury of a ruling people blight their mental powers? Or, did the climate enervate them?

14. As an illustration of the ambiguity of terminology, consider

73

the Latin word *colonus* which meant in the first two periods cultivator (generally owning his land), in the third period free tenant, and in the fourth period serf.

15. The Latin term *villa* is another illustration of verbal ambiguity. It meant (1) any rural homestead, (2) a rural mansion, (3) a town house, (4) sometimes the whole estate attached to the rustic *villa* (just as manor means both the house and the estate), and (5) medieval manor or dependent village.

16. Why is the subject of Roman agrarian history important? If it is so bound up with Rome's destiny, why has it been so neglected by so many historians?

17. Look up the life of Salvian in some encyclopedia. He was the Christian defender of the poor tenant going down before the rich and powerful in our fourth period.

18. For the study of later Roman agrarian history, see the writings of Sir Paul Vinogradoff, *Growth of the Manor* (1905), pp. 48–83, 103–114; his article on the "Manor" in the *Encyclopædia Britannica* (11th ed.), and the *Cambridge Mediæval History* vol. I (1911), ch. xix.

19. In not making the exhaustion of the soil a cause for Rome's fall, are we denying the economic causation of Rome's ruin? Consider the alternative explanation of the general decline of town trade.

20. What are considered to be the essentials of a manor?

21. Wherein did the *saltus* probably fall short of being a manor? Consider the size of the demesne and the extent of the labor rents.

22. Read W. L. Westermann's article, The Economic Basis of the Decline of Ancient Culture, *American Historical Review,* vol. XX (1915), pp. 723–743.

23. Comment: it is not unlikely that the agrarian history of Rome can be summed up in these words: from manor to manor.

For further study, see the references in the notes below.

23. Notes to Chapter III

1. Pliny, *Natural History* (trans. by J. Bostock and H. T. Riley), vol. IV (1856), p. 150. Book XIX, ch. 19.

2. *Ibid.*, p. 8. Book XVIII, ch. 4.

3. The statements of Roman historians are probably guesses, to the effect that Cincinnatus, the patrician dictator in 458 and 439, B. C., had only seven *jugera* and later four, and that Regulus, twice consul and commander in the second Punic war, had only seven *jugera*. The basis of the error probably lies in the acceptance of the small plebeian holding as the normal for all classes.

4. See G. Humbert, *Agrariae Leges, Dictionnaire des Antiquités Greques et Romaines,* vol. I (A–B, ed. by Ch. Daremberg and Edm. Saglio, 1877), pp. 157–161.

5. K. J. Rodbertus, Untersuchungen auf dem Gebiete der Nationalökonomie des klassischen Alterthums, *Jahrbücher für Nationalökonomie,* vol. II (1864), pp. 210 f.

6. V. Simkhovitch, Rome's Fall Reconsidered, *Political Science Quarterly,* vol. XXXI (1916), pp. 221–222.

7. G. Salvioli, *Le Capitalisme dans le Monde Antique* (trans. by A. Bonnet, 1906), p. 97.

8. See above, ch. III, sect. 16, p. 53.

9. Pliny, *Natural History* (trans. by J. Bostock and H. T. Riley), vol. IV (1856), p. 17. Book XVIII, ch. 7.

10. Cf. G. Salvioli, *Le Capitalisme dans le Monde Antique* (trans. by A. Bonnet, 1906), p. 198.

11. It was then called *massa [fundorum],* or lump or consolidation.

12. L. Tarius Rufus, in Pliny, *Natural History* (trans. by J. Bostock and H. T. Riley), vol. IV (1856), p. 15. Book XVIII, ch. 7.

13. C. Cæcilius Claudius Isadorus, in *ibid.,* vol. VI (1857), p. 130. Book XXXIII, ch. 47.

14. See T. Mommsen, *The History of Rome* (trans. by W. P. Dickson), vol. II (1891), p. 436 n.

15. At least six slave uprisings occurred in the period with which we are now concerned. The first (196, B. C.) was the only one north of Rome. The second (185, B. C.) took place among the slave herdsmen. The third (139, B. C.) was in Sicily, a promise of greater trouble ahead. The most extensive up to date was the fourth (133–131, B. C.), also in Sicily. About 200,000 slaves under two slave leaders rose against their masters. They seem to have been chiefly herdsmen who had been left by their masters to plunder and pillage for their own food and clothing. The fifth (103–99, B. C.) occurred again in Sicily, but the total number of slave insurgents was only about 40,000. See W. E. Heitland, *Agricola* (1921), p. 162; and J. Carcopino, La Sicile Agricole au dernier Siècle de la République Romaine, *Vierteljahrschrift für Social-und Wirtschaftsgeschichte,* vol. IV (1906), pp. 161–165.

16. This opinion is held by G. Salvioli (1906), H. Gummerus (1906), and W. L. Westermann (1915).

17. Seven, 10, 15, 20, 30, and 50 *jugera.*

18. G. Salvioli, *Le Capitalisme dans le Monde Antique* (trans. by A. Bonnet, 1906), pp. 100–108.

19. Cato, *De Agri Cultura* (ed. of H. Keil), vol. I, pt. I (1882), p. 24.

20. *Ibid.,* p. 22.

21. *Varro on Farming* (trans. of L. Storr-Best, 1912), p. 54. Book I, ch. 18.

22. For the thesis of soil exhaustion, see the article by V. Simkhovitch, Rome's Fall Reconsidered, *Political Science Quarterly,* vol. XXXI (1916), pp. 201–243. Consider also the theory of E. Huntington (Climatic Change and Agricultural Exhaustion as Elements in the Fall of Rome, *Quarterly Journal of Economics,* vol. XXXI, 1917, pp. 173–208), that Italy suffered from diminished rainfall. While this theory is not to be ruled out, there is so far no real evidence in its favor.

23. T. Mommsen, *The History of Rome* (trans. by W. P. Dickson), vol. II (1891), pp. 441–443. See also A. H. J. Greenidge, *A History of Rome during the Republic and early Principate,* vol. I (1904), pp. 70–73.

24. See M. Weber, *Die Römische Agrargeschichte* (1891), pp. 224–225; G. Salvioli, *Le Capitalisme dans le Monde Antique* (trans. by A. Bonnet, 1906), pp. 173, 180–181; G. Ferrero, *Greatness and Decline of Rome* (1902, trans., by A. E. Zimmern), vol. II (1907), p. 321.

25. Appian (*Roman History,* trans. by Horace White, 1899, vol. II, p. 6) complained in the second century A. D. of the formation of slave plantations out of small holdings. See also G. Salvioli, *Le Capitalisme dans le Monde Antique,* (trans. by A. Bonnet, 1906), pp. 63, 66.

26. Cato (sects. 136 and 137, ed. of Nisard, *Les Agronomes Latins,* 1877, pp. 37–38) speaks of share tenants (*politores* and *partiarii*).

27. Pliny the Younger, *Letters* (trans. by W. Melmoth and W. M. L. Hutchinson, 1915), vol. II, pp. 262–265.

28. *Pignus.* See *ibid.,* vol. I, p. 261.

29. See Columella, bk. I, sect. 7 in *Les Agronomes Latins* (trans. into French by Nisard, 1877), pp. 187–188.

30. See Pliny, *Letters,* bk. II, no. 17 (trans. by W. Melmoth and W. M. L. Hutchinson, 1915), vol. I, pp. 150–165, and bk. IX, no. 36 (*ibid.*), vol. II, pp. 258–263. For plans of Pliny's villas, see Helen H. Tanzer, *The Villas of Pliny the Younger* (1924), pp. 48–135.

31. This is the *Grundherrschaft mit Hörigkeit oder Leibeigenschaft* of German scholarship.

32. The view of M. Weber, *Die Römische Agrargeschichte* (1891), pp. 257–258.

33. The view of Savigny and Seeck. See Otto Seeck, *Geschichte des Untergangs der antiken Welt* (1895, 3rd ed. 1910), vol. I, p. 405.

ROMAN AGRARIAN HISTORY

34. The view of Mommsen and of Rodbertus (Untersuchungen auf dem Gebiete der Nationalökonomie des klassischen Alterthums, *Jahrbücher für Nationalökonomie*, vol. II, 1864, p 207). See W. E. Heitland, *Agricola* (1921), p. 311.

35. W. E. Heitland, *Agricola* (1921), p. 394.

36. F. de Zulueta, De Patrociniis Vicorum, *Oxford Studies in Social and Legal History* (ed. by Sir Paul Vinogradoff), vol. I, no. 2 (1909), pp. 15–16.

37. *Ibid.*, p. 3; F. Thibault, Les Patrocinia vicorum, *Vierteljahrschift für Social-und Wirtschaftsgeschichte*, vol. II (1904), pp. 414–415.

38. Ranch is a reasonably accurate translation because the term *saltus* originally applied to a pasture land, often mountain pasture, and as a developed manor-like institution was commonly isolated.

39. See A. Schulten, *Die Römischen Grundherrschaften* (1896), *passim.*

40. V. Simkhovitch, Rome's Fall Reconsidered, *Political Science Quarterly*, vol. XXXI (1916), p. 239.

41. W. E. Heitland, *Agricola* (1921), pp. 211, 383, 393–394.

42. Such as Pliny's statement concerning the export of the precious metals to the east, the hoarding of gold and silver coins, the government's reduction of the coins, and the development of rents and taxes in kind. Cf. W. L. Westermann, The Economic Basis of the Decline of Ancient Culture, *American Historical Review*, vol. XX (1915), p. 743.

43. Often referred to as the Roman villa, that is, the estate, which, like the manor, took its name from the lord's house. In other words both villa and manor mean house and, as we have already seen.

44. The direct evidence for this period and this development is almost non-existent. We can, however, infer the above from what we know went before, and what we find later.

45. See G. Ferrero, *Characters and Events of Roman History* (trans. by F. L. Ferrero, 1909), pp. 199–200.

46. See above, ch. III, sect. 17, p. 60.

47. V. Simkhovitch has argued that the decline in fertility of the soil was one of the causes, and one of the most potent, of the fall of Rome. See Rome's Fall Reconsidered, *Political Science Quarterly*, vol. XXXI (1916), p. 241.

48. See above, ch. III, sect. 20, p. 68.

49. F. de Zulueta, De Patrociniis Vicorum, *Oxford Studies in Social and Legal History* (ed. by Sir Paul Vinogradoff, vol. I, 1909), p. 10.

50. See M. Rostowzew, *Studien zur Geschichte des Römischen Kolonates* (1910), pp. 375–379.

CHAPTER IV

THE MEDIEVAL MANOR

Meaning of manor   24. ORIGIN OF THE MANOR. The most characteristic institution in the economic history of the Middle Ages, following the fall of Rome, was the manor. When fully developed, the manor was an estate consisting on the one hand of tenants' farms and on the other of the lord's own land (demesne). The tenants, or rank and file of the inhabitants, had small holdings of land which they cultivated for their own use. They were compelled to labor on the lord's holding so many days a week, and during the busy seasons of plowing and harvesting. In return for the right to use their own holdings, the tenants were obliged to cultivate the lord's demesne. Although this duality is at the basis of the whole **Mansio** institution, as here conceived, the name itself comes from the single house or mansion which the lord occupied when in residence. The house was symbolic of the organization: it stood for the lord who at once gave to the tenants and took away from them. He gave them protection and took from them services and produce.

Location and period of existence   The manor, or something much like it, develops here and there when conditions are ripe, in the European and the oriental world, in the eastern and the western hemisphere. It came into existence in Europe as the Roman Empire declined.[1] It arose early in France, England, and Western Germany; it was born late in East Prussia and in Russia. In many districts it lasted 500 years, more or less, not in a static condition, but changing from generation to generation, and yet displaying substantially the same essential constitution.

Its origin obscure   The origin of the manor is obscure. This is partly because any period, in which a manorial organization had any chance of developing, would not be in a high stage of culture; in

78

other words, would not have literary men to record its arrival in the world. Such documents and inscriptions as were composed have come down to us in relatively small numbers or in imperfect condition. All this is in marked contrast to the abundance of information which we have about the manor at its height. Another reason for the difficulty of compassing the origin of the manor is the complexity of the institution itself. Social institutions, especially important ones, present so many sides that it is difficult to say which one stands first in importance and in development. They grow up with so many roots that it is impossible sometimes to say that one is the parent and the others offshoots. The national state, the family, and the manor are examples of such complexity.

One aspect of the problem of beginnings is whether the manor arose out of a servile estate or a free village, out of a private possession or a public community. The issue comes sharply to the front in the interpretation of the words *villa* (private estate?) and *vicus* (public village?) in the centuries just after the fall of the Roman Empire. We have already seen [2] how the manor might develop out of the private estate, more especially out of the Roman villa. In this case the slave plantation added free cultivators, and then both slaves and freemen were levelled off to a middle position of serfs working their own small holdings. Such a group was called a village, but it was not free. Later a demesne or special home farm was added, and the tenants were forced to labor on it for their lord's support. In France, Fustel de Coulanges [3] and, in England, Frederic Seebohm [4] have been notable protagonists of some such theory of growth. On the other hand there have been more scholars, worthy of consideration, particularly in England, Germany, and Russia, who have held the view that the manor grew out of a free village of free men. [5] According to this theory, the public free village of men who had never bowed their heads to a manorial lord, was gradually brought under the sway of some powerful man in the district. This might be done in one of two ways, or in fact by both of the following proceedings. A free man might commend himself and his lands to a lay lord or to a monastery for pro-

Servile or free origin

79

tection.[6] The process might be piecemeal or it might be that the whole free village would in this way pass into the control of a lord at one time. On the other hand the entering wedge of manorialism might come from above: the king might grant to some lord the sole right to hold court [7] in the village, levy and use taxes, and claim sustenance and support. In either case, at first, the men of the village would ordinarily still be regarded as free, but in fact the freedom was curtailed. The formerly free villager became a free tenant; but as long as he remained in the village, he had to use the lord's court and pay the dues belonging to the lord. He could leave the manor, but with no certainty of bettering his condition. The rest of the process was but a matter of time and adjustment. By encroachment the lord could impose the rule that no one should depart from the manor, and could impose one obligation after another upon the tenant who was unfavorably situated. Out of part of the village the lord would carve a demesne, or home farm, to provide grain, animal products, and the like, for his own use. The tenants would be compelled to labor on this land for the lord's upkeep. Thus it really mattered but little whether the lord started with a private estate, provided small holdings for the workers, and then established a demesne, or whether he began with a public village and then added the demesne. The result was the same. An analogy for this is found in the modern national state. In early times the state was created out of diverse elements, later woven into a national unit. In recent times, however, the national basis has in some instances long existed, as in the case of Italy, Czecho-Slovakia, and Germany, and the state has been built upon this developed national feeling. Although the issue as between a private or a public, a servile or a free origin, was once seriously and sharply disputed, it has now come to something like an equilibrium in the recognition of the strong probability that there were two confluents coming together to make up the main stream of manorial growth, the one servile the other free.

Roman or Teutonic origin   In western Europe the controversy has become involved in the issue between Roman and Teutonic culture. Rome has given us the civil law, the Catholic Church, and traditions of a highly centralized government. The Teutonic or German peoples, on the other hand, have contributed their tribal law, local self-government, and ideals of popular democracy. Which is to claim the manor? Generally the Roman theory is identified with growth out of private servile institutions, while the Teutonic is associated with the free public village. Although this is largely justified, it is not, in all probability, the whole truth. There were probably public villages within the Roman Empire and private estates in Teutonic lands that grew into manors,[8] which, when full-fledged, would conform to the general type.[9]

The explanation of the rise of the manor is the need for security, at least that is the one which seems to have most weight.[10] Wherever the lands are accessible and at least fairly fertile, not in sandy Frisia or mountainous Tyrol but generally in Europe, there arises the need of protecting the holdings both of private estates and of public villages. The barbarians, themselves living in free villages, break down the frontier barriers of the Empire and knock at the very gates of Rome. The imperial organization, based on decaying towns, gives way and the only means of saving what is left, the countryside, is to organize locally for defence, each little group for itself.[11] Then, when the barbarians had in turn settled in or near the Empire, they saw their free villages a prey to their kinsmen in the rear, who kept pressing from behind. Thus did Norman hammer Frank at the mouth of the Seine, and Dane plunder Anglo-Saxon in the eastern part of England. Of course, men did not simply say 'there is trouble ahead" and then forthwith create a manor. They worked slowly without plan and doubtless unconscious of the full meaning of what they did.

Cause of manorial growth

Till conquest in 911

Till conquest in 1016

25. THE LORD OF THE MANOR. The strong arm to which society appealed for protection, and around which it rallied for defence, was either secular or ecclesiastical. The secular power was some knight, nobleman (baron, earl, duke), or the king himself. The ecclesiastical was a bishop or archbishop, or a monastery or cathedral chapter; in other words,

Classes of manorial lords

it was either a single church dignitary or a group of monks or canons living together.

Exploitation

The attitude of the lord generally was that the manor was his, to use or exploit pretty much at will, limited only by the slow opposing custom and passive resistance of the tenants. Gradually the lord was able to put pressure upon the manor so that ultimately the exploitation reached a height beyond which it was not profitable to go. Probably the marked general uniformity observed among manors of different countries is due to the resemblance that one completely organized agrarian community has to another. There is precise information about the attitude of the lords of some districts of which the following is an illustration. The Bishop of Beauvais,

1023

north of Paris, wanted to impose the following oath upon the lords of his district:[12] "I will not carry off either ox, or cow, or any other beast of burden; I will seize neither peasant nor merchant; I will not take from them their pence, nor oblige them to ransom themselves; I do not wish them to lose their goods because of wars carried on by their seigneurs, and I

1 Mar.–1 Nov.

will not beat them to obtain their subsistence; from the Kalends of March to All Saints, I will seize neither horse, mare, nor colt from the pasture; I will not destroy nor burn their houses; I will not uproot the vines or gather the grapes under pretext of war; I will not destroy mills, and I will not take the flour therein, unless they are on my land, or unless I am on war service." The lord was bound to defend his tenants against enemies, domestic and foreign, and to succor them in time of dearth or famine, but when the manor was at its height at least, there was little or nothing to induce him to consider their welfare, if his own interests were at stake.

Manor as a unit

The manor was a unit in agricultural production. It had its own name, its own territory, its own officials, and its own customs for the regulation of work and of life.[13] It was a miniature world, a fact recognized in Russia when the dependent village, or manor, was called the *mir,* which signifies both village and world. To what extent the manor was the unit in the thought of the manorial tenant is hard to say, but probably in the more remote districts and everywhere in the

THE MEDIEVAL MANOR

time when towns were insignificant or non-existent, the peasant looked inward rather than outward. He saw the manorial group as the focus of life, all beyond being relatively strange and sometimes quite uninviting.

The symbol of manorial unity was the lord's house, from which, as we have seen, the manor took its name in England.[14] The finest of such dwellings were great castles well fortified, the humblest more like the overseer's house on a southern American plantation. One of the early English manor houses belonging to the clergy, is described at length in a contemporary document. As the visitor approached it, he noticed a pigsty near the outer entrance. Passing the moat, wall, and hedge, he found himself in the outer enclosure. Here he observed a barn for wheat and another for oats; a house with a bed, a stable in good condition and divided up probably into stalls, an old house for servants, and an upper apartment for the bailiff (?*serviens*). Advancing farther toward the center, our visitor passed an inner gate and soon found himself facing the main building or hall, doubtless on one side of an open court-yard. This particular hall proved to be rather a fine one, beautifully adorned with carved oak and furnished with four tables, doubtless for festal occasions, or perhaps also for use when the manorial court was in session. It had the usual hall bed, or chamber having a bed, probably with canopy and testers; there were also a stone fire-place, a wardrobe, a small extra room, a pantry, and a store-room. The chapel, apparently on the other side of the court-yard, had a portable altar and a small cross. Nearby was a fair kitchen provided with a good tiled roof, two tables, a fire box, and ovens, one large, perhaps for bread, the other small for cakes. Opposite was a small house also for baking. It is likely that one of these cooking establishments was for the use of the tenants. There was a new granary covered with oaken shingles; also a dairy-house partitioned off. A pretty good chamber, perhaps in a separate building, was provided for clergymen, along with an adjoining room. We are surprised to find a chicken house within this inner enclosure, like the granary safely located beyond the reach of the servants in the outer yard. All in all, this

Manor house

1265

83

manor house was better equipped in buildings, such as they were, than the modern farmer's dwelling.[15]   And well it might be, because into its establishment and upkeep went much of the labor of the whole group of villagers, who, as a compensation for their efforts, enjoyed the privilege of fleeing for safety, with family and livestock, to the defences of the manor house or at least of the enclosure.

The group of manors   Although there were many instances of a single manor being the only holding of a lord, especially in the early Middle Ages, nevertheless the vast majority of manors came to be mere units within a group.   A king had hundreds, a count or bishop had scores.   A monastery, if large, equalled or surpassed the patrimony of a noble.   But within each of these categories, there were enormous variations.[16]   At first the lay lord with his retinue often went from manor to manor eating up the year's surplus.   But in many instances, and doubtless more and more as time went on, the surplus was sent to favorite manors where the lord's chief residence or castle was located. And in the case of monasteries or cathedral chapters, the produce was from the first sent to the place of residence of the monks or the canons.   This annual tribute was worked out in the form of food "farms," each manor regularly contributing so much grain for bread and beer, wine and ale and so many lambs, pigs, hens, and eggs.[17]   When towns were developing, and the manors coming into the sphere of town economy, the officials of many lay lords and of bishops were ordered to send their produce to the nearest market and to hand over to the lord's treasury the cash received.[18]

Officials   To carry on the work of the group of manors there were at least two officials,[19] the seneschal in general charge and the treasurer who received the net cash yield of each estate.   The individual manor had its own officials.   The bailiff was in general charge as the lord's own representative.   Next under him there was sometimes a reeve [20] who was responsible for getting some of the work done, and who seems to have been to some extent the representative of the tenants or at least to have been concerned with their welfare.   It would probably be fanciful but nevertheless tempting to regard the reeve as the descendant of the old-time free-village elder, who with six villeins and the priest came forth to give evidence for the compilation of Domesday Book. Less prominent were the manorial messenger (radman), the shepherd, swineherd, cowherd, oxherd, dairymaid, and guardian of the standing crops. This array of officials, itself quite incomplete, indicates clearly the existence of the division of labor or employments on the manor.

1086

One part of the manor was set aside, so to speak, as the lord's own holding, in contrast to the lands of the tenants. It was the lord's home farm, the inland,[21] or the demesne. The tenants were compelled to labor on this part of the manor under the direction of the officials, especially the bailiff. The demesne would consist of only forty or fifty acres of arable land on a small manor, but of several hundreds on a large estate. Sometimes it was in one or two blocks of land, indicating that it had originally been carved out of waste land; sometimes apparently it was in whole or in part intermixed with the tenants' land, suggesting that it was made up of tenants' holdings which had fallen to the lord through the extinction of the tenants' families or other such cause. The demesne was really more than arable land; it included the chief messuage [22] of the manor (the manor house and yard), and such other lands as the lord had taken from the waste or otherwise secured. On one English manor the lord's demesne was made up of over 168 acres of arable land, over 25 acres of separate pasture, hay meadow, and peat-fuel land, and over 3 acres around the manor house.[23] The use of this land to provide the lord with sustenance and shelter was called demesne-farming, or more commonly bailiff-farming.

The demesne

1292

Most of our knowledge of manorial conditions comes from manorial documents, of which there are tens of thousands in existence. The "survey" or "extent" was a general statement of the manor's makeup. It indicated the size of the demesne, something about the tenants' resources, the obligations of the tenants to the lord, a number of special sources of income such as the sale of pasture rights on the lord's own demesne and the lease of the mill and fish-pond.[24] The court roll was the

Manorial douments

Survey

Court roll

record of cases decided in the lord's courts and the sums of money accruing to the lord from each case. The bailiff's account was the yearly statement of income and outgo, receipts and expenditures. The receipts included fixed money rents, chiefly from freemen, money received from tenants who had commuted their services from labor to cash, the income from the court and from produce sold. The expenditures were for the purchase and repair of carts, plows, and the like, the payment of wages for special labor performed, and the purchase of seed. Appended to the balanced account was a statement of the grain and livestock, the amount from the previous year, the yield or increase of the current year, the sale or loss for the period, and what remained.[25] These documents are all commonly in Latin and the figures in Roman numerals. The writing material is usually sheepskin. Great care was taken to obtain accuracy: the errors found are indeed relatively few in number. That the many facts needed to go into the yearly accounts could be accurately recorded by bailiffs, who were sometimes villeins, is noteworthy. Probably this was facilitated by the use of notched sticks or tallies, the following of definite formulae for making up the account, and the enlistment of a special scribe, or the parish priest, to copy out the finished record.

26. PEOPLE ON THE MANOR. Besides the lord and his officials, there were various classes of persons resident on the manor. Those usually mentioned first in the surveys were freemen, commonly paying fixed money rents, serving the lord in war, and helping in the plowing and harvesting seasons. As tenants they were usually free, free from the uncertain services which others had to perform. They were always free in their persons, or status. They were free to leave the manor, to marry their daughters to men on other manors, and free to put their sons out to trades in the towns or to have them enter the Church. Normally, they alone, or chiefly, were admitted to the ranks of the army. Next to the freemen came the much more numerous villeins, the normal citizens of the manor. Their name meant villa-men, or manor-men. They were also called serfs and customary tenants. As tenants they

Account roll

Social classes

Freemen

Villeins

owed two or three days of service each week, rarely as many as five days a week. This service was certain in amount but uncertain in kind. They had to work at any task to which they were put, plowing or ditching, spreading manure or cutting the grain, carting the crops or threshing the wheat. In status the villeins were unfree. They might not leave the manor, marry their daughters to men on other manors or to freemen on the same manor, or send their sons to learn a handicraft or to enter the Church; they might not do these things without securing the lord's permission, usually obtained, however, on the payment of a fine. Below the villeins were the potential laborers, the cottars and squatters. These were the occupiers of a house and garden and the holders of a few acres, too small for the sustenance of a family. Accordingly they had to eke out a living by working for others whenever they could. At the bottom of the ladder were the slaves who held no land at all, worked throughout the year for the lord, had few or no rights, and could be sold like oxen.[26] When the manor reached its height, this class was fast dying out, in fact had almost disappeared in western Europe. In the east, however, notably in Russia, the domestic servants were virtually slaves until the emancipation.[27] Slaves cannot be regarded as an important class on the manor; indeed, as we have seen,[28] the growth of the manor involved their absorption into the villein or other tenant classes.

The slaves may have been descended from the unfree workers on large estates which grew into manors; or they may have been originally possessed by the free men of a free village that ultimately grew into a manor. The freemen of the manor, numerous here and scarce there, probably constituted the latest infusion of new blood, especially following in the wake of a conquest. The villeins came either from the slave class below or the free class above. The cottars and squatters, we may infer, were often the younger sons of the villeins or freemen, sometimes the social driftwood of the countryside.

The slave had only status: he held no land by any tenure. The villein had both status and tenure: he was unfree in person, and held tainted or unfree land. The freeman was free

Cottars and squatters

Slaves 12th and 13th centuries

1861

Origins of classes

Status and tenure

both in person and in land. But there were frequent exceptions to these conditions, the most common being that a villein would rent land formerly held by a freeman, or part of the demesne. Status was the first to be debased and, as we shall see, the first to be *entirely* freed. After a man had been bound to the soil, or forced to acknowledge that he was already so bound, he might be easily exploited, because he could not flee, at least not legally. His tenure then might be reduced to the point of exploitation, with uncertainty as to what he might be required to do next.

Tenants' rents

The variety of rents was great, their number legion. They were paid in money, in produce, and in service. A certain abbey in northwestern France received money from one quarter of its tenants, money and grain from another quarter, and money and capons from the remaining half.[29] Ramsey Abbey in England received in produce the following: wheat, bread, barley, malt, fodder, cheese, lard, beans, butter, bacon, honey, lambs, hens, geese, eggs, and herring.[30] The service rents were in plowing, reaping, carting, and carrying to distant places. From another standpoint rents may be classified as arising from personal servitude, from public or ecclesiastical obligation, or from tenure.[31] The first of these, personal servitude, which alone is now considered, is illustrated by merchet, or a payment for marrying a daughter to someone on another manor; chevage, for leaving or residing off the manor; and toll, for the right to sell certain goods. All in all, these manorial rents seem not only bothersome but burdensome. And yet we cannot be sure of the hardship that they involved. Some scholars have thought them moderate. The service of several days a week seems the heaviest. But in case a tenant had an able-bodied son, the obligation could easily be met. Later, when the manor was declining, the chief objection seems to have been the fact that the tenants were prevented from giving all their time to the cultivation of their own holdings, and to the fact that the dues arising out of status reflected unfavorably upon their standing among men. The weight of the burden varied so from place to place and over a long period from time to time that one can come to no definite

88

conclusion on the subject, except perhaps that the manorial lords went just as far as they safely could in taking from classes of dependents whom they so thoroughly despised. When revolts broke out, we can see the effect of pent-up bitterness choking the flow of ordinary human kindliness and holding high the torch of destruction.[32]

The peasants, tenants free or servile, ordinarily lived to gether near the lord's castle or manor house. Because of the proximity of their dwellings, they enjoyed close social intercourse with their fellows. Working in the fields they cooperated with one another and labored according to the custom of the village and probably often according to the decision of their own group. On feast days there was doubtless the usual peasant jollification with a surfeiting of food and drink. At harvest time the lord provided beer and sometimes bread. On Sundays the parish priest, who was sometimes also the lord's chaplain and commonly his appointee, probably emphasised the higher things of life which they tended to forget. As towns grew up, there were occasional visits to stores and shops. Whether these amenities and satisfactions balanced the disabilities of their life in a thatched cottage with mud floor and damp smoky air, we have no means of knowing.

Satisfactions

27. AGRICULTURE ON THE MANOR. The form of the manor viewed from the clouds must have looked like an irregular checker-board, with small blocks or strips of land lying side by side or end to end and, somewhere near the center, the cottages of the villagers and the buildings of the lord.[33] Closer inspection of the plan would show the shots (small divisions, also called furlongs or wongs, perhaps six to 12 in a field), made up of a dozen or a score of parallel strips. A question put to the bailiff would bring out the fact that these shots (still found in Russia) were grouped more or less irregularly into two or three so-called fields (large sections) of hundreds of acres, each one of which was cultivated throughout in much the same fashion. If one of the three fields was planted in wheat, rye, and winter barley, the adjoining one would be devoted to oats, summer barley, mixed grain like drage (barley and oats), and a small amount of beans, peas,

Management of the fields

and vetches. The third field would lie all winter unplowed, and then in spring, summer, and autumn receive in all two or three plowings, primarily to kill off the weeds. While the crops were growing, the livestock was cared for by shepherds, swineherds, cowherds, and the like, and at night impounded in special enclosures. About the use of temporary fences or hurdles to protect the standing grain, there is but little information. After harvest the livestock would be allowed to roam over these open fields, to pick up such nourishment on the fallow and the stubble as could be found. Lying outside this régime of cultivation were the meadow for hay, the permanent pastures or commons, and the waste land.[34]

Tenants' holdings

The tenant had the use of a number of scattered acres, and the right to cut his share of hay on the meadow, to pasture his cow on the commons, and to cut fire-wood in the waste. The scattered strips of arable land amounted to about thirty **Yardland** acres in medieval England. Frequently the holding was only **or virgate** half this size.[35] In this latter case, I presume, five of the acres were commonly in the fallow field and ten in the other two fields under crops [36] Accordingly, from these ten acres, many a family would have to procure its grain for food and drink, for bread and porridge, beer and ale. If the average net yield was eight bushels of wheat and ten of barley per acre, assuming that only the two grains were planted, there would be 40 bushels of wheat for bread and 50 bushels of barley for beer. Such a yield would be obtained only in pretty good years. Along with these, the peasant would have milk from his cow and eggs from his hens and geese. It is of little use to ask whether he could support his family on these products: he actually did get along. Of course, in this connection we should not forget the gifts in food or money made by the lord for some of the services performed. If we are inclined to say that the material compensation for a year's toil was small, we should remember that, barring bad weather, it was pretty certain. No period of business depression came along to rob the peasant of a chance to labor and to enjoy the work of his hands.

Rotation of peasant holdings

Although the peasant held a unit of fifteen or thirty acres, he did not necessarily possess the same acre or half-acre strips year after year. Indeed it is believed that it was a frequent practice to rotate the holdings. Perhaps this was to insure greater evenness in the quality of land possessed by each peasant. Certainly the effect would be to rob the individual of any incentive to improve the soil assuming for the moment that improvement in an open-field system was possible. Such rotation of strips is a very different practice from re-allotment of the number of strips. Rotation was fairly common. Re-allotment was quite unusual and indicated a degree of common ownership or ultimate control that was far from normal, to say the least, though we find it in modern Russia.

28. SELF-SUFFICIENCY OF THE MANOR. One of the commonest generalizations about the manor is that it was self-sufficing, that it produced all the things required for its upkeep. Even if this were true, it would not mark the manor off from the free village. But at most, self-sufficiency is a relative matter. When the manor had grown up in the Roman Empire of the West, that is, when general political power was at its lowest depth, the manorial unit probably had about the hardest shell of localism that it ever possessed. And yet even during this period there was some trade which doubtless trickled through from straggling surviving towns to the manorial villages. It is hard to see how the villagers could get along without certain commodities, such as iron for plows, carts, spades, and knives, salt for table use and the preservation of meat, and medicines, such as sulphur and pitch, for man or beast. Even during the darkest period of the western world, monasteries were being founded and endowed with villages which became manors. These dependent communities had to send to the monks enough for their support. This is not in itself trade, but it indicates the dependence of one group upon another, which is, of course, the antithesis of self-sufficiency or pure localism. To what extent village markets lasted on into the manorial period, we have no way of learning, but it is probable that they continued right through the manorial period as a source of profit to the lord of the manor. Fairs, too, such as Lendit at Saint Denis (north of Paris) [37] were the periodic centers of trade. Later, as towns slowly came to

Trade on the manor

A. D., 400–800

7th century

the front and as nascent states, such as the kingdoms of the Franks and of the Anglo-Saxons, were formed and strengthened, the manor doubtless increased its dependence on the outside world.

Money on the manor

1133 or earlier
991
About 1000

Early 12th century

12th and 13th centuries

There is no surer sign of manorial trade than the possession of money. In England, Peter's pence was collected from even small landholders and sent to Rome. Danegeld was levied from an early date, so many shillings on each hide (120 acres or thereabouts). The lord received fixed money rents from free tenants and in turn paid both goods and money to manorial servants.[38] When the king of England ordered his manors to pay their surplus in cash instead of produce, we may be certain that they were carrying on trade with the towns at least enough to provide them with the cash required by the king. As we read document after document and find well-worked-out services for carrying products to the town for sale, we may feel certain that self-sufficiency, even relative self-sufficiency, is no longer to be stressed.[39] But it was not until towns were well developed, feudalism decaying, and nationalism growing strong, that money economy was enthroned on the manor. When bailiff-farming disappeared and the tenants paid money rents in lieu of services on the demesne, then the last trace of self-sufficiency passed away.[40] The tenants sold their products and, with the money received, paid their rents.

Manorial self-sufficiency and town trade

The self-sufficiency of the manor was real, only when compared with the commercial dependence of the town. Actual intercourse was maintained with the outside world. Trade was carried on periodically in fairs and more regularly on manorial markets. Probably throughout there was enough trade to provide the necessities already enumerated and money with which to pay fines for crimes, as set forth in the barbaric codes of law. With the coming in of towns there arose specialized traders and an increasingly large group of persons, such as merchants, town knights, and professional men, who provided the manorial people with services and goods in return for manorial products. Let us not belittle the amount of trade that survived the destruction of urban civilization and let

us also not regard manorial commerce as anything but important, increasingly important, as towns were re-formed.

29. GENERAL ASPECTS OF THE MANOR. That the manor **Economic**
was a complex social institution and that it had some measure **aspect**
of self-reliance, we have already seen. We may now note
the general aspects of its complex existence and the bases
of its comparative isolation. Economically it was a unit for
exploiting the soil. The tenants helped one another with
their labors, one contributing a plow and another oxen.
And all together they labored on the land of the lord under
the direction of his officials. Foodstuffs, such as grain and
eggs, raw materials, such as wool and hides, and finished
products, such as cloth and carts, were produced on the manor
where consumed.

Administratively the manor was a unit. It had its own **Adminis-**
courts and court officials. It had a place in the tax systems **trative**
of the time. In the tax books it was put down as paying **aspect**
so much into the royal treasury. It contributed so many
knights to the feudal array. It sometimes occupied a definite
place in the scheme of local defence, as worked out with the
towns as the local center. In short, it was the smallest unit
in the feudal state. It came into existence as feudalism was
developing and it declined as feudalism weakened.

On many manors, as time passed on almost all, there was at **Religious**
least one church. Although occasionally it was built and **aspect**
owned by the tenants, at least in England, it was almost always
the lord's. Where rights were divided, the tenants owned the
nave, the lord the chancel. Ordinarily there was a priest,
resident on the manor. The people of the manor had to pay
a tax to maintain the church organization. This was commonly received or appropriated by the lord, but it maintained
its identity.[41] Perhaps in most instances the boundaries of
the manor were coterminous with those of the parish; and,
generally speaking, the parish inherited the local organization
of the manor, and in this form has survived to our day.

The manor was a group of persons who not only worked **Social**
and prayed but visited and made merry together. It was a **aspect**

marriage group, not entirely shut off from kinship with other districts but tending, because of legal prohibitions and the limitations of location, to keep pretty much to itself. The extent to which this inbreeding was a source of weakness to the physique and mentality of the people, we can only conjecture. Some free villages probably were kinship groups from the very first; probably all unfree villages tended to become such. But we must not forget the limitations to social unity. Although the personification of manorial unity, the lord ordinarily dwelt apart from the group, as far as social equality and kinship went. The existence of social classes, even though not vastly different in worldly possession, was a constant reminder of manorial division. When a free man sought a free woman for wife, he probably had to go to another manor to keep from marrying a near relative, so few were the free persons on the average manor. There were probably many events, however, the circumstances of war and peace, which made the whole group laugh and cry together. They not only owed allegiance to the one lord and had to bear the burdens of cultivating the lord's land, but they suffered jointly the ravages of an occasional invasion and regularly joined in the festivities of the numerous holidays.

Periods in the history of the English manor

30. DECLINE OF THE MANOR. The manor may be said to have four ages. Its growth in England was during the period 800–1200. It was at its height 1200–1300. Decline of the most salient feature, bailiff-farming, took place 1300–1500. After 1500 the manor survived only in non-essentials, some of them, however, being of considerable importance. Perhaps the outstanding survivals in England were the open-field system, the cultivation of the arable according to the decision of the whole village group, the joint use of pasture, meadow, and waste, the old courts, the manorial tenures (notably freehold and villein tenures), and, of course, in many cases the manor house often more elaborately re-built. In northern France we find decay setting in earlier than in England, while in Burgundy it took place at about the same time, and north of the Jura mountains in Franche Comté it survived till the French Revolution.[42] In certain districts of

Germany the manor declined only in the early part of the nineteenth century. In Prussia serfdom was abolished by the edict of 1807; the end of bailiff-farming was provided for in 1811; and in 1821 the separation of the lord's lands from peasants' holdings was facilitated. In Russia the manor was abolished by imperial decree in 1861. A decade later it disappeared in Japan along with feudalism.

1868–74

The decline in the western countries came gradually. We shall take England to illustrate this. First came the decay of bailiff-farming and the commutation of services for money rents. Then servile status died out. In 1574, many serfs were freed on the royal estates,[43] and by the end of the next century, if not before, serfdom could no longer be found in England. The rents tended to disappear in the sixteenth century when the value of money fell. The agricultural system was modified in parts of England, in many places being changed from the fallow system or legume rotation to field-grass husbandry at about the same time. The old field system went through two modern periods of enclosure, and by 1845 had practically disappeared. Generally speaking, only the manor house (or its successor), the old name of the manor, and in some places the law courts (the court baron) have come down to the present. Perhaps we may add a measure of peasant subservience in certain parts, which some think goes back to manorial days. In a general way we may say that the manor declined gradually and early in England and Belgium and in most parts of France, and that it was abolished late, by edicts or laws, in northeastern Germany and in Russia.

Decline in different countries

Although it would be true to say that the manor declined because it had outlived its usefulness, we should still want to know what actually brought about its destruction. We have two things to keep in mind. One is that the manor and feudalism in a general way go together; the other that the town and a strong national state are or may be closely connected. As the town rose slowly from the ruins of the Roman civilization, it affected the manor in two ways. It gave to the manor a brisk market, and offered to discontented tenants a place of security within its walls and of opportunity in the

Causes of decline

professions, in trade, and, as time went on, especially in manufacture. In England it broke down bailiff-farming with but little direct public notice of the happening. The town also gave to the government of England (and France) economic resources in the form of taxes and men, which it could use in overcoming the manorial lords. If the towns, however, were small in size and commercial rather than industrial, the situation might be otherwise as in the case of Prussia and Russia. In many parts of Prussia, bailiff-farming was but little affected by the commercial towns and the sovereign did not ally himself with townsmen against the nobility. It required a great national disaster, the Napoleonic invasion, to shock the nation into reform,[44] that is, the abolition of the manor. In Russia, defeat at the hands of the French and British in the Crimean War showed the weakness of an antiquated manorial and feudal state, and led to the edict of emancipation of the serfs and the abolition of the manorial régime generally. In both cases, war showed that the state which was based on trade and which stood for town ideals, was stronger then the state founded on the manor and feudal ideals. It seems that we may associate pretty closely manorialism, relatively little trade, and the feudal state on the one hand, with the industrial town, brisk trade at home and abroad, and the strong national state on the other hand. The lot of the peasant has been improved by the opportunities afforded by both the town and the national state. Economics and politics are the two wings with which the cultivator can fly to success.

1806-13

1853-56

1861

31. Suggestions for Further Study

1. For a list of books and articles on the English manor, see M. F. Moore, *Two Select Bibliographies of Mediæval Historical Study* (1912), pp. 71–167.

2. For brief descriptions of the English manor, see Sir W. J. Ashley, *Introduction to English Economic History and Theory*, pt. I (1888, 1909), ch. I; E. Lipson, *Introduction to the Economic History of England, The Middle Ages* (1915), chs. I, II, III;

and E. P. Cheyney, *An Introduction to the Industrial and Social History of England* (1901, 1920), pp. 29–49, 107–113.

3. Sir Paul Vinogradoff's account of manorial organization in his *Villainage in England* (1892), pp. 223–409, may be read with profit, though many special studies have appeared since he wrote.

4. A convenient and suggestive set of topics and a number of readings on medieval institutions in general and the manor in particular are to be found in H. E. Barnes, *The Social History of the Western World, An Outline Syllabus* (1921), pp. 66–74.

5. For a comparative study of the manor in all important European countries, see M. Kowalewsky, *Die Ökonomische Entwicklung Europas bis zum Beginn der Kapitalistischen Wirtschaftsform*, vols. I–III (German trans. from the Russian, 1901–05).

6. If you are a student of German literature and of German history, work out the meanings of *Erbunterthänigkeit, Leibeigenschaft, Gutsherrschaft, Grundherrschaft, Villikation, Flurverfassung,* and *Hof*. See the articles on *Agrargeschichte, Bauer, Bauernbefreiung,* and *Gutsherrschaft,* in *Wörterbuch der Volkswirtschaft* (1898, 1906).

7. For the manorial courts of England see F. W. Maitland, *Select Pleas in Manorial and other Seignorial Courts,* Selden Society, vol. II (1889), pp. XVI–XLVIII; and Sir Paul Vinogradoff, *Villainage in England* (1892), pp. 362–396.

8. For manorial life and feudal affairs, see W. S. Davis, *Life on a Mediæval Barony* (1923), chs. IX, XIV, XVI. The date is about 1220 and the place northern France.

9. Manorial records have been translated and conveniently reprinted in *Translations and Reprints,* University of Pennsylvania, vol. III, no. 5 (1912), pp. 1–30; and Bland, Brown, and Tawney, *English Economic History, Select Documents* (1914), pp. 5–17, 56–79.

10. Domesday Book is the greatest single source for the study of the English manorial system. See J. H. Round's article on Domesday Book in the *Encyclopædia Britannica* (11th ed.), translations of parts in the *Victoria County History,* and excerpts in Bland, Brown, and Tawney, *English Economic History, Select Documents* (1914), pp. 9–17.

11. For the relation of the manor to the free village and to the town, see N. S. B. Gras, *An Introduction to Economic History* (1922), pp. 70–79, 156–161.

12. See Sir Paul Vinogradoff's chapter on Feudalism in the *Cambridge Mediæval History,* vol. III (1922), pp. 458–484, especially 472–484.

13. What are the essentials and what the incidentals of manorial organization?

14. What was the relationship between manorialism and feudalism? Fustel de Coulanges says that manors came first. Do you find either in great strength without the other?

15. Did the Jews play any part in manorialism or feudalism?

16. What is the difference between the manorial group and the group of manors?

17. Add to the classes on the manor, as explained in the pages above, by reading Sir Paul Vinogradoff's *English Society in the Eleventh Century* (1908). See the index under *bordarii* and sokemen.

18. Enumerate the disadvantages under which cultivators labored on the medieval manor.

19. Whence came the name open-field system? Could you always distinguish the two or the three fields? What arrangement was clearly visible?

20. Explain the reason for the existence of two or three fields, the division of fields into shots, the scattering of a peasant's holdings, and the reallotment of strips.

21. Why were the arable, the pasture, and the meadow, lands kept separate on a medieval manor?

22. Why were there so few cattle on the medieval manor? Was it because they were driven off in time of invasion, seized by high-handed lords, or not easily provided for in the fallow system of agriculture?

23. For a study of prices and wages on the manor in England, see J. E. T. Rogers, *A History of Agriculture and Prices in England*, vols. I–IV (1866–1882); N. S. B. Gras, *The Evolution of the English Corn Market* (1915), pp. 11–17, 261–270. For French prices, see G. d'Avenel, *Histoire Economique de la Propri été, des Salaires, des Denrées, et de tous les Prix en Général*, vols. II–IV (1894–1898).

24. What rights did a villein have? See Sir Paul Vinogradoff. *Villainage in England* (1892), pp. 43–88.

25. What is the significance of the statement that manorial self-sufficiency is quite a relative matter? Compare the self-sufficiency of an American pioneer homestead and a present-day Iowa farm.

26. What is to be said on behalf of the manor? Consider the relative certainty of a living (barring disaster) and the greater measure of social life than American farmers enjoy.

27. Enumerate your objections to the manorial system under the following headings: (1) biological, (2) legal, and (3) economic.

28. Were most of the evils of manorial days due to the manor or the general state of civilization? Consider sanitation, learning, and security of possession.

29. If the manor lasted hundreds of years and arose independ-

ently in different countries, it must have met a great social need.
What was that need?

30. In modern Mexico the *haciendo* is somewhat like the medieval manor. See G. M. McBride, *The Land Systems of Mexico*
(1923), pp. 25–81.

31. Why did the manor decline? Was it because men decided
to abolish it, wished its destruction, or because an unplanned in-
stitutional drift swept it away?

32. Contrast the manor and the slave plantation of the southern states.

33. Enumerate the reasons why a Montana bonanza farmer
could not make his estate into a manor.

34. If European or other nations were to fight another Hundred Years' War, would the manor again emerge?

For further suggestions, see the notes below.

32. Notes to Chapter IV

1. See above, ch. III, sect. 20.

2. See above, ch. III, sect. 20.

3. Fustel de Coulanges, *Histoire des Institutions Politiques de
l'Ancienne France, L'Alleu et le Domaine Rural* (1889), pp. 216,
462.

4. Frederic Seebohm, *The English Village Community* (1883,
1896), pp. 412 f.

5. See the writings of Maurer, Vinogradoff, Maitland, Kowalewsky, and Cunningham.

6. *Precarium* or *beneficium*.

7. *Immunitas* and *jurisdictio* (sac and soc in England).

8. For qualified positions or compromise views of free and
servile, Teutonic and Roman, origins of the manor, see the following: F. W. Maitland, *Domesday Book and Beyond* (1897),
pp. 321, 338; Sir W. J. Ashley, *The Economic Organization of
England* (1914), p. 21; and E. Lipson, *An Introduction to the
Economic History of England, The Middle Ages* (1915), pp.
21–22.

9. There is, of course, no thought of a model manor, a mother
estate, which the daughters closely imitated. Nevertheless, the
similarity of manorial organization arising at different times and
in different places, is sufficiently striking to justify our speaking
of a general type.

10. That scarcity of labor and soil depletion were factors in
the situation, seems very unlikely, for there is no real evidence
for the general prevalence of either.

11. See above, ch. III, sects. 20, 21.

12. G. W. Coopland, The Abbey of St. Bertin and its Neighbourhood, 900–1350, *Oxford Studies in Social and Legal History* (ed. by Sir Paul Vinogradoff), vol. IV (1914), pp. 28–29.

13. It sometimes happened that manorial unity was compromised by the following situations: one manor might belong to two persons, a manor might possess a sub-manor or berewick, and some of the free tenants might have obligations to a lord other than the lord of the manor.

14. In other countries the manor bore various names, in France *seigneurie*, in Spain *haciendo*, in Germany *Rittergut*, and in Japan *shōyen*. In medieval Latin the common term was *villa*.

15. *Ninth Report of the Royal Commission on Historical Manuscripts, Report and Appendix*, pt. I (1883), pp. 35–36.

16. The monastery of St. Germain des Prés (near Paris) had 30 manors, more or less, by A. D., 800 (*Polyptique de l'Abbé Irminon*, ed. by B. Guérard, vol. I. 1844, p. 35). Its 1,646 tenancies are to be compared with those of the following German monasteries: Lorsch about 2,000, St. Gall about 4,000, and Fulda about 15,000 (K. T. von Inama-Sternegg, *Deutsche Wirtschaftsgeschichte*, vol. I, 1879, p. 292). The Abbey of St. Vaast in Arras (northern France) had over 100 villages and at least 1300 *curtilia* or yardland tenancies in the 12th century (G. W. Coopland, The Abbey of St. Bertin and its Neighbourhood, 900–1350, *Oxford Studies in Social and Legal History*, vol. IV, 1914, pp. 66–67). In England in the year 1086 the king had 1422 manors in the ancient demesne; the Count of Mortain had 793, the Count of Brittany, 442, the Bishop of Bayeux, 439, the Bishop of Coutances, 280 (Sir Henry Ellis, *A General Introduction to Domesday Book*, vol. I, 1833, p. 225).

17. *Polyptyque de l'Abbé Irminon* (about A. D., 800, ed. by B. Guérard), vol. II (1844), pp. 703–744; *The Domesday of St. Paul's* (1222, ed. by W. H. Hale, Camden Society, 1858), p. XLVIII; N. Neilson, *Economic Conditions of the Manors of Ramsay Abbey* (1898), pp. 19–21.

18. See Hall's introduction to the *Pipe Roll of the Bishopric of Winchester* (1903); N. S. B. Gras, *The Evolution of the English Corn Market* (1915), pp. 17–31; and a doctoral thesis on the Group of Manors in English History by Mrs. G. T. Droitcour, University of Minnesota.

19. For manorial officials, see the anonymous 13th century treatise, Seneschaucie, in Walter of Henley's *Husbandry* (ed. by E. Lamond, 1890), pp. 85–119.

20. *Fleta* (1647, 1685), pp. 164–166; Seneschaucie, in Walter of Henley's *Husbandry* (ed. by E. Lamond, 1890), pp. 97–

103; and *Domesday of St. Paul's* (ed. by W. H. Hale, Camden Society, 1858), pp. XXXVI–XXXVII.

21. Cf. James Tait, review of *The Victoria History of the Counties of England, Vierteljahrschrift für Social-und Wirtschaftsgeschichte,* vol. II (1904), p. 465.

22. Sir Paul Vinogradoff, *English Society in the Eleventh Century* (1908), pp. 358–361.

23. W. Hudson, Traces of Primitive Agricultural Organization (1101–1292), *Transactions of the Royal Historical Society,* 4th series, vol. I (1918), p. 32.

24. For such surveys brought together in great numbers, see the *Polyptyque de l'Abbé Irminon, Domesday Book,* and the *Hundred Rolls.*

25. English translations of samples of all three types of records are to be found in *Translations and Reprints,* University of Pennsylvania, vol. III, no. 5 (1912), pp. 1–30.

26. See G. W. Coopland, The Abbey of St. Bertin and its Neighbourhood, 900–1350, *Oxford Studies in Social and Legal History,* vol. IV (1914), p. 51.

27. For a brief analysis of manorial classes in England, see Sir W. J. Ashley, *An Introduction to English Economic History and Theory,* pt. I (1888, 1909), pp. 7 f.

28. See above, ch. III, sect. 20, p. 65.

29. G. W. Coopland, The Abbey of St. Bertin and its Neighbourhood, 900–1350, *Oxford Studies in Social and Legal History* (ed. Sir Paul Vinogradoff), vol. IV (1914), p. 68.

30. N. Neilson, *Economic Conditions of the Manors of Ramsay Abbey* (1899), p. 20.

31. See N. Neilson, Customary Rents, *Oxford Studies in Social and Legal History* (ed. by Sir Paul Vinogradoff), vol. II (1910).

32. See below, ch. V.

33. For a study of field systems and agricultural technique of the medieval manor, see the following:

Walter of Henley, 13th cent., *Husbandry* (ed. by E. Lamond, 1890), pp. 7–9, *et passim;* G. Hanssen, *Agrarhistorische Abhandlungen,* vol. II (1884), ch. on Die Ackerflur der Dörfer, pp. 179–329; F. Seebolm, *The English Village Community* (1883, 1896), chs. I, IV, X, and maps; K. Lamprecht, *Deutsches Wirtschaftsleben im Mittelalter,* vol. I, pt. I (1886), pp. 331–385, 532–584; C. M. Andrews, *The Old English Manor* (1892), ch. V; Sir Paul Vinogradoff, *English Society in the Eleventh Century* (1908), pp. 279–304; G. W. Coopland, The Abbey of St. Bertin and its Neighbourhood, 900–1350, *Oxford Studies in Social and Legal History,* vol. IV (1914), ch. VIII and map at end.

34. See above, ch. II, sect. 9, p. 27.

35. This would be the half virgate (or bovate), so common in England. G. W. Coopland (The Abbey of St. Bertin and its Neighbourhood, *Oxford Studies in Social and Legal History,* vol. IV, 1914, p. 37) found that the *mansus* or holding in 17 cases in northern France in the twelfth century averaged about 16 acres.

36. For bovates (half virgates) of 20 acres (in the two-field system?), see F. M. Stenton, *Documents illustrative of the Social and Economic History of the Danelaw* (1920), pp. XXVIII–XXX.

37. Charter probably granted 629, confirmed 710. G. Fagniez, *Documents relatifs à l'Histoire de l'Industrie et du Commerce en France,* vol. I (1898), pp. 43–44, 47–48.

38. *Rectitudines Singularum Personarum,* in Bland, A. E., Brown, and Tawney, *English Economic History, Select Documents* (1914), p. 7. For Peter's Pence, see O. Jensen, The Denarius Sancti Petri in England, *Transactions of the Royal Historical Society,* N. S., vol. XV (1901), pp. 184–188.

39. See above, ch. IV, sect. 25, p. 84.

40. See T. W. Page, *The End of Villainage in England,* Publications of the American Economic Association (1900), pp. 58 f.; H. L. Gray, The Commutation of Villein Services in England before the Black Death, *English Historical Review,* vol. XXIX (1914), pp. 630 f.

41. Cf. S. O. Addy, *Church and Manor* (1913), pp. 153–156, 424–426, 432, 437.

42. See M. Kowalewsky, *Die ökonomische Entwicklung Europas,* vol. II (1902), p. 131; Cf. H. Sée, *Les Classes Rurales et le Régime Domanial en France au Moyen Age* (1901), p. 384.

43. A. Savine, Bondmen under the Tudors, *Transactions of the Royal Historical Society,* N. S., vol. XVII (1903), pp. 271–276.

44. On agrarian conditions in Prussia and the great reforms, see G. S. Ford, *Stein and the Era of Reform in Prussia, 1807–1813* (1922), chs. VI and VII.

CHAPTER V

PEASANT REVOLTS

33. EARLY REVOLTS IN THE NETHERLANDS. One of the telling commentaries on the manor is the series of revolts that took place sometimes to avoid manorialization but more often to escape from the manorial servitudes. These are the green risings [1] of history in contrast with the red revolutions of urban workmen and the white revolts of reactionary landlords and capitalists. They illustrate rural discontent and the use of force as a solution of the cultivator's problems. They prove the futility of radical efforts, suddenly made and badly planned. They show some of the inherent weaknesses of farmers' movements that are even now in evidence in our very midst.

Importance of peasant revolts

It is difficult to choose the initial uprising, because the early ones were not so clearly social and economic and because the information is general and vague. The revolt in West Frisia may be taken as typical of many, though of unusual significance because of the likelihood of its being widely known in western Europe and therefore a potential influence upon other peoples. West Frisia is roughly that part of Holland west of the Zuider Zee. It is a sandy stretch of land with easy access to the sea. Its inhabitants, whether peasants or fishermen, merchants or pirates, were noted for their love of local freedom and their persistent refusal to submit to near-by princes. They had long enjoyed special privileges, but broke out in revolt, either for further concessions or in fear of a possible feudalizing process in the future. In a long contest the Count of Holland subdued them, virtually incorporating their district into the Countship of Holland. The submission meant the payment of taxes, the acceptance of forced services, and the acquiescence in the construction of roads and castles.

Revolt of West Frisia, 1254–88

1254

1272–78

Thus did one more province fall before the organizing in-fluences of the Holy Roman Empire. The peasants and fish-ermen and plunderers of West Frisia had long held out against Christianity, against political conquest, and against feudalism. Reluctantly they had to submit to some extent to them all. Frisia is of interest in the history of agriculture on account of this struggle for local liberty, the long survival of free peasant proprietorship, and in recent times on account of the black and white cattle now so famous for their milking qualities. In that part of the Netherlands which we call the Dutch Nether-lands, or Holland, the revolt under consideration was one of the few peasant uprisings that the country had to witness.[2] Hap-pily changes were slow evolutionary processes, while in other western European lands social turmoil and strife were periodic occurrences.

Revolt in West Flanders, 1323–28

Farther along the coast to the south, a revolt occurred at a later date, that was more social than the one in West Frisia. This was in West Flanders, also a sandy coast-land district. Here in this flat infertile country, the cultivators were free men, not serfs. There were many nobles in the land, but the nobles did not possess manors; they held estates, to be sure, but these were either cultivated directly by free laborers or were rented out to tenant-farmers. This practice of renting to free tenants gave to many freemen, not owning holdings of their own, the means of independent existence. That the re-volt was against the nobility is evidenced by the fact that the peasants attacked the nobles. Just what their grievances were is hard to state precisely. To what extent the objection was to the nobles in their capacity of landlords or in their capacity as leaders in the civil and the military organization, is not clear. Certainly the peasants wanted only free men like them-selves. They were prosperous and were ambitious for even better conditions. Their chief leader was Clais Zannekin who himself possessed a small free estate. The revolt on the whole was well-ordered. The middle-class cultivators had less desire to change the system of government than the personnel. The contest grew until it included many elements with which we are not directly concerned. The town of Bruges aided the cultivators, while the town of Ghent was a bulwark for the nobles. The latter also had the assistance of the Count of Flanders and his feudal chief, the King of France. The Pope placed the country under an interdict. Under such circumstances, the wonder is how the peasants held out for nearly five years. Finally, however, they were defeated in the bloody 1328 battle of Cassel. Large sums of money were later paid by the survivors for pardons, and a perpetual rent was imposed upon the remaining peasants, a rent which was collected for about three centuries.[3] In a sense the peasants lost, but from another viewpoint they were victorious. They spoke very clearly their hostility to a threatening feudal-manorial system. This system was not really destined to engulf them, however, because at the time it was already beginning to decline in western Europe. Another favorable result was the example given to neighboring countries, notably France and England, of the common man's love of freedom.[4]

34. JACQUERIE OF 1358. The Jacquerie was the first outstanding uprising that has attracted wide-spread attention. It took place in northern France and occupied not quite five weeks. The name comes from the soubriquet borne by the French peasant. Just as Americans call a farmer Si, so the French called the countryman Jacques, or James. The Jacquerie was the revolt of the Jacques. It was so called at the time and has never lost the appellation.

Meaning of Jacquerie 21 May- 24 June, 1358

The immediate background of the Jacquerie is the political situation of France. The English king was fighting to obtain the French crown. The English had won a second notable battle at Poitiers, still memorized by the English school boy. After that event France lay almost prostrate, the English in possession of the western parts and holding the King of France prisoner. Government in that section of France still independent of the English, was uncertain and weak—in the face of rapacious nobles and ambitious townsmen. In many parts of the north, even up to the walls of Paris, brigands roamed at will. Some of them were English, some French. Many French nobles joined their ranks, for the business in which they were engaged was both profitable and honorable in their

Brigandage as the occasion
1356

day. Bold knights found favor in the eyes of French ladies for their harrying of the countryside. Great companies of brigands were formed who marched now north, now south, plundering as they went. It was the defenceless village, the monastery, and the isolated homestead that fell as easy prey before them. The lord in his castle escaped, sometimes because of his rank, sometimes because of his security behind strong walls. The raids were so little heralded, so unexpected, that villagers had little or no time to withdraw with their families and livestock to the lord's fortifications. In the case of villages at a distance from the lord's chief residence, such refuge would under all circumstances be impossible. Young men and old were killed either because of their resistance or for sport. Virgins and nursing mothers, even nuns, were violated with impunity. Those peasants, who with their children escaped to the woods or to swamps, returned to homes that were pillaged and burned, to barnyards that were emptied and wrecked, and to fields with grain trampled underfoot and vines uprooted. In the spring of the fatal year, the land was unplowed, the vines uncultivated, and such animals as remained were not driven to the pastures. So awful was the recollection of past atrocities and so fearful the anticipation of new ones that the church bells did not ring—except to warn the people of another raid.[5]

1358

Ranks of the Jacques

Many a beast will run when attacked, but will fight when cornered. Desperation drove the peasants to hit back. Fortunately for them, they had allies, merchants from such towns as Paris and Senlis, and even a few nobles; probably the tradesmen, such as butchers and cheesemongers, and the priests, were more numerous, though individually less influential.

Leader of the Jacquerie

A war, a rebellion, in fact any upheaval of society, brings forth new leaders, men who under ordinary conditions are quite undistinguished. The Jacquerie produced William Cale, or William Charles, a peasant hailing from the country north of Paris. He was handsome and eloquent. With some education and at least a little military experience, he made an excellent leader. The excesses of the rank and file of his growing army, he sought to check. He seems to have been more in-

terested in winning a victory than in wreaking vengeance.
His peasant followers had unqualified faith in him.   If Cale
had possessed a disciplined army and proper equipment, a
larger measure of success might have been his.

The chief single group of allies that the peasants had were **Etienne**
the rich merchants of Paris.   Their plans and ambitions were **Marcel**
personified in Etienne Marcel, one of the outstanding political **as ally**
figures of the day.   As the provost of the merchants of Paris,
he had power and influence.   As a draper trading with the
proud and haughty towns of Flanders, he had ambitions for
Paris and indeed for the French communes generally.   As a
Frenchman he longed for a better government in his native
land.   What sympathies he had for the Jacquerie, we can only
surmise.   Both Marcel and Cale were the enemies of feudal
lords.   Marcel wanted to build up a state on the basis of town
civilization and influence to take the place of the monarchy
founded on feudal estates.   Cale sought a reformed feudalism
or perhaps the overthrow of the whole system of master and
man, landlord and service-giving tenant.   It is a question
whether Marcel instigated the peasants to revolt or simply took
advantage of their insurrection to further his own ends.   At
any rate his courage and intellect, as well as the wealth of the
class to which he belonged, were probably a source of great
comfort to the peasants in revolt.

Marcel destroyed the castles of feudal barons near Paris, but **Peasant**
he sought to cause no needless loss of life.   Cale, the peas- **attroci-**
ant leader, was also moderate, as we have seen.   The peasants, **ties**
however, infuriated by the wrongs suffered at the hands of the
brigands, knew almost no bounds.   The chronicles of the
day, whether written by friendly or by critical hands, agree
in the horror of their deeds.   The mild, sullen, passive tiller
of the soil had become a furious beast.   There is no reason
to question the description given by Froissart, though we
should remember he was a courtly writer, contemptuous of
the villein mob.   Let us paraphrase and shorten his account
of the uprising, as follows.   Certain people of the common villages, without any head or ruler, came together near Beauvais,
at first not over 100 in number.   They said that the nobles,

knights, and squires were a disgrace to the realm and should be destroyed. Shame is on him who does not do what he can to destroy the gentlemen of the country. Without any other counsel and without arms, except staves and knives, they went to a knight's house, and breaking in, slew the knight, his lady, and all his children, and burned the house. Then they went to a second house, bound the knight to a stake, violated his wife and daughter before his face, slew the lady, daughter, and all the other children, and then killed the knight. Such crimes continued, and soon 6,000 peasants were on the warpath and the gentlemen fleeing for safety. They slew another knight and putting him on a broach, roasted him over a fire in the sight of his wife and children. Ten or twelve of them ravished the wife and then forced her to eat of her husband's flesh. Then they killed her and her children. Wherever these ungracious people went, they destroyed good houses and strong castles.[6]

End of the Revolt

Meaux

The peasants suffered two defeats that broke both their ranks and their resistance. One was at Meaux on the River Marne, where the cause of nations and classes has often been at stake. Within the castle of Meaux were many noble and royal ladies who had sought safety in flight. Outside were the peasants and their Parisian allies. Some of the peasants had withdrawn with William Cale to the north of Paris to protect their fellows and their homes from another danger. The accidental arrival of a band of knights gave to the defenders of the castle a chance to resist the attackers. A few well armed knights fighting on foot cut down the peasants and their townsman supporters, as grain before the scythe. The town of Meaux, which had abetted the peasants, was sacked and burned, and with it the peasants who had hidden in the houses. The second disaster was north of Paris whither William Cale had led his peasant warriors when they left Meaux. Their enemy was the King of Navarre (in northern Spain and southern France) who was a claimant to the throne of France. Some of his noble friends having been murdered by the peasants, this king now sought revenge as well as the prestige of victory. The royal troops numbered 1000 knights;

the peasants could muster about twice that number of badly equipped men. Nevertheless the peasants were confident of victory under the leadership of Cale. The wily king of Navarre, however, invited Cale to a conference and then made him a prisoner. The peasants lost heart at once and what might have been a battle, became a massacre. The scattering bands were hunted down like wild beasts. About 300 were burned in a monastery in which they had taken refuge. Those who escaped either went back to burned houses and deserted fields or withdrew to other districts.[7] The Jacquerie was over. It had begun in massacres of the peasants and it ended thus. It failed as an effort, but it was a pledge of the fact that peasants were men and that manorialism and feudalism had been challenged.

9 or 10 June, 1358

It is, of course, perfectly clear that brigandage was the immediate occasion of the Jacquerie. The more enduring causes are difficult to state. The part of France, in which the revolt took place, seems to have been prosperous. It was studded with fair towns and crowned with the capital itself. For two hundred years and more the peasantry had been going upward as the towns grew in size and wealth. Then came the invasion by the English, national humiliation, the temporary breakdown of feudal power, and devastating brigandage. The Jacquerie seems to have been the peasant's sudden reaction to the loss of security and happiness and of the slowly developing emancipation from servile status and tenure. The peasants had been bettering their lot. Suddenly the tide turned against them. The despised countrymen having tasted of better things, refused to accept worse.

Causes of the revolt

35. THE SOCIAL REVOLT IN ENGLAND. As long as the English were victorious in the Hundred Years' War against France, they could look with complaisance upon the Jacquerie and could ignore peasant complaints and suffering at home. But when the tide turned and England was losing in France, in fact having difficulty in defending its own coasts, then the peasant problem in England came to the front with dramatic violence.[8] The movement has borne various names, Wat Tyler's Rebellion, the Peasant Revolt, the Great Revolt, and

Outbreak in England, 1381

the Social Revolt.[9] It was more than the revolt of Wat Tyler; it was not confined to peasants; and when compared with other revolts generally, it was not great. But it was social, not simply economic and political, but religious and legal as well.

Wat Tyler Of the several local leaders, Wat Tyler was clearly the most powerful. Probably a tiler by trade, a soldier by fortune, and a highwayman by choice, he soon rose to a position of leadership among the peasants of Kent. He was self-reliant, quick-witted, and eloquent. In other words he was a born leader. He kept order within the ranks and feared no rival. Like Cale, he was a tower of strength in himself, for his lieutenants obeyed him and his peasant followers felt victory in his presence. But Tyler was an insolent fellow, with no clear vision of the cause he served, more fit to lead a mob to violence than to bring final victory to a popular revolt.[10]

John Ball John Ball was the prophet of the movement which Wat Tyler for a brief period controlled. The "mad priest of Kent" had for many years preached poverty and discontent. He was one of the numerous poor preachers, who was neither Friar nor Wyclifite but an enemy of the established Church of Rome. His great opportunity came when he was allowed to address the multitude just before it marched on London. His sermon was as memorable for its substance as inflammatory in its effect. He made bold to ask:

"When Adam delved and Evé span
Who was then the gentleman?"

In other words, originally there were no lords or serfs, just free men. At last, the time had come for restoring freedom to the world. Men of power and rank, notably the lords, judges, and lawyers, who had abused their position, were to be done away with. Bishops, abbots, monks, and canons were to go with the others into the rank and file of citizens. But there was to be an archbishop; some said (perhaps slanderously) that it was to be John Ball himself.[11]

John Wraw A third leader, operating off by himself in Suffolk to the northeast of London, was John Wraw. Apparently he had been in London when the followers of Tyler and Ball were approaching. Hurrying homeward, he raised his county in revolt. His chief concern seems to have been the opportunity for personal gain that the revolt presented. Like Ball he was a priest; like Tyler he was a leader. With a loud voice and a ready tongue, he gained an effective following. But he was vain and cruel, and in the end turned against his own fellows to save himself.

The peasants and fishermen of Essex, on the east, were the first to rise. They refused to pay the poll-tax demanded by the royal officials, and after some high-handed acts took to the woods and finally, gathering in large bands, marched toward the capital. Southeast of London, the men of Kent were soon in arms. They took Rochester Castle, opened Maidstone jail, and chose Wat Tyler as their leader. Having seized some manorial rolls and burned others, they marched toward the capital, heard John Ball's sermon, and made ready for an attack. Accomplices within London lowered the drawbridge to the Kentishmen and opened the nearest gate to the Essex crowd. Once in London, the peasants and others burned and plundered. Some were so drunk that they could not leave the cellars of their victims before the flames reached and consumed them. The lawyers and their legal records alike suffered from the mob. As many as could be got together marched beyond the walls to the eastward to set their demands before the king. These demands were formally granted by the king. Having returned to the city, the mob murdered four of their enemies in the Tower, the archbishop, the treasurer, and two others. All of these were fiercely disliked because of their failure as administrators or because of their connection with the poll-tax. Flemings and Lombards were massacred as hated foreigners. After sacking many houses, the mob again left London, this time going westward to a spot where the whole group could interview the king again. Wat Tyler who had been present at Mile End and at the Tower massacres, was now the dominant figure. He made his famous demands, to which the king gave no clear-

Events of the Revolt, 30 May–28 June

Conference at Mile End

Smithfield conference

111

cut reply. An altercation arose which led to the climax of the whole revolt. One of the king's servants called out that he recognized Tyler as a notorious thief. Tyler in a fury drew his dagger, but was crossed by the Lord Mayor of London. Tyler's dagger struck the mayor's armor concealed under his garments. The mayor in turn dealt Tyler a telling blow with his sword. When the peasants, alarmed at the noise and the danger to their leader, drew their bows to shoot at the royal party, the youthful king—he was only fifteen—rode out boldly, proclaiming himself as their king and ordering them to follow him. He led them off to another field, while the Lord Mayor raised the London militia, captured and beheaded the wounded Tyler, and brought his head on a pole before the king and the peasants. Then a strange thing happened. The peasants completely lost heart, as they had years before in France when Cale had been seized. Falling among the wheat and on their knees, they implored the king's mercy. The king then kindly dismissing them, sent them home like naughty children.[12] The crisis was over: London was saved. The revolt continued in the north [13] and in the west,[14] but the result was a foregone conclusion. Officers were sent out to many parts to see that the guilty leaders were punished. Many lost their lives, but there were no such massacres as followed the Jacquerie in France.

Reasons for failure   The revolt was a failure in so far as the demands were not granted or immediately attained. It had some measure of success in so far as the temper of the peasantry was now known to all. Again the manorial and feudal system had been challenged, but not overthrown. The failure to put through the plans of reform was due to several causes. The peasants lacked leaders of their own class; in fact, they lacked leaders from any source, able to visualize their needs. They had few resources at their command and probably no local or national organization. The revolt had been stirred up by priests and brought to a head by the stings of heavy taxes, but no effective preparation had been made to overthrow the established order of king, nobles, and church.

Causes   It is much easier to record the outstanding events of this uprising than to determine the causes. A study of the demands made at Mile End and at Smithfield [15] helps to explain the situation, where the events at the time do not indicate the forces at work. The chief single cause was serfdom. Peasants were still villeins or serfs liable to all the obnoxious dues of old. Above all they had to labor on the lord's demesne, whilst they would have preferred to pay a money rent. They went so far as to say what the rent (4 d.) per acre should be. Gradually they had been commuting their services to money payment at a small sum (often 1 d.) for each day's labor. But this movement was not proceeding fast enough, and had probably been somewhat checked by the Black Death which made labor scarce and the lords unwilling to take such small sums in lieu of service.[16] The general movement was upward, but the speed had slackened.

The peasants demanded that there should be free purchase and sale in towns, cities, and other places. It is difficult to decide whether the restriction that they sought to remove had been imposed by the towns or by their manorial lords.[17] The only restrictions that the towns imposed were tolls on goods exposed for sale (or brought into and taken out of the town), and the rules about the time, place, and honesty of sale and purchase. The lords allowed their tenants to sell their own wares, except those commodities such as horses and oxen, needed for the performance of obligations. Sometimes a toll was charged on all beer brewed for sale. But on the whole both lords and towns profited by the trade of peasants and were willing to allow it to continue, under the conditions outlined. But the peasants apparently chafed at even these limitations. They wished to buy and sell freely and with their money to pay their lords money rents instead of services. In short, they wished to engage in commercial agriculture. *Restriction on sale as a cause*

There is evidence that some of the followers of Wat Tyler were concerned chiefly with wages. Soon after the Black Death, attempts had been made by legislation in 1349 and 1351 to maintain the old wage scale, thereby cheating the surviving laborers of the high current market wage. In Kent where there never had been much or any villeinage, this was the prin- *Statutory wages as a factor* cipal economic grievance. Lawyers were attacked during the revolt, court records containing the cases were destroyed, and at Smithfield there was a demand that the harsh legal procedure used should be abolished.[18]

Other causes

The poll-tax of 1381 had imposed an unequal burden on the manorial villages. Some suffered while others got off lightly. The result was that there was a widespread effort to dodge the tax. The attempt to collect it properly was the occasion of the revolt.[19] But if there had been no other causes, the trouble resulting from the tax situation would have been slight. The failure of the government of England to maintain the honor and dignity of the realm, even to defend the shores and northern borders, was at least a source of unrest and discontent. The poor priests, such as John Ball, were teaching evangelical poverty and the equality of worldly possessions. The followers of the reformer Wyclif, it is not unlikely, were applying in their own fashion the doctrine of property held by their leader, namely, that property had been entrusted by God to the nobles and others as good stewards, and that they were to retain it only so long as they made good use of their wealth and position.[20] It is probable that the chief effect of such teaching was to make vocal the thoughts of the peasants, to express what they felt and thereby to carry them a step nearer action. But townsmen rose in revolt as well as countrymen. In London it was hostility to rivals in trade, notably foreigners. Sometimes it was one group of trades against another; sometimes the workmen against their masters. In the towns belonging to monasteries, towns such as Bury St. Edmunds and St. Albans, the people rose to secure more liberal charters than the conservative churchmen had been willing to grant. Personal animosities are not to be forgotten as factors in any revolt. Tenants rose against cruel masters in the country and all who felt themselves oppressed saw a chance for revenge. The criminal, having nothing to lose, found prospects of gain in the period of turmoil and strife. It would be hard to find a movement more truly social, more comprehensive in its bearing, except perhaps the French Revolution. Even then the difference may lie in the magnitude of results rather than in complexity of social forces.

The Jacquerie of 1358 and the Social Revolt of 1381 were alike in that both took place near the capital cities of the respective nations. Both lasted but a few weeks. In each case much depended on a single leader. And townsmen both in France and England played an important part. On the other hand they differed in many respects. In England the peasants fought no battle, they shed little blood, had better formulated demands, and apparently had grievances that were much more complex. Jacquerie and Social Revolt compared

36. THE GERMAN REVOLT OF 1524–1525. The German revolt broke out in the south, quite near the Swiss border. This was in July and August, 1524. It spread northward along the Rhine into Alsace and even into the very heart of Germany. Eastward it did not go far, but it spread to the southeast into Tyrol. By May, 1525, the revolt was at its height; by December of that year it was practically over, except for Tyrol where the end was not reached till 1528. The revolt broke out after Luther had begun his protest against the Catholic establishment. It took place in those parts of Germany where the peasants were relatively the best off. Time and place of the revolt

The number of leaders in this revolt was as great as the number of bands or mobs of which it was composed. The nearest approach to *the* leader was Hans Müller who came to the front at the beginning and remained till almost the end. For about eleven months, he was in command of peasants operating near the Swiss border. Starting with a few hundred, he soon came to have thousands obeying his orders. He seems to have been a man of capacity, who believed in impressing his followers not only by his success but by his appearance. He wore a red hat and mantle and surrounded himself with a miniature court of men in gorgeous attire. Originally a peasant, he had gained skill in war and so was a logical leader for his fellow villagers. We may take him as a representative of his type, of which there are many illustrations. Götz von Berlichingen was the outstanding knight to join the peasants. Without such help as his, the movement Leaders

115

would not have gone far. He had less love for the peasants than hatred of their enemies, the Church dignitaries, the rich burghers, and the powerful princes. His courage, military experience, and moderation proved a tower of strength. Prominent among the preacher-captains was Thomas Münzer, who was a dreamer of utopias and an orator of great eloquence. Like Luther he denounced the Catholic Church, but was himself attacked by Luther. His ideal was not middle-class independence, but a communistic theocracy, that is, a state or group of persons owning in common and advised by priests. Although his chief interest was the souls of poor men, he took up the worldly cause of the peasants and became a local

15th March, 1525 leader of prominence. His defeat at Frankenhausen was the turning point in the insurrection. About 5,000 of his followers were slain and he himself was executed.

Occasion The occasion of the outbreak was some petty tyranny on the part of a nobleman, traditionally the Count of Lupfen. This occurred at a time when the German nobles, and knights, and experienced warriors were in Italy campaigning against the French. Here and there crop failures, and, quite generally, heavy taxes stung the peasants to action.[21]

Characteristics The events of the conflict are so diverse and the contests so isolated that no general account of the course of the struggle can be given, that is both inclusive and brief. At first the peasants stormed, sacked, and burned castles and monasteries. They seized court records and amassed military supplies—money, cannon, and camp equipment. They slew nobles and knights, monks and women. They listened to fierce sermons, fought local engagements, and when successful drank themselves senseless. Their leaders pleaded in vain for moderation. The peasants, however, had suffered at the hands of their lords; this was their day of vengeance. Their women shared in their dangers and in their intoxications. As time went on, the poorer townsmen joined their ranks and opened the town gates to them. Once within the towns, as in the monasteries, the peasants often destroyed works of art and books of learning as the products of an aristocratic and theological system, from which they themselves had suffered.

But the tide turned in March. After the Emperor had won the battle of Pavia and captured the King of France, German troops were released to oppose the peasants. By spring the nobles were ready to take the field with their followers and hired soldiers. During the summer they captured one town after another, defeated one band after another, and executed nearly all the outstanding leaders. Whilst the peasants had slain hundreds, the lords massacred thousands. Whilst the peasants had beheaded the noble lords, the princes burned the peasant leaders. 24 Feb., 1525

The peasants lost because of their disunion. They had many able leaders, but there was no unity of plan and little concentration of forces. The peasants like their leaders were, generally speaking, more interested in their local salvation than in the general emancipation of their class. Some of the leaders and many of the peasants grew excessive as the struggle continued, so that moderate persons were turned away from their ranks. This in itself would have been fatal in the southwestern part of Germany where the middle class was so strong. The destruction of personal property, of commerce and manufacture, and of art, was threatened; and townsmen could not brook seeing their civilization undermined. Nevertheless the real immediate occasion of the defeat was the successful issue of the imperial arms in the great contest against the French. The power of the Emperor was at the moment identified with that of the nobles and knights who had fought under his banners in foreign fields. Now he was to reward them by helping to put down the peasants. **Why the peasants lost**

The results of the revolt were the loss of perhaps 100,000 lives and the imposition of heavier burdens, but again there was established a precedent, the greatest on record up to that time, for emancipation. Sometimes many matches have to be lighted before the fire is started. One of the tragedies of history is the fact that those who wage the battles rarely enjoy the fruits of victory. **Results**

The prime cause of the revolt was that the emancipation from manorialism and feudalism had been checked. For over two centuries the growth of towns had given unprecedented **Check of emancipation as a cause** opportunities to the peasants, for escape from agriculture if they fled to the towns, or for better rural conditions if they remained on the soil. The peasants had been raising their standard of living, adding luxuries to necessities,[22] and improving their system of cultivation. Their agriculture was becoming more intensive. Their holdings in some parts were becoming smaller and their fallow land decreasing in amount. They were raising more sheep, producing more garden stuff for the town market, and cultivating more vines.[23] This economic prosperity was threatened by the efforts of the lords to obtain a share of the added income. The lords demanded more days of service on their demesnes,[24] at the very time when the peasants needed all their labor to intensify their own agriculture. In other words, lords and peasants were competing for the town market. The lords were favoring the introduction of Roman law [25] which in disputes with tenants was on their side, while the peasants were depending on local custom which hitherto had been slowly changing in their favor. Just how far the turn in the tide of the struggle had gone by the outbreak of the peasants' war, it is, of course, impossible to say.

Obnoxious survivals as a cause The personal side of serfdom had largely disappeared in the southwest by the time of the revolt. Except here and there, peasants were free to move about and to marry their daughters as they would. But they had not gained all the elements of freedom that they desired. They were subject to week work, whilst they would have liked to give only boon-work at the plowing and harvest seasons. They had to hand over to the lord tithes or tenths of the increase of cattle, whilst they would have preferred to pay only the tithe of grain. They were prevented from fishing in flowing waters, even though their wives when pregnant longed for a fresh trout. They could not hunt nor cut wood to supply their own needs. The meadows and fields which they traditionally regarded as theirs, had been encroached upon by the lords and sold or leased out for their own profit at the expense of the peasants. And the old-time heriot was claimed long after its original occasion had passed away.[26]

PEASANT REVOLTS

The peasants were unlearned men, boors by occupation and by taste. They had words for their implements and their livestock, their pots and pans, but very few terms for abstractions. Their language could express their hopes, and their hopes formulate plans, only in so far as they could provide themselves with terms, symbols of aspiration. The Church came to their aid. The theological and ecclesiastical revolt from Rome was a lesson in expression, as well as an example of action. Poor priests who suffered from the order of affairs were ready to revolt and preached rebellion. Luther led a movement which defied Rome, and poor Lutherans were friendly to the peasants' revolt. Anabaptists who were downright socialists or communists in their teaching, supplied the peasants with expressions, leaders, and recruits. Peasant revolts had appeared years before Protestantism showed itself, and died out long before Protestantism was well established, but the two movements, economic and religious, were for a while closely associated.

The revolts of 1381 and 1524–25 were similar in many respects. In both, the upward swing had been checked; religion had come in to give expression to aspiration; socialism appeared to urge man to extreme action; and foreign wars weakened the government. In both, townsmen participated; churchmen were attacked; and castles captured. Both countries had the standing example of freedom near at hand; Germany had Switzerland, while England had Kent, one of its own counties, and across the channel the Dutch and Flemish Netherlands. Both countries had precedents of revolts for freedom; Germany had its own numerous contests of the preceding two generations and England had the uprisings of West Flanders and of the Jacquerie. But the German revolt was largely directed at tenurial disabilities, while the English was also aimed at servile status. Germany was suffering from the revival of Roman law, which affected England hardly at all. In Germany prices were rising and driving the lords to higher taxes and higher rents, while in England wages were rising and forcing the lords to check the commutation of services to money payments. In Germany much blood

Religion as a factor

1476, 1491, etc., to 1514

Comparison of revolts of 1381 and 1524–25

119

was spilt, while in England the loss of life was very slight.

Revolts in England

1549, 1607

1535, 1549, 1569

37. LATER PEASANT REVOLTS. The number of peasant revolts occurring since 1525, as well as those before that memorable year, is legion and could be described, even briefly, only in an extensive treatise. In England, the peasants rose to maintain their system of cultivation as against the enclosure movement [27] and to uphold their Catholic faith against the inroads of Protestantism.

Swiss Revolt, 1653

In Switzerland, the peasants broke out in revolt in those cantons just south of where trouble had started in Germany in 1524. As in Germany, there was much bloodshed and no immediate success. The causes were the heavy taxes imposed on the peasants by the towns and the general loss of political rights suffered by the peasants. The revolt was precipitated by the hard times that followed the Thirty Years' War which had ended in 1648.

Revolt in Russia, 1773-74

In Russia the manorial system had grown up late, beginning probably about 1500. When it had reached its height in the eighteenth century, it was even more extreme than in England and northern France in the thirteenth century. The peasants might not marry off the manor, sometimes not within it, without the lord's consent. They might not leave the manor without paying a fine. They had to obtain permission to borrow money, enter trade, the Church, or the University at Moscow. They had to give many days of service each week. When punished they were sometimes put to torture. They were often sold off the estates to work in factories or in mines. Their children were forced to enter the lord's household, virtually as domestic slaves. But the tide was turning: the greater freedom of the west was being discussed. When the lords were relieved of compulsory military service in 1762, the peasants said that they too had been included in the emancipation and that their lords were withholding their share of the Tsar's gift. Only sporadic revolts occurred until Pugachev came to the front to lead the peasants.[28] The son of a Cossack landowner, Pugachev was ignorant of books and schools, but he had seen service in the army, wandered about a good deal, and lived in monastic establishments. He proclaimed himself

Peter III, the Tsar who had really been slain some years before. He burned churches and monasteries and executed many noblemen. He captured forts and sacked towns, notably Kazan. Industrial establishments he destroyed, as also the imperial forces sent against him. His success depended not only on the fury of his bondmen followers and on the aid given him by the clergy, who had been angered by the secularization of some of their property, but on the fact that the government of Russia underestimated the movement and was engaged in a war against Turkey. Finally, betrayed by a follower who sought the reward offered for his capture, he was imprisoned and executed. He had been in himself a tower of strength, but even he, in the long run, would have been helpless against imperial forces, unless he had been able to enlist the support of the towns which refused to join his cause. Although his efforts came to naught, he is still dimly remembered as the champion of a popular cause which finally won, only when the edict of emancipation was issued in 1861.

The French Revolution was more than a peasant revolt, though the part played by the peasants was important.[29] When the Revolution started, the peasants, especially in the east, burned castles and records of the manorial system. That system survived in France in varying degrees of strength. In the east, serfdom as a status as well as servile tenure still remained,[30] though it had been abolished on the royal domains in 1779. In the north and west, the servile status had disappeared and also service on the lord's demesne, but quit rents had still to be paid in lieu of services rendered centuries previously. Commonly in France there were many petty servile dues or obligations that had survived, such as market tolls and the compulsory use of the lord's mill and oven, or the payment of a sum of money to avoid it. Apparently some of the old forgotten dues of this kind had actually been revived in the eighteenth century, an unpardonable sin in the eyes of an ambitious peasantry. Then, too, there were the manorial courts which the peasants still had to attend and appeal to for justice. All manorial elements were now swept away by various laws, and French peasants remained henceforth free in their persons

Peasants in the French Revolution, 1789 f.

4 Aug., 1789– 17 July, 1793

and free in their tenure of land.[31] Henceforth no one stepped in between the peasants and the state. The power of the nation was henceforth based on the middle class of townsmen and peasantry. Here at last was a revolt in which the peasants had won. But, if we could measure the influences, we should probably have to allot the greater share to the townsmen.

Revolt in Russia, 1918

The latest great revolt in which peasants have gained took place in Russia. This time apparently the change was instigated and carried through by the proletariat of the towns. Since 1861, the lands occupied by the peasants had been legally owned by the village group. Gradually, but particularly since 1906,[32] the communal ownership gave way to individual peasant proprietorship. The revolution of 1918, however, established national ownership and added to the peasant holdings the lands formerly owned by the lords.[33] At present there are no landlords in Russia, unless we regard the Russian state as such. Again, as in the French Revolution, the peasants profited by the action of townsmen.

Conclusions

Peasant revolts have flourished in the stages of town and metropolitan economy. There seems everywhere to have been a rising standard in economic and social conditions, which was checked, at least temporarily, by legal, political, or military events, sometimes by a turn in the economic situation. Religious thinking, about the highest form of mental exercise known to the peasant, has rarely been absent and often vitally important. The leaders of the revolts have commonly been either peasants with experience of a non-agricultural nature or non-peasants, especially of the professional classes. Purely peasant revolts rarely succeed, largely because of the lack of good leaders and because of lack of unity. There is a tendency toward individualism. As democracy increases, peasant revolts give way to farmers' movements. In France and Germany the recent movements have been for the protection of farm products by means of national tariffs. In Norway they have been in favor of native civilization and rural dialect. In America they have been for advantages in tariff regulation, cheaper transportation, the provision of rural credit, and direct government participation in the purchase of grain.[34]

Enough has perhaps already been said to indicate, if not to prove, the existence of powerful material situations driving the peasant to act. Another general force may have been the survival of a half-submerged love of freedom. This may have been set off by the existence of a few freemen on the manors and by the free townsmen. One peasant revolt may have stimulated another, though it would be rather difficult, if not impossible to prove that a revolt in one country actually brought about an uprising in another at a very much later date. Moreover, an unsuccessful revolt, and we have seen that they were all unsuccessful, would hardly have a stimulating effect. On the whole, it seems safer to infer that like situations bring about like results, whether in England or France, Europe or America.

Causes of peasant revolts

38. SUGGESTIONS FOR FURTHER STUDY

1. Study a map of Europe to note especially the geographical proximity of the early revolts.

2. See the articles on Wat Tyler and John Ball in *The Dictionary of National Biography* (ed. by Sir Leslie Stephen and Sir Sidney Lee).

3. For a contemporary account of the Social Revolt in England (1381), see *The Chronicle of Froissart* (The Tudor Translations), vol. III (1901), pp. 227–244.

4. For the revolt of 1381, see *A Dream of John Ball* (1888) by William Morris. Obviously the facts in this work are not up to date.

5. The following historical novels depict aspects of the revolt of 1381: Annie M. Meyer, *Robert Annys, Poor Priest* (1901); Florence Converse, *Long Will: a Romance of the Days of Piers Plowman* (1903). For juvenile readers: G. A. Henty, *A March on London: a Story of Wat Tyler's Insurrection* (1898); Dora M. Jones, *The Duke's Ward: a Romance of Old Kent* (1896).

6. For a biographical study of the German Revolt of 1524–1525, see the lives of Hans Müller, Thomas Münzer, Martin Luther, and Götz von Berlichingen in the various encyclopedias or biographical dictionaries.

7. For a favorable description of the German Revolt of 1524–1525, see E. B. Bax, *The Peasants War in Germany* (1899). An excellent critical Catholic account is found in J. Janssen, *History of the German People at the Close of the Middle Ages* (trans. by A. M. Christie), vol. IV (1900), pp. 121–369.

8. For the cultural and religious background of the German Revolt of 1524–1525, see Preserved Smith's *Age of the Reformation* (1920), chs. I and II; for the Revolt itself, pp. 87–95.

9. Compare the slave revolts in ancient Italy with peasant revolts. See above, ch. III.

10. Search for peasant revolts other than those dealt with in this chapter. Consider Spain, the Scandinavian countries, and China.

11. May we expect to hear of peasant revolts in the near future? Is there any serfdom in the world to-day?

12. Could there not develop peasant revolts in Mexico, if the peons sought to emancipate themselves?

13. Did the American Civil War show any elements of a peasant revolt?

14. What similarity do you observe running all through the revolts of this chapter?

15. Were the peasant revolts religious in any real sense?

16. Does it seem that there was any ideal of freedom in the minds of the peasants or only a blind groping for better conditions?

17. Is there not something rather futile in peasant revolts, if we agree that they took place when peasant disabilities were disappearing and that they rarely attained the immediate result sought?

18. Why did the peasant not revolt to any great extent when the manorial and feudal system was being established, instead of waiting till it was declining?

19. What was there in the life of the peasant, the dirt farmer, that unfitted him for leadership?

20. Compare peasant revolts and farmer's movements as to nature of the conflict, objects, and results.

21. Did the revolts take place in backward or progressive districts, far from or near to towns?

22. What is the chief economic background of peasant revolts? Is it technique of agriculture, tenure, personal status, or the commercial side of agriculture?

23. Study the Mexican revolt of 1910–11, to learn how far it was rural and agrarian.

For further suggestions, see the notes below.

39. Notes to Chapter V

1. Cf. Helen D. Irvine, *The Making of Rural Europe* (1923), p. 213.
2. See P. J. Blok, *History of the People of the Netherlands* (1892, trans. by O. A. Bierstadt and Ruth Putnam), vol. I (1898), p. 208.
3. Kervyn de Lettenhove's *Histoire de Flandre,* vol. II (1874), pp 99–121, has been supplanted (as far as the peasants are concerned) by H. Pirenne. Le Soulèvement de la Flandre Maritime de 1323–1328, *Academie Royale de Belgique, Commission Royale d'Histoire* (1900), introduction and documents.
4. Cf. A. Hyma, The Disappearance of Serfdom in England, *The Quarterly Journal of the University of North Dakota,* vol. XIV (1924), p. 135.
5. See *The Chronicle of Froissart* (The Tudor Translations, 1901), vol. I, pp. 399–400; S. Luce, *Histoire de la Jacquerie d'après des Documents Inédits* (1859, 1894), pp. 9–38.
6. *The Chronicle of Froissart* (The Tudor Translations, 1901), vol. I, pp. 403–405.
7. S. Luce, *Histoire de la Jacquerie d'après des Documents Inédits* (1859, 1894), pp. 133–159.
8. At least the two following contemporary chronicles, both translated into English, should be read : *The Chronicle of Froissart* (The Tudor Translations, 1901), vol. III, pp. 227–244, and The Anonymous Chronicle of St. Mary's, York, in C. Oman, *The Great Revolt of 1381* (1906), pp. 186–205.
9. G. Kriehn, The Social Revolt of 1381, *American Historical Review,* vol. VII (1902), pp. 254 f., 458 f.
10. C. Oman, *The Great Revolt of 1381* (1906), pp. 36–38.
11. *Ibid.,* pp. 12, 20, 51–52, 190.
12. The Anonymous Chronicle of St. Mary's, York, in C. Oman *The Great Revolt of 1381* (1906), pp. 186–205.
13. E. Powell, *The Rising in East Anglia in 1381* (1896), pp. 9–66; A. Réville, *Le Soulèvement des Travailleurs d'Angleterre en 1381* (ed. by C. Petit-Dutaillis, 1898), pp. 3 f.
14. C. Petit-Dutaillis, Introduction Historique (1897) in A. Réville, *Le Soulèvement, des Travailleurs d'Angleterre en 1381* (1898), p. CX.
15. See G. Kriehn, The Social Revolt of 1381, *American Historical Review,* vol. VIII (1902), pp. 280–285, 477–484.
16. J. E. T. Rogers (*History of Agriculture and Prices in England,* vol. I, 1886, pp. 81–84, and *Six Centuries of Work and Wages,* 1884, pp. 253–254), maintained that commutation had

gone far by the time of the Black Death (1348–49) and that thereafter the lords not only refused further commutation but actually sought to go back to the old labor services. The peasants, he thought, rose in revolt against this. In other words they were fighting against a loss of what had already been attained. T. W. Page, on the other hand (*End of Villainage in England*, Publications of the American Economic Association, 3rd series, vol. I, no. 2, 1900, pp. 323–387), sought to prove from statistics that there had been very little commutation, that it really took place in the 15th century. The revolt, therefore, was to attain something new, not to retain what was threatened. H. L. Gray (Commutation of Villein Services in England, *English Historical Review*, vol. XXIX, 1914, pp. 650–651), making a second statistical study, came to a third conclusion. Rogers' view, that there had been commutation, was correct, but it applied to only one part of England, the north and west, the district where the revolt had been least prominent. Page's conclusion, he held, applied to the south and east. Here commutation had not gone far and peasants rising in this part of England, sought to attain fully what they had only slightly tasted before. Gray and Page are in substantial agreement on the aspect of the question and the part of the country with which we are at present concerned.

17. This latter view is held by G. Kriehn, The Social Revolt of 1381, *American Historical Review*, vol. VII (1902), p. 281.

18. This was outlawry as a process of law. The outlaw might be killed, if he resisted, and he lost his right to his land and chattels.

19. C. Oman, *The Great Revolt of 1381* (1906), ch. II.

20. G. M. Trevelyan, *England in the Age of Wyclif* (1899, 1900), p. 199.

21. Cf. W. Stolze, *Der deutsche Bauernkrieg* (1908), p. 49.

22. J. Janssen, *History of the German People at the Close of the Middle Ages* (trans. by A. M. Christie), vol. IV (1900), p. 148.

23. W. Stolze, *Der deutsche Bauernkrieg* (1908), pp. 46–49.

24. See the sixth of The Twelve Articles, *Translations and Reprints*, University of Pennsylvania, vol. II, no. 6 (1902), p. 29.

25. Cf. the ninth of The Twelve Articles, *ibid.*, p. 29; J. S. Schapiro, *Social Reform and the Reformation*, Columbia Studies in History, Economics, and Public Law, vol. XXIV, no. 2 (1909), pp. 40–53.

26. See the Twelve Articles, *Translations and Reprints*, University of Pennsylvania, vol. II, no. 6 (1902), p. 29.

27. See below, ch. VII, sect. 49, pp. 168 f.

28. J. Mavor, *An Economic History of Russia* (1914), vol. I, pp. 181, 262, 301, 310, 442; vol. II, pp. 40–62.

29. See H. A. Taine, *The French Revolution* (trans. by J. Durand, 1878), pp. 9 f.

30. See Voltaire, *Œuvres Complètes,* vol. XXIX (1785), pp. 457–511, especially pp. 499 f., for an account of serfdom on the lands of the Abbey of St. Claude, Franche-Comté.

31. *The Constitutions and Other Select Documents illustrative of the History of France* (ed. by F. M. Anderson, 1904, 1908), pp. 11–12; A. Esmein, *Précis Élémentaire de l'Histoire du Droit Français de 1789 à 1814* (1907, 1911), pp. 57–74.

32. Al. A. Tschuprow, The Break-up of the Village Community in Russia, *The Economic Journal,* vol. XXII (1912), pp. 173 f.

33. See the Russian Constitution of 10 July, 1918, and The Russian Land Law going into force September, 1918. *International Conciliation,* no. 136 (March, 1919), pp. 73, 91.

34. See below, ch. XVI, sect. 118, pp. 418 f.

CHAPTER VI

METROPOLITAN AND NATIONAL ECONOMY IN ENGLAND: THE ECONOMICS AND THE POLITICS OF MODERN AGRICULTURE

Metropolitan marketing and national political influences

40. THE CONCEPT OF METROPOLITAN ECONOMY. Before proceeding with the story of agriculture, we need to consider at least two of the factors that are dominant in the modern period. On the one hand, there is the development of economic organization; on the other, the growth of a political frame-work. There arises in the early modern period a remarkable duality of economic interest and political policy, which though distinct are not separate. These two ingredients of modern social growth in general and of modern agriculture in particular are metropolitan economy and national economy.

Some towns became metropolitan centers

The economic background of agricultural progress up to this point has been the four stages of general economic organization, outlined above.[1] The fifth stage, the one following town economy, is metropolitan economy.[2] The large town, the outstanding urban center, slowly grew into an economic metropolis. Outwardly the difference between the metropolis and the town was chiefly a matter of size. Sometimes the old walls were torn down in places and extended outward to include the new houses, shops, and stores. Often there were complaints of the rapid increase, and efforts were made to check it. Such were the growing pains of a new institution. The old two-story building of shop and upper dwelling was rebuilt with three or four stories. The number of market places was increased. More vehicles entered the metropolis than the town. Business was brisker and bore heavier risks with larger gains and greater losses. The artisan-trader or petty merchant of town economy saw himself subordinated to the man of big business, against whose activities loud outcry

128

was raised. In fact, his operations are only now, in our time, being made acceptable to the small man of affairs in town or country.

Before a town could develop into a metropolis, it had to possess certain outstanding advantages. It had to be reasonably healthful. The town located on the seacoast or a tidal river obviously had a great asset in the matter of drainage. No considerable progress could be made unless there were facilities for transportation by land and by water. Location between large groups of consumers and producers was also necessary. London lies between the rich European market and the less developed lands overseas. New York stands with its back to a bountiful area and its face to Europe and the rest of the world. A middle position is not in itself sufficient, as is illustrated by the Phœnician and Greek cities. They had no extensive or rich area of supply behind them, no hinterland as a base of operations. Metropolitan economy is, indeed, an informal organization of people having a large city as nucleus (just as town economy had a town as its center) and beyond an extensive, accessible, and fertile area. It is a mutually dependent group of producers and consumers who exchange goods and services by means of the orderly arrangements worked out in a large city which is the focus of local trade and the center through which normal economic relations with the outside are established and maintained.

What a metropolis needed

When town economy arose, village economy disappeared but not the villages: they remained, but subordinate to the urban center. And so with metropolitan economy: while it destroyed town economy, it left the towns, not with their old-time independence but economically subordinated to the metropolitan center. The towns remained to perform commercial, industrial, and cultural services for the country round about. Some of them developed special functions in commerce, transportation, or manufacture. They were the divisional centers of the metropolitan area, looking much as of old but bowing before the towering dominance of the metropolis. Through them the metropolis kept its hold on farmers and foresters, miners and fishermen. Through them the farm and the mine,

Subordination of towns

the ranch and the humble cottage obtained their supplies of material goods and cultural stimuli.

Metropolitan unit

The metropolitan unit is made up of the central city and a wide area of communities round about. From the standpoint of metropolitan economy the center is the vital part, but from the standpoint of society the area is of greater importance. If the metropolis declined and passed away, the area could still survive—in town or village economy. But the loss of the center would mean great economic and cultural retrogression. The metropolis and its district are mutually dependent. Without one the other would fall—as a part of metropolitan economy. For agriculture it is obvious that the area is of greater importance than the metropolis, and yet, as will appear, the influence of centralization in marketing is becoming greater and greater in the life and work of the cultivator.

Four phases in London's development

41. DEVELOPMENT OF METROPOLITAN ECONOMY. A new economic system, so important for agriculture as metropolitan economy, merits considerable attention. It was London and the area round about which first developed into a metropolitan unit and which have gone through all the changes of function anywhere to be observed. In the process of metropolitan growth we can observe four phases, which, whether as clear or not as in the case of London, seem to be widely prevalent. The first of these is the development of a marketing

1550–1750

system which occupied about two centuries in the London unit.

Specialized wholesalers

In such a wide market, or exchange area, as the metropolitan, a specialized wholesaling class is required. In the Middle Ages, or that part of it dominated by town economy, there was wholesaling but not a well developed class of wholesalers. Traders bringing a shipload of grain or wine were commonly required by town regulations to sell to consumers who might come to the ship to buy. After the latter had been satisfied, sale to the "trade," that is, local retailers, might take place. The peasant was forced to expose his grain for a while, so that the consumer might take his choice. Then he might sell to a corn dealer, if he had any grain left. Even during the stage of town economy, it had been hard to keep wholesalers from specializing. In metropolitan economy, division of labor between wholesalers and retailers became more or less hard and fast. The wholesaler arose to serve the widening market. If he was in the wine business, he either imported the wine or bought it on arrival, and then sold it to taverners in single casks. If in the grain business, he bought the supply of the peasant, allowing the latter to go home sooner than he otherwise would, or he purchased a whole cargo of grain on arrival. This wholesaler was the man of big business who made the larger (metropolitan) unit possible. Although he specialized in wholesaling as distinct from retailing, nevertheless he combined merchandising with other functions. For example, he was not only a trader but a carrier and warehouseman. As further specialization grew, he hired the common carrier, whether ship owner or carter, to transport his goods, and often employed a warehouseman whose sole business it was to store for other persons.

Merchants having long distances to go or trafficking afar and accordingly bearing great risks, had a business peculiar unto themselves. To meet their particular needs, exchanges grew up, at first on a street or a square, later in some enclosure or building. In the medieval town there were exchanges where a merchant could go to trade the coin of one country for that of another. Such a place with its money changers came to contain a motley group of dealers, not only exchanging money but arranging for the sale of jewels or fine cloth, valuable leather or wine. Retailers joined the group, selling out of hand or inviting prospective customers to their stores or shops. As the exchanges became better organized and as they erected special buildings for their use, reserving at least one floor for their own particular benefit, the retailers were pushed out or eliminated. Then the advantages of specialization showed themselves, so that one exchange came to deal in securities only (the stock exchange), one in cotton, and another in grain or produce. When located in metropolitan centers, these exchanges dominate the trade of wide areas. Examples are the London Corn Exchange, the Liverpool Cotton Exchange, the New York Produce Exchange, and the Chicago grain exchange (Board of Trade).

Exchanges

**Joint-
stock
com-
panies**

The same merchants who were founding exchange associations were establishing joint-stock companies, notably for col-
onization and trade. Although the joint-stock company was
used before the metropolis existed, it was not an important
factor in trade till the metropolitan stage. Any venture that
required much capital and encountered great risk, was difficult for one man even though rich. Accordingly, a joint-
stock was formed. When well developed, this joint-stock
was made up of a specified number of shares of equal value,
and available for sale. Although the first joint-stock company

1553

in English commerce was probably the Russia Company, the
earliest of importance was the East India Company, founded

1600

chiefly by London merchants, to trade directly with India,
Ceylon, and the East Indian islands. Shortly after this, the
Virginia Company was created to colonize and develop Virginia. English noblemen and London merchants were the
backers of the company and sank a good deal of money in their
venture which was financially unprofitable.

**Joint-
stock
companies
facili-
tate con-
centration**

Joint-stock companies were of great aid in the establishment
of metropolitan economy. Enterprises of unprecedented magnitude were possible with their assistance, to explore unknown
lands, to colonize the most promising parts, and to carry on
trade over distant seas at great risk. With their use in mining and manufacturing we are not now concerned. The various commercial fields were given to the several companies to
develop as they might. The companies usually bore the names
of the district that they were to exploit. Some of them are
well known—the Eastland, Russian, Levant, East India, West
India, and Virginia Companies. When these companies got
under way, the wares of distant lands poured into London, and,
of course, goods or cash had to be sent out to pay for what
was brought in. Never before did so many parts of the world
pay tribute to one city, and never did so many districts derive
such advantage from one trading center. The capital required
for enterprises of such magnitude could be raised only by
tapping all available sources, the surplus of nobleman and
merchant, priest and orphan. In London, merchants were
usually in general charge of such companies and many suc-

132

cesses resulted, but in Paris the nobles and state officials had much to say and many failures are to be recorded.

Such trade, as has just been described, was beyond the metropolitan area itself. It may be called "extended" or extrametropolitan. As explorations continued south and west, the extended trade of metropolitan or incipient metropolitan centers grew. Lisbon, London, and Amsterdam were all eager competitors, throwing out their tentacles to the uttermost parts of the earth, trading with the villages of Africa and America and the towns of India and Russia. When the commerce was between two metropolitan centers, for example, London and Amsterdam, we may speak of inter-metropolitan trade. Some of the old type of local trade necessarily remained, and remained of great importance. This was between town and country or town and town. A fourth kind of trade, and most significant of all was the hinterland-metropolis commerce. This was the concentration of products from the hinterland and the radiation of wares from the metropolis. This exchange was brisk and decisive. It opened up new avenues of transportation and communication, and established a new cultural association in which local peculiarities tended to give way before metropolitan habits and tastes. The exact delimits of such an area are difficult or impossible to set forth. In the case of London the metropolitan area included well nigh all of England, at least in the first part of metropolitan development. *Kinds of metropolitan commerce*

A metropolitan city which focused upon itself the products of so many kinds of trade must be a vast storage center. Always playing an important rôle in commerce, storage now became a vital part of metropolitan trade. More wares and goods in greater variety were stored up. They came, on the average, longer distances than commodities exchanged in town economy. In the town stage, storage had been in the hands of artisans, retailers, and wholesalers in the town itself, and of cultivators in the country. In the metropolitan period there arose specialized warehousemen who stored not on their own account but for others at so much per bushel, barrel, or hundredweight. Enormous sums have been invested in this new *Storage* business which also requires special knowledge and which has been much subdivided. There are to-day grain elevators, cotton warehouses, cold-storage plants, and the like in great plenty, all at the service of townsman or countryman.

New methods

As metropolitan economy came into being, many new methods were adopted. Advertising became a valuable aid to merchandising. Merchants began to hustle for business, instead of just sitting with folded hands waiting for it, as had been the case in town economy. In other words competition became patent and noisy. The manufacture of new cloth out of old clothes, long banned as unprofessional, came to be a regular business, the shoddy trade of modern times. An eagerness to venture new enterprises and a willingness to make new experiments, created a business enterprise that was dynamic beyond precedent. Many were the losses incurred; but the tales of gains from being first in some new undertaking, lured men on, some to success, some to bankruptcy.

London's supply of grain

While the new developments in business organization were going forward, the government, both national and local, looked on with only periodic interference and only in respect to a few matters. The civic magistrates did not think it safe, however, to leave the grain trade of London to develop unassisted or unregulated like the spice, fur, or fruit, trades. London in the days of town economy brought its grain from the near-by counties of England, and only occasionally from abroad. Metropolitan London, however, had to look farther afield, especially to the Baltic. The national government's aid was enlisted to assist in bringing grain into the country, in conserving the domestic supply, and in transporting the surplus of the hinterland to London. After a fairly long period (1514–1660) of municipal regulation and storage, it seemed safe to leave the supplying of the metropolis with grain, to the private grain merchants. Capital, enterprise, and knowledge had so developed that government aid was superfluous and government regulation more of a hindrance than a help. London had become a grain center through private initiative and had enough and to spare. Agriculture had played its part by increasing production. Country buyers and metropolitan merchants stood ready in fat years to export unlimited quantities abroad and in lean years to provide at home or abroad all that the metropolis needed. In the period of market adjustment and food scarcity, it became clear to the authorities that a rich producing area was vital to the growth of large cities. Without the farmer's surplus there could, indeed, be no metropolis. For a time both in Europe and America there was competition between actual or incipient metropolitan centers for the grain and meat supplies of the intervening territory. London and Bristol drew grain from the same section, also Paris and Rouen, New York and Montreal. In the period of plenty that has intervened since the adolescence of metropolitan economy, the importance of a grain supply has often been forgotten. There is a possibility that in the future the large city, the central metropolitan market, will again face a stringency and will again be compelled to make adjustments that will try the patience and ingenuity of those in positions of responsibility.

Closely connected with the organization of the market was the development of manufactures, which, however, came as a movement somewhat after the general market changes. The industrial progress consisted in the giving up of much household manufacture, the growth of many new industries in the metropolis, the improvement of industrial organization, and the application of power machinery, especially in the making of textile and metallic wares. *The second phase of metropolitan economy*

The metropolis, like other large cities, develops manufactures in its very midst. The demand within the confines of the metropolitan center itself is stimulus enough to give rise to new industries. The manufacturer has right at hand a consuming public and he can utilize the metropolitan marketing organization to purchase raw materials and secure labor as well as to dispose of all surplus not used by the people of the metropolis. The manufacture of luxuries thrives in the central market city, that is, the making of wares such as fine clothing, jewelry, and various confections. For example, when knitted hoisery and fine coaches were introduced into England, they were first made in London. *Industries in the metropolis*

Many industries are obliged to leave the metropolis because

135

Industries in the hinterland

of the high cost of manufacture. The silk industry of London in the eighteenth century and the printing of books in New York in the twentieth are instances of this. As is to be expected, many new industries of a staple variety are never, or rarely, set up in a metropolis. The cotton and iron and steel industries of England belong to the north, not to London. To accommodate these and other manufactures, industrial satellites, some of considerable prominence such as Birmingham in England and Pittsburgh in America, have sprung up. Many of the new industries lent themselves to power-machine production and the use of unskilled labor. The latter often came from the farms when cultivators lost their holdings or when agricultural laborers were invited by higher wages to enter central workshops or factories. The power machinery was provided in large part by the capital accumulated in commerce and agriculture, which was now turned into the promising business of manufacture. This phase in the growth of metropolitan economy in and about London occupied the period roughly from 1750 to 1830. That part of it connected with the use of power machinery is known as the industrial revolution.

Third phase, transportation

Although the general market development of the first phase of metropolitan economy and the industrial progress of the second phase were accompanied by many improvements in transportation, nevertheless in England, and in western Europe generally, the revolution in transportation succeeded that in industry, as will be apparent from what follows.

Congestion in the metropolis

As traffic of men and vehicles increased in the metropolis itself, there arose difficulties which were hard to meet. Streets had to be widened as carts and wagons multiplied, and roads had to be paved more solidly when heavy wagons and later heavy motor trucks appeared upon them. New thoroughfares running long distances had to be constructed to handle the traffic. London has solved this problem less drastically than Paris, at least on the surface roads. The old walls, and especially the old narrow gates, had to go, as more space was needed, as railroads demanded entry, and as houses grew beyond them so far as to render them useless for protection.

In spite of all the ingenious contrivances of engineers and officials, in spite of the outlay of capital on viaducts, overhead railroads, and underground tubes for freight and passengers, the problem of transportation is getting more, rather than less, serious, largely because of the increase of motor cars.

During village economy roads had been largely trails. In town economy more effort had been put forth to keep the highways in repair, but in rainy weather the roads were often impassable and in backward parts they were never convenient or smooth. There was no central plan and no central authority active in constructing great arterial highways, except for the purposes of war, until metropolitan economy came into existence. Horses had carried loads up and down the old neglected trails and carts had struggled through the mire with the peasant's grain. All agricultural products had been taken to the nearest town market for sale, or were sent to the most convenient coast town or river for transportation by water. This had been roundabout and expensive. As highways were improved for long distances, goods could be sent directly by wagon to the place where they were to be used. Common carriers arose to do the work formerly performed by farmer or by trader, not simply within the towns, where they had long operated, but in the country as well, where until the time of metropolitan economy they had been few in number or non-existent. These special carriers transported either goods or passengers. Stage coaches began to ply regularly in England, centering particularly in London. And hard it was to keep the miserably constructed roads in good condition when they were regularly used, in wet as in dry weather. In the eighteenth century, however, engineers, such as Metcalfe, Telford, and Macadam, came to the rescue, constructing highways which were at once smooth and well drained. It is true that improvements have had to be made in very recent years to accommodate our heavy vehicles, still the highway since their time has been an effective metropolitan agency.

Highways could not alone provide adequate transportation to growing metropolitan centers. Two proposals for a canal were made as early as the seventeenth century, to connect Lon-

Country roads

17th cent.

Canals

1782

don with Bristol which was her somewhat independent rival in the west. When finally constructed, the expense was born largely by rich London merchants, showing not only that London was rich but most concerned with the enterprise. The first considerable canal building in England occurred in the north, partly to assist in the opening up of coal and iron mines and the development of the new industries, and partly also to make connections by sea with the metropolis. Later many canals were built with London as an immediate focus, so that directly or indirectly canals helped the farmer, the factory owner, and the miner send his wares to London, and to receive back supplies needed in the provinces or hinterland. But canal barges, drawn by horses or pushed by hand, were too slow. In summer the canals dried up, at least in part, and in winter they were in danger of freezing over and shutting off all traffic.

Railroads

1837 f.

The earliest important railroad used by a steam locomotive connected Liverpool and Manchester in 1830. Later a veritable network of lines was built with London as the center in England, and Paris in France. To the towns and to the metropolis these railroads sent fresh fish from the seacoast, vegetables and fruits from districts where they could be most profitably grown, and eggs, fowl, dairy products, and meat from the countryside generally. To the farmer this meant opportunity for sale that had never been known before. Although a few countrymen—the country gentlemen were most vocal—objected to the new means of transportation, the grateful people accepted them as few things have been received before. The railroad has been one of the greatest emancipators of the human species, although to-day we think of it chiefly in terms of petty grievances of faulty schedule or excessive rate.

Steamships

What the railroad did for land traffic, steamships did for water transportation. Although America made notable progress in river steamboats—the *Clermont* went up the Hudson in 1807,—still it was England that did the chief pioneering on the sea. Englishmen were the first to make the Atlantic liners a continuous success, the first with iron and then with steel ships, and the first to apply the screw propeller to com-

138

mercial steamships. As was to be expected, England reaped her reward for priority in freight from goods and fares from passengers carried all over the world. To this day England has retained preëminence, though America, Germany, and Japan are potential and actual rivals. For English agriculture the result of the new ocean steamships with their holds full of grain and meat was threatening, even temporarily disastrous. English cultivators with heavy expenses could not compete successfully with American, Argentinian, and Australian farmers using up the bountiful fertility of a virgin soil that had never known the weeds or parasites that blight the crops of man. What English and, we may add, European agriculture lost, the American farmer gained. Many of the old-world farmers left for the new lands to partake of the promised fortune there. The great steamship lines concentrated in the metropolitan center of London or on tributary ports which were in effect London ports. Or they helped to develop rival centers, notably in the northwest of England, at Liverpool and Manchester, which, with close railroad connections and a ship canal, were essentially one economic center.

Post office Using now-a-days both the railroad and the steamship but nevertheless antedating them by centuries, is the post office, a potent instrument for the expansion of metropolitan influence and service. As a public utility the post office dates from about 1637 when it became a government monopoly and was already used by London merchants. From the carrying of letters, the English post office has extended its services to the transmitting of money, the keeping of deposits, the sending of telegrams, and the use of the telephone. The Englishman of to-day thinks more about some petty annoyance that he petulantly complains of than the great service which he enjoys and his ancestors had never experienced.

Parcel post In order to use railroads and steamships effectively there had to be some means of sending small parcels. The rank and file of producers and consumers had only occasional packages to send and these went to various parts of the world, both far and near. At first private express companies undertook to provide this service. Later the post office in England

and elsewhere took it over. Accordingly to-day it is possible for the farmer to send his honey and eggs, fruit and fowl to the adjoining town or to the brisker central market for sale. And it is equally convenient for him to receive parts for his machinery, clothes for himself and family, and even groceries and many other supplies for general use, either from the local town or from the metropolitan center, from the local dealer or from the big mail-order house of a great commercial city. All this is a tremendous help for agriculture.

Significance for the farmer

Generally speaking, the development of metropolitan economy has affected the farmer more than anything that has happened since the growth of towns. It has given him a market for his wares that he never knew before, that is, a place to sell practically all he can produce—at the prevailing price. It has brought him into competitive relations with farmers in his own nation and in many other parts of the world. Cheaper rates for transportation have been made possible not simply through the economy of locomotion, but through the saving involved in concentration in one large center. If town economy had prevailed, railroads and highways would have had to be built and equally well kept up between town and town much in the fashion of a checker-board. But in metropolitan economy, saving is possible through the effective concentration in a large city. Everywhere this is at least vaguely understood, or at any rate unconsciously accepted. Efficient and economical transportation in the long run means cheaper supplies and a higher net price for products than would otherwise prevail. It means that the goods purchased and sold are fresher and generally in better condition. Economic and cultural isolation is banished. A more commercialized agriculture and a more business-like cultivator are now possible. In a very general way the various new services in transportation, although they developed early, nevertheless fell chiefly within the period 1830–1890 in the case of London. They still continue to be performed and to be improved, but now another movement seems to have supplanted them, not in operation but in the newness of service, as will appear below.

Along with the general development of the market and rev- **Fourth** olutionary changes in industry and transportation went finan- **phase,** cial progress. Exchanging and loaning money had been com- **financial** mon in town economy, but now in metropolitan economy financial machinery became more elaborate, extensive, and effective. In so far as we can mark such a development off from the others, we must say that it came to constitute a phase of metropolitan growth only in the latter part of the nineteenth century. In the case of London, we may probably ascribe the outstanding financial period to the time since about 1890. It is an axiom that finance is the handmaid of commerce, industry, and other forms of production, but it is well known that, once established, financial institutions and habits of thinking have great power and influence through the agency of credit extended to this enterprise, withdrawn from that. And financial middlemen, such as bankers and brokers, have a psychology of their own. For instance, nearly all bankers, where they have a choice, especially those in metropolitan centers, tend to neglect agricultural interests and to foster trade and industry. They commonly have a preference for free trade as against protection. They promote enterprises that are often more effective in paying dividends than in serving the people.

Apart from money, the oldest financial instrument that was **Bill of** important in metropolitan economy is the bill of exchange. **exchange** It is simply a draft or call made by one dealer against another for a sum of money to be paid within a short time. During the period it has to run, the draft may circulate from hand to hand as paper money. If both dealers concerned, the payor and the payee, are well known and trusted, the draft is readily accepted by all, the last man to receive it, however, making sure that he presents it at the time and place it is due. Even in the town economy of the Middle Ages the bill of exchange was used in inter-urban trade. A Florentine cloth merchant sold a piece of fine cloth to an English draper. He then drew up a draft on the draper who proceeded to sign it, as did the cloth merchant. The bill was due at a certain fair in Champagne in northern France. In metropolitan economy such a bill was used in trade between one metropolis and another and between a metropolis and a distant town, but also, and more characteristically, between the metropolis and the hinterland. There were two kinds of brokers handling such paper, discounting it for the period it had to run, the foreign bill brokers and the domestic bill brokers. Such instruments while of great value to commerce have had little to do with agriculture until the recent development of business-like farmers who have a large turn-over in cattle, dairy products, or in grain.

Stock exchanges and speculation

The stock exchange took its start in town economy but became a vital instrument only in metropolitan economy. Developing first for the sale of spices, gold, cloth, and other staple and standard commodities, it came to deal also in securities or credit paper—such as bills of exchange, certificates of government debts, and private company's bonds and stocks. Here on the stock exchange merchants and brokers, traders and stock-jobbers, stood side by side engaging in their hectic and often nerve-racking business. The Royal Exchange in London, **1568** which had been established in the days of Queen Elizabeth, somewhat before the planting of the American colonies, came to contain all the divers sorts of traders. So obnoxious, however, did the speculators become that they were forced out—to **1698** do business on the streets. After meeting for a long time in the coffee houses, they erected a building of their own, the Stock Exchange, which, of course, still is a vitally important institution in metropolitan economy. Paris, New York, and many other cities have constructed exchanges of various kinds. These tend to increase in number as business becomes more keen, some devoted to paper securities, such as stocks and bonds, and others to staple commodities, such as grain, cotton, coffee, and produce. Against some of these, farmers have been very hostile, partly because of evil practices and partly because of ignorant prejudice as to the functions they perform. Without them there could have been no smooth market machinery for the purchase of farmers' products and the sale of farmers' supplies. Whether such a system, so helpful in the past, will be equally necessary in the future is nevertheless a very different matter.

As the market area widened, and as the number of persons **Business** in metropolitan economic groups multiplied, the affairs of **cycles** business became increasingly uncertain and risky. Men bought and sold on the stock exchanges and elsewhere in anticipation of failure of crops, disaster to foreign governments, and wrecks of cargo ships. There was a constant change in the amount of produce raised and the amount of wares manufactured and imported. Such fluctuations in supply, with resulting changes in demand, were reflected in variations in price. The upshot was a wave-like movement in trade, which has now received the name of business cycle. This cycle is made up of prosperity, inflation (rising prices), crisis (sometimes a panic), and deflation. For 150 years or more London experienced fluctuations, but it was only in 1720 that the modern phenomenon of the crisis occurred with all its violence and disaster. At times the farmer has lain almost secure from such eruptions; but as metropolitan influences have reached out and brought him within the circle of brisk and continuous marketing, and as the business-like farmer has taken the place of the older types, the countryside has come to experience the ups and downs of commercial fortune involved in the business cycle. The urban merchants, the manufacturers, bankers, and others have taken many generations to adjust themselves to the vicissitudes of fortune, so it may be expected that the business farmer will require time to learn the necessary lessons. Because of the fact that we know much about the cycle and have many agencies of enlightenment, the farmer may escape with but a few singeings and scalpings.

Playing an important rôle in the business cycle and supreme **Banks** in metropolitan finance are the banks. In flourishing towns of the Middle Ages we already find banks, notably in Genoa and Venice, with varying degrees of fortune. The oldest in London were private banks that grew out of the practices of **Early** goldsmiths, who first loaned out their own capital and later **17th cent.** loaned money received on deposit. The Bank of England then came as a semi-public, and semi-official institution to loan **1694**

143

1826

money to the government, receive deposits, and make commercial loans. It was a long time before the Bank of England established branches in the hinterland and participated directly in the hinterland-metropolitan finance of London. From first to last the Bank of England has been a banker's bank. Indeed it is the coping stone of private finance rather than the system itself. The banking business of the merchant, manufacturer, and farmer has been done by the private banks, at least at first, and gradually more and more by joint-stock banks owned by many security holders. The latter are hardly 100 years old, but they have grown in power and prestige. At first they were local independent institutions, then they established branches. The large banks with many branches amalgamated one with another until there have come to be just five great joint-stock banks, all with head offices in London.

Since 1826

Financial concentration and radiation

By means of the network of banks the financial resources of the metropolitan unit have been made fluid for the use of all the parts according to their varying needs. Capital from one section, chiefly in the form of deposits, flows from one district to another where it is in greater demand. An agricultural community at one season of the year will have a surplus for a manufacturing district; at another time it will have to borrow. Regardless of the amount or the direction of the movement, the transaction is commonly effected through London, or through machinery devised in London. In this way towns, countryside, and metropolis are knit together into one effective whole.

Metropolis visualized

From the standpoint of a resident in the central city, the metropolis is a group of persons and a collection of buildings which are very busy with local and outside affairs. For the services performed, a considerable toll is charged. Opportunity lies there for brains and energy. For the farmer the metropolis is usually a great busy hive of complicated institutions which seem somehow to depend in the last analysis upon agriculture (and mining and fishing), but which appear nevertheless to carry on their affairs without consulting or considering the farmer. In fact metropolitan economy is a

144

network of private and public institutions finely integrated for the economical performance of functions necessary to a highly specialized existence. It has no written constitution. Its spirit is private gain and competition, either free or modified. The farmer exists on the outskirts, either in geographical location or in power to control. When village economy had given way to town economy, the cultivator of the soil was forced to turn his eyes away from his abode to a near-by town where he bought his supplies, sold his surplus, and received news and ideas. Then metropolitan economy established an even greater and generally more distant center. The farmer was now even more remote from the vital point of material and cultural affairs. His subordination to the mechanism, which he could hardly know much about, was greater than ever. From one point of view he was a fly caught in a gigantic spider's web, the center of which was far away but made none the less fearful and threatening by the presence of the big business man who "determined" the ups and downs of trade, fixed prices and rates of carriage and storage, and commanded for himself a handsome reward from the whole area. As the old-time cultivators have given way to more business-like farmers, this idea has been modified or even dissipated. The farm, however, still remains a long way off in one way or another from the effective control of business.

42. SIGNIFICANCE OF METROPOLITAN ECONOMY FOR AGRICULTURE. While the metropolis was developing, the farmer was growing grain, raising livestock, and generally trying to make ends meet. Although quite unconscious of the nature of the change in the economic organization of society, the farmer was profoundly affected by it. The most general expression of the effect was the more complete commercialization of agriculture, with varying degrees according to circumstances. Although we can say that the metropolis affected agriculture directly according to the distance of the farm from the metropolitan center (or more accurately, according to the ease of access), nevertheless we have to make many exceptions because of variations of soil and

Metropolitan economy and agriculture

climate. Metropolitan centers grew up at points convenient for trade and always within reach of food-stuffs and raw materials. But the metropolis often had at its very door considerable stretches of unproductive soil, although fertile fields lay not far off. London had the rich valleys of the Thames and the Ouse, but many barren heaths lay near-by. New York had fertile stretches to the east and south and the rich Mohawk and Genesee Valleys farther off; but just to the north there were rocky districts and to the south some swamps and forest areas that were largely unproductive.

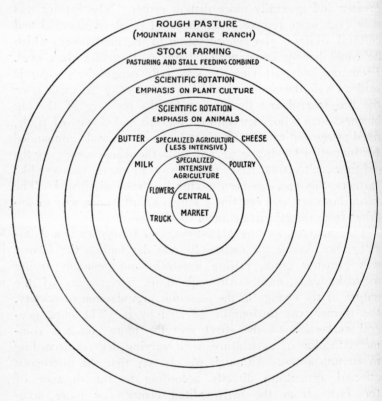

TYPES OF AGRICULTURE
SURROUNDING
A CENTRAL OR METROPOLITAN MARKET

METROPOLITAN ECONOMY IN ENGLAND

In a general way, the technique of the farmer is determined, at least in part, by the *accessibility* of central markets, usually metropolitan centers. What a man will do with his land in a system of commercialized agriculture depends on his opportunity to dispose of his products.[3] If he is near a metropolis, under normal conditions, he will work his land intensively, carefully managing every acre and applying large amounts of labor and capital to it. Such are the gardeners who serve the metropolis with flowers, fruits, and vegetables. Of course, we know that special advantages of soil, climate, and aptitude of labor have enabled the fruit grower of the southern part of France and the vegetable grower of Belgium to rival the producers of Kent on the markets of London. These are, of course, the exceptions that point to the rule. Beyond the gardens are the dairy farms which provide fresh milk and cream. Then there is the wide stretch of general farms producing cereals and livestock. The livestock may provide the metropolis with meat or with butter and cheese. In some metropolitan areas there lie at the extreme confines mountainous or other lands fit only for grazing. Here is found perhaps the least intensive method of using the land.

Metropolitan economy and agricultural technique

It can be stated in a general way that land values are highest near the metropolis, because of the greater intensity of agriculture, although there will necessarily be many exceptions owing to differences in the fertility of the soil. Truck-gardening land bears a high rental, while at the other extreme rough grazing land can yield but a very low income. What part of the rental is due to fertility and what part to accessibility to the market cannot in practice be determined.

Metropolitan influence on land values

It would be tempting to deduce that the nearer we go to a central market the greater the amount of tenancy we find. The argument is that, as the system of cultivation becomes more and more intensive and the value of the land higher and higher, the more the cultivator is compelled to invest his capital in equipment (especially in general agriculture) leaving little or nothing for purchasing land.[4] An exhaustive study might show that such was on the whole the case, but so many exceptions would probably be discovered that the rule would

Effect on tenancy

147

not be worth much.[5]   We actually find, in America at least, not a few gardeners near central markets owning their small farms.   Fruit farms are generally operated by owners, because the trees require careful handling over a long period of time.   It is a matter of common observation that there is more tenancy on small and medium farms where the emphasis is on cereals, cotton, tobacco, and plant culture generally, than on farms on which livestock is raised in considerable numbers.

Effect on well-being

It is difficult to make any general statement about the well-being or plane of living of the cultivators as they radiate out from the metropolis.   There certainly are advantages in being near the big center where goods in great variety can be purchased and where highly specialized personal service is available.   On the other hand, the intensive labor system on small farms near the metropolis is often so exacting and sometimes so unremunerative that there is but little opportunity for enjoying what lies near at hand.   At the same time, away out on the edges of the area, there are farmers and grazers who engage in an extensive system and manage to enjoy the real luxuries of living in a spacious house, riding in fine vehicles, and spending part of each year in the very midst of the metropolis.   Theirs is a nature and a capital system which often yields an income sufficient to compensate for remote geographical location.

Metropolitan and national economy

43. NATIONAL ECONOMY AND AGRICULTURE.   Metropolitan economy grew up as an economic system in which the farmer played an important, though generally an inarticulate, part.   He was an operator in the hinterland of the unit, providing food-stuffs and raw materials and requiring manufactured goods and distant products.   But he was also a citizen of a state.   The state was a great social and cultural organization which had gradually developed out of the crudest relationships of peace and war.   It was based on the twin pillars of nationality and conquest.   It was older than the metropolis, older even than the town.   The old village-state, the feudal-manorial state, was decentralized, that is, it was stronger in local defence than in concentrated aggression. But the towns had helped the process of centralization by pro-

viding the national government with revenue in the form of money, and by mobilizing the personal property of the people for the support of an army, navy, and civil service. The growth of metropolitan economy continued the process. Within the fold of the state one town grew to be a metropolis and pointed the way to a commercial policy. Those states not having a strong metropolis, or not having even flourishing towns, might imitate the metropolitan state, but they could hardly be successful. England was the paramount example of a metropolitan state. The action of metropolis and state was reciprocal: the metropolis helped to strengthen the state, while the state made possible the development of a great economic organization.

Metropolitan economy is an example of informal organization, the state of formal organization. The metropolitan unit had no constitution, no parliament, no civil or military service, unless it became coterminous with the state itself, as is suggested somewhat by the development of such a city state as the Venetian Republic. The metropolitan unit could hardly have a policy, though it might have an interest which at times could be formulated and expressed. On the other hand, the state had a great advantage in the possession of a government (executive and legislature), a foreign service, a civil and military home service, recognized leaders, and a policy, shifting and not unchallenged but definite and formulated as championed by one statesman or another. While such a policy often reflected metropolitan interests, either of the metropolis itself or of the hinterland, it was often independent, as the personality of a leader or the opposition of recalcitrant communities made itself felt. Such a policy has been an influence at once in the guidance of state affairs and in the theorizing of economists about the getting of a living. It has been much studied,[6] and at least in outline deserves to be understood by all persons interested in history, whether the history of society in general or of agriculture in particular.

The first policy of the modern state was mercantilism. It developed in England in the latter half of the sixteenth century during the period when Burghley was Queen Elizabeth's

(marginal note:) Metropolitan and national policy

(marginal note:) Mercantilism 1558-98

adviser. In England it assumed internal free trade; in France it tried to bring internal free trade about. It emphasised foreign trade everywhere, and we to-day, in retaining such an emphasis, have not recovered from the mercantilism of our ancestors. It was particularly the export of manufactured goods that was desired so as to bring about a favorable balance of trade. This favorable balance, or excess of exports over imports, was to bring in gold and silver in abundance, for use as coins and in the arts and as treasure for the state. All people, not nobles or gentlemen or clergy, were to be kept busy in order to increase production and in order to prevent any uprisings that might trouble or weaken the government. All commodities that the state might require were to be within reach, that is, raw materials at home or in the colonies, and manufactured wares in the home country. In other words, the state was to be self-sufficing, at least in essentials. In times of peace the state was to prepare for war, by developing independence in the production of goods, by strengthening the army and navy, and by filling the national treasury. Power not plenty, security not well-being, was the aim. Agriculture played its part according to the country and the leaders of thought and action. In England the state did not neglect agriculture, at least not for long. The ousting of cultivators from the soil during the early enclosure movement in England was combatted by the government, though without great success.[7] A policy favorable to the export of grain was developed as soon as and whenever conditions seemed to warrant exportation.[8] The middlemen who handled grain were finally allowed relatively free action. Foreign corn was heavily

1663 taxed on importation unless prices were high in England.[9] In France on the other hand the mercantilism of Colbert was un-

1661–83 favorable to agriculture, because it discouraged the export of grain. Fearing that France might suffer from a lack of cereals, if exportation was allowed or encouraged, Colbert prohibited exportation. The result was that the cultivator raised the minimum crop, what he thought France itself would require in normal years; and accordingly he failed to produce sufficient for years of poor crops.

150

Mercantilism went to such extremes that a reaction set in. **Liberal mercantilism** Publicists and statesmen and even legislatures had come to judge foreign trade in terms of a favorable balance. If England seemed to import more from France than it exported to France, or if England sent silver to India to pay for imports, then the trade with these countries was condemned. For a time much of the trade with France was absolutely prohibited, **1678–85, 1688–96** while the merchants trading in India had to fight for their position. A group of Londoners protested against such a narrow view of foreign trade. These Tory Free Traders, as they have been called,[10] did not seek to overthrow restrictions or **1678–1713** monopolies in foreign trade, but just to liberalize the old mercantilism. They made national prosperity the criterion of public policy, and a general favorable balance the test of a successful foreign trade. In France, at a later date, another **1750 f.** liberal mercantilistic school arose. Gournay, a merchant, and Turgot, an administrator and statesman, sought to make trade free, both foreign and domestic. They had no thought of abolishing export and import duties, but just of allowing the merchant to buy and sell where and when conditions warranted. This would have freed French agriculture from the curse of an uncertain or prohibited export trade. It would have created a more stable demand for French grain.

Following liberal mercantilism genetically, but historically **Physiocrats** almost coterminous, came the school of physiocratic writers who emphasised not trade but agriculture. In so far as there must be commerce, it should be free. But the main aim was to build up a strong agricultural system of landlords, large tenant farmers, and numerous agricultural laborers. Agriculture was regarded as practically the only form of production. In so far as this school is described at length elsewhere,[11] it may be passed over here.

There developed in England a school of economists, of **Liberal economics** whom Adam Smith was the distinguished leader, who believed that both agriculture and commerce were productive and who held that both should be free to develop as cultivators and merchants thought best. All parts of the nation's resources were to be exploited freely, without direction by the government and with no thought of public policy, except that involved in private gain. The logical result of all this was the abolition of monopolies at home and abroad and the establishment of international free trade. The remarkable industrial growth of England made it possible for that country to get rid of every vestige of tariff protection for its manufactures, but the situation was somewhat different when, by the repeal **1846** of the corn laws, English agriculture was put on a competitive basis. Because of the high cost of transportation and favorable national conditions, the effect was not at once felt, but when the railroad and the steamship were perfected to the **1876 f.** point of landing cheap American grain in English ports, English agriculture began to suffer. Although many adjustments have been made, English agriculture still is under a cloud.

Protection Nearly all European countries followed England into the free-trade camp, but almost all deserted sooner or later. Indeed few have been willing to make the sacrifices necessary, and few have been able to compete with England, notably in manufacturing. When it was observed that England had such a headstart in industry as to give it substantial protection, and when it was realized that the price of free trade in England was the loss of a vigorous agriculture and a virile rural population, the other countries went back to mercantilism or to neo-mercantilism, as it is sometimes called. The most essential feature of this new system is the protection of national production by import tariffs. Germany imposed a protective **1879** tariff on both agricultural and manufactured goods brought **1881,** into the country. France established protection, notably to **1892** enable its cultivators to hold their own, especially in the face of American rivalry.

Agricultural or industrial state The great issue, and it has been very consciously formulated,[12] is whether the nation shall be agricultural, industrial, or maintain a balance. Denmark, Holland, Ireland, Russia, and Italy are notable examples of agricultural states. The lack of metals and cheap fuel and, in the case of Russia, general backwardness have kept these countries agricultural. England, on the other hand, possessing natural resources in abundance and being favorably located commercially, plunged into

152

manufacture, and in its race for wealth bargained to ruin its agriculture. To be sure, the agricultural resources of England could not completely support a growing industrial population. For the aid of English leaders there was also no precedent and no warning of the evils of industrialism. Conservatives and many Socialists in England would gladly restore the nation's agriculture; Liberals and workingmen seeking a cheap dinner pail refuse to make the sacrifices that are necessary. Some countries have kept the balance, France by circumstances and Germany partly at least by policy. After the loss of Alsace-Lorraine, France had but little iron. Its coal was limited in amount and far from such iron as it did possess. French aptitudes have been in the direction of luxury production, for example, of fine silks, millinery, porcelain, and art goods generally. So there has been little inducement and less opportunity to develop manufactures at the expense of agriculture. It may be that in the future, if mechanical power can be secured, France will have a real industrial revolution, instead of the apology sometimes designated by that name. Many Frenchmen are willing, but others think that the national predisposition for hoarding rather than for investment, staying at home rather than venturing into foreign fields for markets, and making goods for quality rather than in quantity, will maintain the balance of manufacture and agriculture that their ambitious compatriots would destroy.

1825–70

Alarm was expressed in Germany that the national agriculture would be ruined and the rural virtues would be lost to the empire, if industrialism went on unchallenged. In a short period, 1897–1902, several books were written dealing with the subject of agrarian policy.[13] Programs have been drawn up, articles of national faith, set down by individuals and supported by the agrarian party and by others. One of these programs is in part as follows:[14]

Agrarian and agricultural policy in Germany

1. Agriculture is fundamental.
2. The state should promote agriculture.
3. The agricultural policy should be slow working and forward looking.

4. There should be a wise division of the land so as to maintain large, medium, and small estates.

5. The rural population should have every local advantage in administration and government.

6. Opportunity should be provided for married agricultural laborers to possess some land.

7. There should be a strong and continuous increase in the production of raw materials.

8. The agricultural policy of the nation should be a state, not a party, issue.

9. There should be a clear understanding between the state and the agricultural interests.

10. Many evils exist; the solution depends on a satisfactory agrarian policy.

Such a program is not without significance for both England and America. In the former country for a score of years there has been a serious discussion of going back to a rural emphasis. In America the issue is in the minds of the leaders [15] and may soon come to the consciousness of the people. In the chapters that follow, there will be evidence of drift, of futile efforts of governments, and one-sided theories of economists. In the history of the past as well as in the situations of the present, we may expect to find the solution of the national problem.

44. SUGGESTIONS FOR FURTHER STUDY

1. For a series of questions on the content of this chapter, see N. S. B. Gras, *An Introduction to Economic History* (1922), pp. 269–273.

2. Do you think that the cultivator has played a dynamic part in the development of metropolitan economy?

3. Could there be a metropolis located far from a fertile district?

4. Can you enumerate instances of special soil conditions that interfere with the ordinary rule that intensive cultivation is found near the metropolis?

5. Investigate the subject of the well-being of the cultivators as they spread out from the central markets, so as to see whether

you can arrive at more definite views than those expressed in the preceding pages.

6. Why has the cultivator been so slow in bringing forth a national policy favorable to agriculture?

7. Distinguish the modern protective system (neo-mercantilism) from the early modern mercantilism.

For further references, see the notes below.

45. NOTES TO CHAPTER VI

1. See above, ch. I.

2. For a fuller account, see N. S. B. Gras, The Development of Metropolitan Economy in Europe and America, *American Historical Review,* vol. XXVII (1922), pp. 695–708; and *An Introduction to Economic History* (1922), chs. V and VI.

3. See the accompanying diagram based on J. H. von Thünen's *Der isolierte Staat,* pt. I (1826, 1875), pp. 390–391. Von Thünen's systems are *Frei Wirtschaft, Forst-Wirtschaft, Fruchtwechsel-Wirtschaft, Koppel-Wirtschaft, Dreifelder-Wirtschaft,* and *Vieh-Zucht.* The *Forst-Wirtschaft,* or forestry, was for the provision of firewood and building timber. In the pre-railroad days the supply, especially of an interior (German) town, had to be close to the large centers. See B. Youngblood and A. B. Cox, *An Economic Study of a Typical Ranching Area in the Edwards Plateau of Texas* (1922), p. 87. See also, below, ch. VIII, sect. 53, p. 184.

4. Cf. B. H. Hibbard, Farm Tenancy in the United States, *Annals of the American Academy of Arts and Sciences,* vol. XL (1912), p. 32.

5. See C. L. Stewart, *Land Tenure in the United States with Special Reference to Illinois,* University of Illinois Studies in the Social Sciences, vol. V, no. 3 (1916), p. 71. Cf. also *ibid.,* pp. 27 and 78.

6. Consult the following works, in addition to the sources referred to in ch. X below: A. Oncken, *Geschichte der Nationalökonomie, Die Zeit vor Adam Smith* (1902); J. K. Ingram, *History of Political Economy* (1885, 1915); W. Cunningham, *Growth of English Industry and Commerce, The Mercantile System and Laissez-Faire* (1903); Sir W. J. Ashley, The Tory Origin of Free Trade Policy in *Surveys, Historic and Economic* (1900), pp. 268–303; C. Gide and C. Rist *A History of Economic Doctrines* (1909, translated 1915).

7. See below, ch. VII, sect. 48 p. 165.

8. N. S. B. Gras, *Evolution of the English Corn Market* (1915), pp. 221 f., 242 f.

9. *Ibid.*, pp. 148–149.

10. Sir W. J. Ashley, *Surveys, Historic and Economic* (1900), pp. 268 f.

11. See below, ch. X.

12. Adolf Wagner, *Agrar-und Industrie-Staat* (1902).

13. Buchenberger, 1897, Brentano, 1897, Von der Goltz, 1899, and Adolf Wagner, 1902.

14. Theodor Freiherr von der Goltz, *Agrarwesen und Agrarpolitik* (1899, 1904), pp. 324–326.

15. See E. G. Nourse, The Place of Agriculture in Modern Industrial Society, *Journal of Political Economy,* vol. XXVII (1919), pp. 466–497, 561–577.

CHAPTER VII

ENCLOSURES, CHIEFLY IN ENGLAND

46. KINDS OF LANDS ENCLOSED. The enclosure of the scattered strips of land which had characterized the village, both free and manorial, went through some very dramatic episodes in England and played its part in all countries that have developed modern agriculture. Without a knowledge of the movement we cannot understand some salient features of the great middle period of agricultural history in which the old was being given up and the new slowly taken on. It is not only on the technical but also the social and cultural side that the enclosure of lands had great and lasting effect. Impor-
tance of
enclosures

The enclosures can be understood only after attention has been given to market changes. The most vital summary of these can be expressed by the formula of metropolitan economy. The new opportunity for gain, the growing individualism, and the increased specialization, all beginning in town economy, reached their full development in metropolitan economy. In a sense, the enclosures were part of this centralizing change, in which a group of big business men located in a great city and possessing an elaborate mechanism for carrying on commerce, reached out their hands and brought the cultivators and especially the land owners within their sphere of influence. The background of the peasant revolts sets out in clear relief the actual destruction of medieval agricultural arrangements. What the peasants had sought to do by uprisings—to destroy the manor, was done by the lords and some of their tenants, not by war but by more or less peaceful enclosures of fields. In order to comprehend how this was allowed to pass, to be perpetrated in states possessing orderly governments, we must know something about the policy or brand of national economy existing at the time. We must Enclosures
and
related
subjects

157

realize that at one time the government of England was negligent, at another hostile but impotent, at a third favorable and even helpful.

Manorial background

The technical and social background of the story of enclosures is the manor with its little plots of land located here and there in the open or unenclosed fields. The manor had evolved as a social unit of families knit together by co-operation and maintained by a feeling of comparative equality. All shared in labor and in the holding of good and bad land. The result was anything but individualism, anything but efficiency. No one man could cultivate as he thought best or make improvements that occurred to him. The basis of the manor was group welfare on a relatively low scale rather than individual progress on a comparatively high scale.

Consolidation

The enclosing of holdings involved the consolidation of scattered parts, so that a villein, for example, would have twenty or thirty acres in two or three large enclosed fields, rather than twenty or thirty acre strips in the open fields. In England the hedge rather than the fence was the common means of marking and protecting the consolidated farms.

Engrossing

Sometimes enclosure involved much more than consolidation. A manorial lord, for example, might succeed in enclosing the holdings of his tenants for his own use. He might engross these, that is, throw them together by the wholesale, so as to form one big farm which he would then rent out to the most promising tenant. Of course this involved great hardship and, as we shall see, complaints and revolts.

Enclosure of arable

There were four kinds of tenants' land affected by enclosure: arable, meadow, common pasture, and common waste. The arable land usually lay in two or three large fields or sections, which were open or unfenced. The holdings of each tenant, and often of the lord, were distributed in the various fields with only a balk, or side ridge, separating one strip from another. Just how each tenant knew his strips from his neighbors', we can hardly say, but know them he did. And yet there were disputes as to holdings. How the peasants could be content for so long to plow this little bit and then move on some distance to plow that, we can not imagine, unless we assume that no other scheme occurred to them. But the idea did finally occur and gradually made headway till virtually all the strips were consolidated and hedged or fenced. The advantages in doing this are obviously the saving of labor, the chance to initiate new methods, and the reduction of disputes.

It might be that only the arable would be enclosed. In that case there would still be the common use of meadow land, pasture, and waste. But on the other hand, each of these might be enclosed either individually or along with the arable. As in the case of the arable, it was necessary to unscramble the manorial egg, to pull apart the lord's share from the tenants' and to allot to each tenant his individual part. On one manor the arable might be enclosed and the other kinds of lands left untouched. In such a case a tenant would have two or three (say) ten acre closes or fields for plowing and sowing as he wished, and the old right to cut hay from two or three acres of meadow according to the allotment made by the village, to keep sheep and cows on the common pasture, and to turn various animals (sheep, goats, cows, pigs) on to the waste land (rough pasture, woodland). On another manor only the waste might be enclosed, or only the common pasture or some part of it. In still another case, perhaps unusual until recent times, all kinds of lands would be completely enclosed by one arrangement and each tenant would have a few enclosed fields in lieu of all his previous claims. *Enclosure of meadow, pasture, and waste land*

The enclosed lands might be used in various ways. They might be sowed down to grain, or used as pasture or meadow. They might be used permanently for one or all of these purposes or, much more commonly, alternately or in some kind of rotation. Indeed one of the reasons for enclosure came to be the alternation of one crop with another so as to improve the technique of cultivation.[1] And yet, the use which attracted most attention at one time did not so much involve improvement in technique as use for one purpose, pasturing sheep. At times the enclosed land was used not for cereals, nor hay, nor cattle, nor sheep, but for wild animals, such as deer and rabbits. In other words some lands, we may infer *Uses of enclosed land* the poorer sort, were enclosed as deer parks and rabbit warrens, for the sport of rich owners. Against such enclosures the complaints were many and bitter.

Earliest enclosures not a movement

47. EARLY ENCLOSURES. About the earliest enclosures we have very little precise information, largely because they did not constitute a movement, to say nothing of an agrarian revolution. There was little or no engrossing of holdings and therefore no classes of persons who greatly suffered from the results of these enclosures. Taking place piecemeal and by arrangement, they were little heeded at the time. In the revolts of 1381 and 1450 it seems that enclosures did not constitute an issue.

Lords enclose, 1236 f.

These enclosures began sometime before 1236. For in that year a law was passed, the Statute of Merton,[2] which gave to the lords of manors the right, perhaps already being exercised, of enclosing part of the common waste, woods, and pasture, provided they left enough for the use of the tenants. This law seemed to imply the existence of more land than was being used. Enclosures of such a nature would involve the use of hitherto neglected resources and would be of benefit to the whole state. Nevertheless the enclosing activity of the

1285

lords was challenged by the tenants, when at night and otherwise in secret the more determined of the tenants filled in ditches and uprooted hedges.[3]

Tenants enclose

An even more obscure class of enclosures was made by the tenants. This was of the nature of reallotment and was locally arranged,[4] doubtless to the satisfaction of all concerned. How far it involved just arable and how far it included the other kinds of land, cannot now be determined. It took place, apparently, in the coast counties, such as Essex, Kent, and Devonshire.[5] Like the enclosing activity of the lords at this period it was an adjustment for the advantages involved in production, and seemingly brought forth no big questions of rights or privileges as between individuals or classes. How far it was due to a desire to produce a larger surplus for the local town market and for transportation by sea, we can only infer from the prominence of the coast counties. To what extent it was due to the mere improvement of technique, such as might be involved in the introduction of a lighter plow, drawn by two oxen rather than eight, we can hardly venture an opinion.

48. TUDOR ENCLOSURE MOVEMENT: FIRST AGRARIAN REVOLUTION IN ENGLAND. Enclosures began early and even in our day occasionally occur. The movement with which we are now concerned reached its height during the period of the Tudor kings and may therefore be designated the Tudor enclosure movement. As a movement it began somewhat before the Tudors came into power and lasted somewhat after the line had died out. It reached its climax at about the middle of the period in Ket's rebellion. *Period of the movement*

1485– 1603

1549

Although enclosures in the sixteenth century probably occurred in all parts of England, the spread was very uneven. The area which had been least affected in the past was the one now most concerned. This was the Midlands or interior of England, from Berkshire to Leicestershire and Nottinghamshire and beyond. Although the enclosure movement included other parts, from the Isle of Wight to Northumberland, it had most continuous influence on the central district. The evidence for localizing the movement comes from the statutes, from the investigations of special commissions (1517, 1549, 1607), and from the careful studies of modern scholars. *Where the movement occurred*

As in the early enclosures, so in these, the tenants and lords were both active. The tenants left little evidence of their work, while for various reasons the lords gained more prominence. The greed and heartlessness of the lords were the occasions of loud outcry. Uprisings took place to check the highhanded action of the country gentlemen who were everywhere held to be displaying unwonted and unchristian selfishness. *The en- closers*

It is not now possible to determine exactly the use to which the enclosed land was put. There is little doubt that much of it, possibly most, was for pasturing livestock, especially sheep. Contemporary complaints in sermons, pamphlets,[6] and statutes, were almost exclusively against enclosure for pasture. Pasture land yielded a higher profit than arable. Rents were higher for pasture land than for arable.[7] Modern investiga- *Enclosure for pasture* tors have emphasised pasture: Ashley [8] following contemporary statements, Gay [9] carefully working over the existing fragmentary statistical data, and Tawney [10] using both quantitative and qualitative evidence.

Enclosure for legume rotation

Although most of the evidence is in favor of enclosure for pasture, we should be careful not to overlook another movement which was going on with less dramatic and less spectacular results. While enclosure for pasture was revolutionary in so far as sheep came to take the place of men, and flocks the place of families, nevertheless there was a slow-moving evolutionary change in the direction of better technique that doubtless had its effect. If the lords were chiefly interested in enclosure for pasture, their tenants were largely concerned with enclosure for better general farming. Perhaps if we had more evidence we should find that while up to about 1560 enclosures were characteristically for pasture,[11] after that they tended to be more and more for field-grass husbandry.[12] Although there were many complaints of scarcity of grain, we may set them down to failures of crops or to the changing marketing conditions of the times.[13] During one of the most active parts of the whole movement, the export of corn was continuous and increasing.[14]

Net technical result of enclosures

Probably the net result of the enclosure movement, at least on the technical side, was the more careful use of a greater amount of land than had been available before, including especially the waste land. On the whole, when we consider both enclosure exclusively for pasture and enclosure for alternating pasture and tillage in the new field-grass system, we must conclude that the Tudor movement was primarily for pasture. It is likely that a smaller acreage of tilled land under the new system actually produced a larger surplus than before the movement began.

Extent of the movement

1455–1607

Difference of opinion exists as to the extent of Tudor enclosures.[15] Certainly many open fields were left for subsequent generations to consolidate and hedge. But in any case we may apply the term agrarian revolution, because an accelerated movement of enclosure changed the nature of many villages and threatened the whole fabric of surviving manorialism. It was an agrarian rather than an agricultural revolution, because the change involved was more far-reaching on the side of field-systems and tenancy than on the side of agricultural technique, though the difference is obviously one of degree.

When economic systems change, social evils result. An alteration in productive agencies involves adjustment that many find difficult to make. The peasant is less apt in meeting new situations than are the other classes, more accustomed to change. Being the victim of routine, especially in the old open-field system, he has developed no flexibility. Accordingly, when the lord enclosed his holdings for sheep walks, the peasant was adrift on an unmanageable sea. He might go to the town to become an artisan, he might hire a cottage in the country without any land, but very frequently he actually became a vagrant. The increase of poverty is one of the features of the Tudor period, though doubtless it has been exaggerated. It seems likely that the tenant suffered even when he received a piece of enclosed land in lieu of his scattered holdings. Adjustments were difficult for him and heavy expenses were involved in ditching and hedging. Perhaps many who made the effort to farm under the new conditions, in due time followed their fellows who had been supplanted by sheep.

Social dislocation

The rights of the freeholder were protected by the royal courts. In case of enclosure he received a compensating share of the land enclosed. The leaseholder, who rented or farmed out the demesne or the waste, could, on the other hand, be turned out whenever the term of his lease had expired. The copyholder class, the most numerous of all, admits of no such simple statement.

Legal aspect of enclosures

The copyholder was ordinarily the descendant of the old-time villein or customary tenant. He was called copyholder because at one time or another he came to have a copy of the (manorial) court roll in which his tenancy was set forth. According to one part of the document, he held at the will of the lord. This, taken with the fact that he was often dispossessed by his lord on the occasion of enclosure, might indicate that the copyholder had no legal protection at all.[16] In another

Copyholders

part of the document, however, it was stated that he held according to the custom of the manor. If the royal courts would only step in and carry cases of dispute out of the manor itself, then the tenant might have his custom and hold his land. Certainly the national courts (both common law and equity) did step in, did recognize the cause of the copyholder.[17] On those manors where the custom was in favor of the tenant, he was protected, but where custom was against him the royal courts could or would do nothing. For them to have gone beyond local custom in the development of a common law of landed property would have seemed to many to savor of an attack upon the institution of private property itself. Where local custom gave to the copyholder a tenancy by inheritance (from father to son indefinitely), the copyholder could never be legally dispossessed. If a copyhold was for life or for lives, the lord had simply to wait till the end, and then dispossess the holding family and enclose and farm out (or rent) his land. The copyholder, or customary tenant, had to pay a rent, practically always fixed by custom and therefore not easily changed. Of the fine or payment for entry upon the land, however, custom rarely stated any definite amount. Originally the fine was a trivial sum paid when a copyholder entered upon his holding, but in the sixteenth century the lord seized upon this fine as a means of getting his due share from the land. Prices were rising and so should rents. But the rents were fixed and accordingly the elastic fine was seized upon as a means of recouping the lord for loss in rent. The lord might demand from the tenant a few shillings, or two, three or four pounds, per acre in the form of a fine.[18] Where the demand was high, the tenant was ruined and forced sooner or later to get off the holding. Ultimately, but too late to help a great many, the royal courts decided that a reasonable fine was two years' value (rent?).[19] Some copyholders, probably a small percentage, held their land both by inheritance and at a fixed fine or entry fee. These could look to the future with equanimity. The courts would see that they got justice.

Legally the copyholder, with a favorable manorial custom

164

behind him, could weather the storm, but economically he often fell by the wayside. Such was also the case with many a freeholder. The expenses of enclosing and the difficulties connected with an independent system of agriculture requiring both initiative and good judgment, were often too much for these old-time citizens of the manor. And in their places there arose a gradually increasing host of farmers, or tenant-farmers as they are sometimes called. At first these had arisen to farm out the lord's demesne or the waste land, but now they were coming to supplant the holders of that land which had always been tenant land. Legally the most insecure, economically they were the most potent. Subject to rack, or competitive, rents, they were the instruments that the landlord looked to for a larger income, and later they or their descendants became the devotees of a more scientific agriculture. Promising as they were—the agricultural upper middle class—they did not become very numerous until the next enclosure movement swept them into a position which they hold to this day. It would be a mistake to push back the disappearance of the freeholders and copyholders to the sixteenth century. As a class they held their ground, though the writing was on the wall: victory belongs to the efficient cultivator regardless of his claim upon the soil.

Economic forces favor the tenant-farmer class

The government was not opposed to enclosures as enclosures. It objected to them only when they led to obvious evils. It feared the depopulation of such a district as the Isle of Wight because the foreign enemy (the French) might get a footing there.[20] It was alarmed at idleness and the decay of churches and religious services.[21] It thought that, when cloth-making in the country was decaying and population declining before the armies of sheep, action was necessary even to the extent of prohibiting any one from keeping over 2,000 sheep.[22] It seemed to the government dangerous to stand aside and see squatters deprived of their land of 3 acres, more or less,[23] and other tenants of their 20 to 40 acre holdings,[24] even though they were allowed to keep their cottages. To the government a landless proletariat was no substitute for a small tenantry.

Attitude of the government

From what has been said, it is clear that the government of the day was anxious to keep the realm strong in actual tax payers and potential soldiers. It is also likely that the Tudor monarchs, turning away from the feudal nobility as the support of their political power, were forced to look to other classes for good will, for moral support if not for much actual direct assistance. The lords and gentry might control parliament, but public opinion was even then a source of strength that no monarch could afford to neglect, or parliament single handed to flout.

Increased demand for agricultural products as a cause

The explanation of the Tudor enclosure movement does not admit of either a single or a simple statement. The growing demand for wool both at home and abroad, was a factor. English wool was the rival of Spanish in the making of fine cloth. The old retail handicraft was giving way to the new wholesale handicraft in which large numbers of persons were producing for a market of unprecedented dimensions. So prosperous was the textile industry of England and western Europe that it was clearly a safe plan to enclose land for the raising of sheep which produced such golden fleece.[25] In addition, the textile industry was creating an unprecedented demand for vegetable dyes, such as saffron and woad which could be best produced in enclosed fields.[26] The demand for English grain was continuous abroad [27] and increasing at home.[28] The number of consumers of grain, engaging in manufacture, was increasing especially in the country. The metropolis, London, was going ahead by leaps and bounds, demanding more and more corn as it increased in size. The opportunity for gain from enclosing the land either for pasture or tillage was assured.

General rise in prices as a cause

1520's

After a long period of two hundred years of low stable prices, an upward general swing began, which, with a few exceptions, has been continuous up to the present. At first the rise in England was due to the debasement of the coinage. But soon the effect of the influx of Spanish bullion [29] came to be felt. The lords who received their income from the land in the form of money were hard put to it to maintain their accustomed standard of living from agriculture alone. Accordingly, they had either to turn to commerce or deal drastically with their estates. As we have seen, what they did was to charge their tenants excessive fines, or enclose the lands for sheep pasture or for renting out to tenant-farmers. The inundation of Europe with American gold and silver was one of the first and one of the heaviest of many blows that the new world was to strike against the old.

The town was the first to develop a measure of economic rationalism but the countryside was to follow surely though slowly in its footsteps. To adapt the best means to the economic end was an urban device of marked success. To get most for the least effort became a somewhat more conscious attitude in life. The individual became the focus of life, and a good income (not inordinate, however) an assumed necessity. In business, art, and letters, even in government, men were matching their strength, in the effective utilization of the forces at their command. And so perhaps we may see in the agricultural and agrarian changes of Tudor England an effort to attain success. Here and there arable land was almost exhausted and needed the recuperating holiday that pasture affords.[30] In some places, doubtless, land that was fit only for pasture, had been providing a meagre existence under an arable system. It would obviously yield more as good pasture. Some waste land was hardly used at all. It would make tolerable pasture if improved and enclosed. Tenants who were unwilling and unable to pay high rents, who could not get the most out of the soil, were dispossessed in favor of those who could progress. We may regret the dispossession, the uprooting of family ties, the shock to age-long habits, but the fact remains that a more efficient agriculture resulted, not everywhere, it is true, nor at once anywhere, but gradually and generally. The light of the sun is flashed through space, but the light of better methods of work seeps struggling through the inertia and prejudice of centuries. The effect of the exchange mechanism was telling on the country as on the town. Local necessities and foreign luxuries had long been on the market. Now land and labor were made available to the highest bidder. For better or for worse, both were becom-

Economic rationalism as a cause

ing articles of commerce, commodities of the market place. The marriage of inefficient labor to misused land was divorced by enclosures and their accompaniments. The Tudor movement was revolutionary not because it was extensive—for it was not—but because it ushered in an economic situation that was as threatening as it was strange.

49. ENCLOSURE REVOLTS. Four of the six revolts that occurred in the period 1536–1607 were occasioned in whole or in part by the enclosure movement. One in 1549 (in the West Country) and the other in the north in 1569 were religious. The first that was in any way colored by the enclosure movement was The Pilgrimage of Grace. The people of the north, especially of Lincolnshire and Yorkshire, rose under Robert Aske, a lawyer and a country gentleman.[31] Their banner bore the picture of Christ and their chief complaint was of the religious changes, notably the dissolution of the monasteries which are thought at this time to have been more serviceable and virile in the north than generally in England. The rebels also complained of enclosures and fines for entering upon possession of land. Important as these were in the minds of many of the malcontents, the rebellion never became a full-fledged enclosure revolt.[32] This was because both the gentlemen and the tenants were in arms, the former primarily because of the religious changes and the latter probably because of the enclosures quite as much as anything else. Royal troops were sent against the rebels who are said to have numbered about 20,000, but a sudden downpour of rain swelled the streams to the proportions of rivers and kept the two armies apart. A second uprising in the north was abortive. The usual result of peasant revolts occurred: the uprising was speedily put down and the leaders executed.

The second of the revolts was by long odds the most important of them all. It occurred in the eastern part of England, chiefly in Norfolk. The leader was Robert Ket,[33] a tanner and country gentleman, who seems to have headed the revolt almost by accident. A large army, perhaps 16,000 strong, took the field, but of course badly equipped and led. The chief men, however, did keep order. They held a law

1536
Pilgrimage
of Grace

Ket's Rebellion, 1549

court under an oak tree, and chaplains preached to the multitude of followers. Fences were torn down and hedges uprooted. Norwich was besieged and captured, but defeat came in due time when the undisciplined commoners met the king's mercenaries on the open field of battle. The number of peasants killed is said to have been 3,500.[34] There is no question about the tenor of this uprising; it was primarily an enclosure revolt. Over a score of delegates had drawn up articles of complaint which are living witnesses of the trouble at hand: Some of the complaints or demands are as follows. No manorial lord should pasture livestock on the commons. The lords are not to force the freeholders to pay unusual rents. The fines for entering upon an estate are to be small, such as a capon or a reasonable sum of money. The lords are not to buy land to let out again as copyhold. The lords are not to charge excessive rents, nor (unless they are knights or better) are they to keep pigeons or rabbits. All bondmen are to be free, as are the rivers for the purpose of fishing and passage.[35] These demands are general and resemble those of 1381 [36] and 1525.[37] The heart of the trouble, however, was the enclosure movement which the lords had been carrying on, at least in part for sheep pasture. The lords were not to dispossess tenants through excessive fines or rents, nor were they to buy off the old tenants in order to get in new ones whom they could rack-rent. The very first article, however, stipulates that there was to be no objection taken to enclosures for growing saffron (yellow vegetable dye), probably because they had been carried out by the tenants themselves.

When it was rumored about that Queen Mary was to be married to the Catholic Philip of Spain, the English Protestants and other Nationalists were alarmed for England's new religion and for her national independence. There was to have been a general uprising, but only the men of Kent actually took the field. Their leader was Sir Thomas Wyatt, an impulsive gentleman of Kent.[38] The rebels marched upon London and made demands for reform, one of which is that the pasture lands seized by persons in power were to be restored to the people.[39] Although enclosure had begun early

Wyatt's Rebellion, 1554

in Kent, there was evidence that it continued in the sixteenth century. The rebellion was put down, the leader executed, and enclosures continued.

Midland Revolt, 1607

The last of the enclosure revolts of any importance occurred in the Midlands of England, in Northamptonshire, Warwickshire, and so on. Groups of as many as 3,000 and 5,000 men gathered together. Although they were moved by some religious considerations, their chief concern was to prevent further enclosures and restore lands to their earlier condition. A certain Captain Pouch was the chief leader. He wore a leather pouch which, he said, contained something that would defend all his followers. On his capture, only a piece of green cheese was found in the pouch. The bands of levellers, as they were called, were easily put down, and the executions as easily made to follow. On this occasion as in 1549, one real result was the appointment of commissioners to investigate the extent of village depopulation, conversion to pasture, and the separation of land from rural cottages.[40] The work of these commissioners, however, was doubtless more potent in providing the modern scholar with information than in effecting any lasting change in the enclosure movement.

Period of the final movement

50. THE FINAL ENCLOSURE MOVEMENT: THE SECOND AGRARIAN REVOLUTION. The movement which finally enclosed almost all the remaining common fields, meadows, pastures, and waste lands, began in the seventeenth century and ceased in the nineteenth. Perhaps we may roughly place it in the period 1650–1850. It probably reached its height in the years 1761–1815. Of course enclosures still continue, under the Ministry of Agriculture, but they are no longer of sufficient importance to justify their inclusion in the movement.

Place of this enclosure movement

Those parts not enclosed previously were in this movement fenced or hedged. Hardly a county escaped some kind of enclosure, though in some of the southern coast counties the total area affected was slight. In the Midlands and in the north, the movement was more important than elsewhere.[41]

The enclosers

As before, both tenants and lords enclosed the land. But the lords were unquestionably in the ascendant. They were active in putting through enclosure schemes whether by private agreement or by act of parliament. Because of the fact that the lords were dominant in government, (especially since 1689), it was easy to put through a measure to provide for enclosure. Although the first of the acts providing for enclosure goes back a long distance, they became numerous only in 1606 the eighteenth century. From 1727 to 1801 there were 577 acts, enclosing pasture and waste, and from 1801 to 1845 there were 808 more.[42] After 1801 these acts were standardized and made uniform. Since 1845 enclosure has taken place under the General Enclosure Act of that year, not by a special parliamentary act but through special commissioners.

Because of the great diversity of soil, the enclosed land was **Purpose of the enclosures** put to different uses, pasture or tillage, or the two in some kind of relationship. During the earlier part of the period, it seems that there was somewhat of a balance of the two. But when the movement was at its height the enclosure was for **1761– 1815** grain growing. The price of grain was high and the demand during the war period exceeded the supply. But after the war **1793– 1815** there was a tendency for grain growing and animal husbandry again to be more evenly balanced. But animal husbandry, as we shall see,[43] no longer required much pasture, especially in the case of cattle and pigs. Enclosures, then, were largely for the growing of grain to feed both man and beast.

The third enclosure period saw all kinds of lands enclosed, **Kinds of lands enclosed** arable, pasture, meadows, and waste. Although there are no reliable figures of the proportions, it would seem that the enclosure of waste land was the most significant. Soil that had been reclaimed from the sea, fen land, and wild unbroken land that had to be pretty much made over, lands that were in some cases very rich, others that were relatively poor, were hedged about for cultivation.

Perhaps about one half of the land available for agricultural **Extent of the enclosures** purposes in England and Wales was enclosed by 1700. In the period, 1700–1845, about 14,000,000 acres are thought to have been enclosed.[44] This is somewhat less than the other part, but not a great deal less. In 1874, about 264,000 acres still lay in open fields, and 883,000 acres were useful waste land.

The two enclosure movements compared

The Tudor movement was for pasturing sheep and growing grain, while the final movement was for growing grain and raising cattle. The Tudor movement saw parts of manors enclosed, the later movement whole manors at a time. The Tudor movement was to bring higher rents to the lords and somewhat to bring about better tillage, while the later movement was to bring in larger returns to the lords through an improved system of cultivation. The first was for wool and field-grass husbandry, the later for the scientific rotation of crops. Both movements were agrarian revolutions, the first one leading to agricultural improvements, the second to the agricultural revolution.[45]

Results

It is often said that this enclosure movement led to rural depopulation. This is probably not the case, if we mean that fewer people actually resided on the land than had lived there before the movement.[46] It is doubtless true, however, if we imply that many people left the farms for the factories. Here and there, doubtless, an actual and absolute loss in population occurred, but probably not in England as a whole. The most frequent lament is that the yeomanry of England disappeared. They had begun to go in the sixteenth century and are now practically non-existent. It was in this final enclosure movement that they declined most rapidly. The first to go were the small yeomen, the last the larger ones. In the nineteenth century they declined rapidly.[47] Some of them became tenant farmers, and some agricultural laborers; others left to work in the towns or to migrate to America or the colonies. The cottars went like the yeomen, most of them, sinking into the ranks of the protelariat. When they lost just their few acres of arable, they continued to work for an enterprising farmer. Their wages, supplemented by the income from their cow, geese, chickens, pigs, and garden, were enough to support them tolerably well. When they lost the common pasture and common waste, however, they could keep few or no animals and had no free fuel. The agricultural laborer with only a house and perhaps a miserable garden was a pitiable and hopeless creature, in manhood dependent upon outdoor poor relief and in old age consigned to the poor house. Such was the price that England paid for the efficiency she secured from enclosures.

> "The mournful peasant leads his humble band,
> And while he sinks, without one arm to save,
> The country blooms—a garden and a grave.
>
> .   .   .   .
>
> If to the city sped—what waits him there?
> To see profusion that he must not share." [48]

Whether the compensation was equivalent or not, it was nevertheless real. It consisted of a larger yield of grain per acre and better livestock. In short, the compensation was the agricultural revolution, that is, for those who remained on the soil. For those who had to leave to work in the towns, the alternative was the industrial revolution. The two revolutions are truly supplementary. The coincidence of the application of more capital and better management to both agriculture and manufacture is as remarkable as the result was outstanding. The net effect upon England was leadership in production and the acquisition of wealth. Although we have less enthusiasm for these material commodities, when we reflect that they were attained at the expense of social deterioration, still we cannot fail to acknowledge the economic advance.

The medieval manorial arrangement had recognized the lord as the driving force in agrarian and agricultural affairs. All the tenants had paid him rent in money, produce, or service. Then he had given up bailiff-farming and became a rent taker. At first he had been content with his income from the old-time tenants—the freeholders and villeins—on the one hand, and from the new class of tenant-farmers leasing the demesne on the other. Anxious to secure more from his position of landlord, he had enclosed such waste lands as seemed beyond the necessities of the tenants. Realizing that the old-time tenants were paying him a low customary rather than a high competitive rent, he had sought to get possession of their holdings. At first this was during the Tudor enclosure movement and later in the movement now under consideration. The lord did not seek to go back to bailiff-farming; he did not want to

The threefold English system

become an agriculturist. He became a taker of competitiv
rents. His ally was the tenant farmer, who first of all, from
about 1450 onwards, leased the demesne, and then, as enclo
sures proceeded and the old tenants were dispossessed or los
their holdings, leased their land as well. On those manor
which had grown out of free villages, the lord was a lat
comer who served the villagers but exacted a heavy toll. H
took the land of his tenants and rented it out to other tenants
Now we cannot accuse the lord of doing this without assist
ance. Some of the old-time tenants (free holders and copy
holders) conspired with their lord to ruin their fellow tenants
Those joining in the conspiracy (if we may call it such) wer
effective in doing three things: giving the lord, or, as we ma
now call him, the landlord, a larger income per acre, improv
ing the technique of agriculture, and reducing his fellow ten
ants, who chose to remain in rural parts, to the rank of agricul
tural laborers. Gradually after about 1450, and rapidly sinc
about 1760, the threefold system of landlord, tenant-farmer
and agricultural laborer has been developing in England. The
lord lives away from the manor in most cases; the tenant
farmer comes to have a separate homestead near or on hi
holding; and the agricultural laborer is left to occupy the rud
cottages of the old-time village. The landlord supplies the
land and permanent improvements such as houses, barns, sta
bles, hedges, and larger drains, while the tenant-farmer fur
nishes the capital for livestock, machinery, and operating ex
penses, and the knowledge of cultivation and marketing. The
laborer has only his labor to offer, and for this he receives a
very low wage. His cottage is frequently inadequate and his
outlook for the future without hope of improvement. His
failure is in part the price that England has paid for the ad
vantages enjoyed by the landlords and the farmer class. Of
course, the landlords and the tenant farmers have made the
contributions—they have been the hammers; while the laborers
have lagged behind—they have been the anvils. Social selection allowed the lord to hold his own. Some tenants of capacity and ambition rose in the economic scale, and other tenants
without ability or energy fell to the bottom of rural society.

ENCLOSURES, CHIEFLY IN ENGLAND

Efforts to raise the laborer have been made by the back-to-the-land movement—the provision of good land on favorable terms, but so far the laboring class has shown little inclination or aptitude to rise out of the rural proletariat.

At the present time the English countryside is made up of palatial residences, scattered homesteads, and villages. The villages are occupied by farm laborers, tradesmen, a few tenant-farmers, and officials of landowners. The fine residences of the rich owners, and the scattered homesteads of the poor, or moderately circumstanced, farmers are offshoots of the village, the former of the manor houses, the latter of the humble cottages of peasants. The number of homesteads built out in the fields and convenient for the practices of agricultural work has been increasing, ever since the enclosure movements enabled the cultivator to separate himself from his fellows. From the seventeenth and eighteenth centuries onward they have constituted the visible evidence of a more individualistic rural system and existence. To the American, Canadian, and other upstart peoples, of course, the separate homestead is the rule, the village of agricultural laborers or cultivators the remote exception.

Scattered homesteads as a result

On the Continent of Europe lands have been enclosed at various times. In northern Germany, the enclosure movement came after 1821. In France enclosures have been going on slowly, not as a movement at all, but as a gradual process that is not even yet complete. In Czecho-Slovakia enclosures have been made, but much remains to be done. Something has been done in Russia to get rid of the open-field system and to enclose the land; but taking Russia as a whole, we can hardly say that the process has made more than a beginning.

Enclosures on the Continent

In America there have been enclosures, but they have been different from those in the old world. In New England the problem has been largely to pick the stones from the fields for use as fences. In the more fertile forested area, it has been, first, to fell trees and split rails or to dig up the roots for barriers, and later to construct more economical fences. On the prairie, it has been to secure wooden posts and barbed wire for separating one estate from another, or one field from an-

Enclosures in America

175

other within the estate. The problem in America has been to
find the time to do the work of fencing and in some parts to
secure the material. In one section there was the additional
issue of man against man. In the vast range area from Texas
to the Canadian boundary, ranches came to be created, partly
out of the temporary holdings of cowboys and others, secured
free or almost so from the government, and then purchased
and consolidated by rich cattle owners. The owners of the
ranch frequently fenced their holdings with barbed wire, but
had to contend, often physically, with those who still drove
their flocks and herds up and down the range. In other
words, the ranchers were the lords encroaching on the common range, much as the medieval and early modern manorial
lords encroached upon the common pasture and waste lands
claimed by the tenants. But generally speaking, apart from
this situation, America has had no enclosure problem involving, as in Europe, changes in human relations, ownership, business conditions, and technical processes, with their accompanying social losses and economic gains.

51. SUGGESTIONS FOR FURTHER STUDY

1. Read Sir Thomas More's *Utopia* (1516, trans. by Ralph
Robinson, 1551, 1904), bk. I, pp. 18–21.
2. For contemporary documents of great value, see Bland,
Brown, and Tawney, *English Economic History, Select Documents* (1914), pp. 247–277, 525–542.
3. For maps of enclosed villages or manors, see R. H. Tawney,
The Agrarian Problem in the Sixteenth Century (1912), following pp. 172, 220, 222; and H. L. Gray, *English Field Systems*
(1915), pp. 26, 75, 77, 144, 146, 147.
4. For a valuable account of the copyholder and his legal status,
see R. H. Tawney, *The Agrarian Problem in the Sixteenth Century* (1912), pp. 287–301.
5. On the English agricultural laborer (the cottar) during the
period 1760–1800, see W. Hasbach, *A History of the English
Agricultural Labourer* (1908), pp. 116–147.
6. Compare the enclosure revolts with the peasant revolts of
Chapter V, as to connection with religious movements and results.
7. What kinds of lands were enclosed?

8. Why were lands enclosed for parks (rabbit warrens and deer parks) in the sixteenth century? Why did the peasants not object and the statutes not prohibit their enclosure?

9. Is there any necessary connection between the breakdown of bailiff-farming and the enclosure of holdings?

10. Compare the Tudor and the final enclosure movement as to causes, social dislocation, and economic results.

11. What is the meaning of the word farmer? What part did he play in the enclosing of land?

12. Comment: the farmer was the chief single instrument in the break-up of the manor. Consider both bailiff-farming and enclosures.

13. What were the weaknesses of the old tenants and the strength of the new farming class?

14. Oliver Goldsmith's *Deserted Village* (1770) might profitably be studied with the enclosures in mind.

15. Why was right to use the common pasture of more value to the cottar than a few acres of arable land?

16. What was the relation between the agrarian revolution and the agricultural revolution, both in eighteenth century England?

17. Why was the industrial revolution in the towns about as disastrous for the small yeomen and some cottars as the agricultural revolution in the rural parts? Consider the loss of subsidiary or joint occupations.

18. Why was enclosure delayed so long? What finally started it going?

19. Comment: the rise of prices in the sixteenth century gave to the tenants an unearned increment. Trouble arose when the lords sought their share of the advantage.

20. What do you consider the underlying or basic factor in bringing about enclosures, operating in a general way and over a long period? Was it the growth of a marketing system, the increase of knowledge and efficiency, the incoming of more individualism, or something else?

21. If in explaining the enclosures in England you emphasise the rise in prices, how do you account for the fact that enclosures were so late in arriving in Prussia and Russia where prices rose long before enclosure began in those countries?

22. Why then did enclosures come so early in England and so late in Prussia?

23. Why did England enclose in a revolutionary manner, while France followed an evolutionary policy?

24. Why have enclosures received so much attention at the hands of students of English economic history? Does the explanation lie in intrinsic interest or current emphasis? Consider the

problem of food supply and the back-to-the-land movement o:
recent years.

For further references, see the notes below.

52. Notes to Chapter VII

1. See above, ch. II, sect. 11, p. 38.
2. *Statutes of the Realm,* vol. I (1810), pp. 2-3.
3. *Ibid.,* p. 94.
4. R. H. Tawney, *The Agrarian Problem in the Sixteenth Cen*
tury (1912), pp. 172, 180-182, 405.
5. [John Hales], *A Discourse of the Common Weal of thi.*
Realm of England (1549, 1581, 1893), p. 49.
6. See [John Hales], *A Discourse of the Common Weal of thi.*
Realm of England (1549, ed. by E. Lamond, 1893), pp. 49, 57
7. I. S. Leadam, *The Domesday of Inclosures, 1517-1518,* vol
I (1897), pp. 62-67.
8. Sir W. J. Ashley, *Introduction to English Economic His*
tory and Theory, pt. II (1893, 1909), p. 286.
9. E. F. Gay, The Inquisitions of Depopulation in 1517, *Trans*
actions of the Royal Historical Society, N. S., vol. XIV (1900)
pp. 246, 256-257.
10. R. H. Tawney, *The Agrarian Problem in the Sixteenth*
Century (1912), p. 224.
11. Cf. E. C. K. Gonner, *Common Land and Inclosure* (1912)
p. 137.
12. See above, ch. II, sect. 11, p. 38.
13. N. S. B. Gras, *Evolution of the English Corn Market*
(1915), pp. 219-220, 225, 232.
14. *Ibid.,* p. 112.
15. Ashley and others think the enclosures extensive in amoun
as well as far-reaching in effect. Gay has demonstrated statisti
cally, however, that they were probably slight in extent (under
3% in 24 counties), though threatening in their results. E. F
Gay, Inclosures in England in the Sixteenth Century, *Quarterly*
Journal of Economics, vol. XVII (1903), pp. 586, 588.
16. Cf. the position of Sir W. J. Ashley, *Introduction to Eng*
lish Economic History and Theory, pt. II (1893, 1909), pp
274 f.
17. I. S. Leadam, The Inquisition of 1517: Inclosures and
Evictions, *Transactions of the Royal Historical Society,* N. S.
vol. VI (1892), p. 261.
18. A. Savine, English Customary Tenure in the Tudor Period
Quarterly Journal of Economics, vol. XIX (1904), p. 55.

19. A. H. Johnson, *The Disappearance of the Small Landowner* (1909), p. 67.

20. 4 Hen. VII, ch. 16 (1488–89). *The Statutes of the Realm,* vol. II (1816), p. 540.

21. 4 Hen. VII, ch. 19 (1488–89). *Ibid.,* p. 542.

22. 25 Hen. VIII, ch. 13 (1533–34). *Ibid.,* vol. III (1817), pp. 451–454.

23. 3 and 4 Ed. VI, ch. 3 (1549–50). *Ibid.,* vol. IV, pt. I (1819), pp. 102–103.

24. 39 Eliz., ch. I (1597–98). *Ibid.,* vol. IV, pt. 2 (1819), pp. 891–893.

25. Leadam, using Rogers' materials, maintained that the price of wool had risen, while Gay, after examining Rogers' entries carefully, rejected the existing data on wool prices. See E. F. Gay, The Inquisitions of Depopulation in 1517, *Transactions of the Royal Historical Society,* N. S., vol. XIV (1900), pp. 262–263.

26. See below, ch. VII, sect. 49, p. 169.

27. N. S. B. Gras, *Evolution of the English Corn Market* (1915), p. 112.

28. *Ibid.,* pp. 73–77, 104–109.

29. C. H. Haring, American Gold and Silver Production in the First Half of the Sixteenth Century, *Quarterly Journal of Economics,* vol. XXIX (1915), p. 468.

30. The view of Denton, Gardiner, and Miss Harriett Bradley. Miss Bradley (*The Enclosures in England: An Economic Reconstruction,* Columbia Studies in History, Political Science, and Public Law, 1918) maintains that the land was enclosed because the old fallow system had failed to maintain the fertility of the soil, which could under the circumstances be restored only by such a new system of tillage as enclosure afforded. Doubtless exhaustion had taken place here and there.

31. See James Gairdner, "Robert Aske" in the *Dictionary of National Biography* (ed. by Leslie Stephen), vol. II (1885), pp. 189–190.

32. E. F. Gay, The Midland Revolt of 1607, *Transactions of the Royal Historical Society,* N. S., vol. XVIII (1904), pp. 196–199.

33. Mandell Creighton, "Robert Kett," in the *Dictionary of National Biography* (ed. by Sidney Lee), vol. XXXI (1892), pp. 76–77.

34. See J. A. Froude, *History of England,* vol. V (1860, 1906), pp. 194–206.

35. For the text of the articles see Bland, Brown, and Tawney, *English Economic History, Select Documents* (1914), pp. 247–250.

36. See above, ch. V, sect. 35, p. 113.

37. See above, ch. V, sect. 36, p. 118 (notes 24–26).

38. Sidney Lee, "Sir Thomas Wyatt" in the *Dictionary of National Biography* (ed. by Sidney Lee), vol. LXIII (1900), pp. 187–189.

39. E. F. Gay, The Midland Revolt of 1607, *Transactions of the Royal Historical Society*, N. S., vol. XVIII (1904), p. 210, n. 1.

40. *Ibid.*, pp. 212–221.

41. For a brief survey see W. H. R. Curtler, *The Enclosure and Redistribution of Our Land* (1920), pp. 183–223. See the maps at the end of E. C. K. Gonner's *Common Land and Inclosure* (1912).

42. G. Slater, *The English Peasantry and the Inclosure of Common Fields* (1907), p. 267.

43. See below, ch. VIII, sect. 53, p. 182.

44. G. Slater in *The Land: The Report of the Land Inquiry Committee*, vol. I (Rural, 1913), p. LXXII.

45. See below, ch. IX, sect. 60, p. 208.

46. E. C. K. Gonner, *Common Land and Inclosure* (1912), pp. 396 f., especially p. 411.

47. A. H. Johnson, *The Disappearance of the Small Landowner* (1909), pp. 144–147.

48. Oliver Goldsmith, *Deserted Village* (1770).

CHAPTER VIII

LATER STAGES OF AGRICULTURE AND THE PROBLEM OF SUBSISTENCE

53. THE SCIENTIFIC ROTATION STAGE. A consideration of metropolitan and national economy and the enclosure of land has brought us to a point where we want to know more about the technique of agriculture. The early methods of cultivation have already been considered in the form of stages.[1] These are natural husbandry, the naked-fallow system, legume rotation, and field-grass husbandry. Two additional stages seem to complete the development of agricultural methods up to our time. These two latest stages are here called the scientific rotation of crops and the specialized intensive system. {Early and later stages of agriculture}

As the need for rural products increased with the continued growth of towns and the development of metropolitan economy, the cultivators in the most accessible districts found themselves just as strongly impelled to establish a new system as they had been previously. The same problems of increasing the surplus and at the same time retaining the fertility of the soil existed as before. The new type of agriculture that arose to meet the need was the scientific rotation.[2] {Problem of surplus}

Crops had been rotated in all of the stages, with the possible exception of the first, but in the one now considered the rotation becomes very effective, or as we may express it, scientific. In other words, one crop was carefully chosen to follow another and the total number—in good husbandry from four to ten—was selected so as to bring about several desirable results. Each crop was, as far as possible, to prepare the soil for the one that followed; for example, clover planted before wheat provided the food needed by the wheat. At first this was known only empirically, that is, that the wheat really did {Advantages of scientific rotation}

181

grow better on land formerly sown to clover. German chemists explained in 1886 how this happened: the clover plant took nitrogen from the air and deposited it in nodules on the clover roots. When these were plowed under, they were available for the wheat, together with the rest of the clover plant. Putting in one crop after another helps to rid the land of weeds. It happens that certain weeds have about the same life history as important food plants. They sprout, blossom, and go to seed at the same time. If the main crops are changed, wheat to turnips, for instance, the weeds accompanying wheat are eradicated in the cultivation given to turnips. And so with fungi and other parasites. In warm countries wheat rusts will live in the soil at least one year, while flax wilt survives even the coldest winters. If a wheat crop is followed by other crops, for example, oats, for two or three years, the parasites are destroyed and the land cleaned for another wheat crop. A large variety of crops carefully selected utilizes the moisture and, some believe, the fertility of both the surface and the subsoil; it also enables the cultivator to use his own labor and that of his helpers throughout the year, so that the labor burden is more evenly divided. And pasturing the land, a rather wasteful use of the soil, is almost wholly eliminated. Pasturing is a restorative and a tonic, but it is wasteful. Much of the grass is injured by the hoofs of the animals. And not a little of it is covered up by the droppings of the cattle and spoiled for immediate use. In the scientific rotation, the fields are used to grow fodder for the cattle, horses, and sheep, which are fed within folds or in stalls where they are protected from weather and beasts of prey, where their food is given to them according to a well-worked-out plan and in such a way that little is destroyed. The manure is carefully stored up and applied to the land at the right time, so as to avoid the waste that comes from fermentation and leaching before the plowing season comes.[3] Thus the cultivator has a system of maximum returns and minimum losses for both plant and animal cultivation. Moreover, he has his eggs not only in more than one basket but in more than one kind of basket. He has a money crop, say wheat, the other crops such as oats, turnips, barley, and corn being fed to the live-stock. The livestock constitutes the second money income. It is hard to imagine a year in which both will fail the farmer. Accordingly, the monetary position of the farmer is better than ever before. He can obtain loans at lower rates, loans for improvement and expansion.[4]

The history of such a system is hard to write. Here and there the scientific rotation has come to the front, as the cul-mination of experiment, trial and error, the experience of cul-tivators, and the research and theorizing of agricultural stud-ents and writers. It arose in ancient China on large estates,[5] perhaps in medieval Lombardy and Tuscany, in parts of Spain, northern France, and Switzerland, in the Rhineland, and no-tably in Flanders since the fifteenth or sixteenth century.[6] Not far from towns and in districts with a dense population, the scientific rotation or something like it, first developed. The scientific rotation system that has meant most for the modern world, the model for western Europe and America, was de-veloped in England. Just as the Romans borrowed much agricultural lore from the Carthaginians, and the Spaniards from the Moors, so did the English get from the Flemings the two new essential ingredients of their scientific rotation, clover and turnips.[7] The best known variety of the scientific rotation, and also probably the oldest in England, is the Nor-folk rotation of clover, wheat, turnips, and barley, developed in the eastern county of Norfolk and at the end of the eight-eenth century, made famous in Europe and America by Arthur Young. Like many good things, it was overdone. Found applicable to Norfolk, it was introduced into many other coun-ties where, as William Marshall and Sir James Caird pointed out, some other rotation would have been better. It was the task of the eighteenth century to popularize it, and of the nineteenth century to adapt it to local conditions. In the county of Norfolk, however, it is still the dominant type, though not unchallenged.[8]

Progressive cultivators in many parts of the world, accord-ing to prevailing conditions, have introduced and practised the scientific rotation of crops. Nevertheless this system prevails

History of scientific rotation

About 1800 1851

1919

Where found to-day

in some countries much more than in others. We find it in England, Germany, France, and Italy, but not well developed in Russia, the Balkans, or Spain. It is not evenly spread within a state, but tends to occupy a position nearer to the central markets, especially the metropolitan markets, than all other types so far considered.

The balance within this type

As one gets away from the historical model of Norfolk husbandry, and examines the different rotations, all scientific, that are practised, he is impressed with the variety within the type. This occurs in detail in the particular crops cultivated and in general in the emphasis on plant or animal cultivation. The stress may be on plants, generally cereals, or on animals. Or there may be an effort to maintain a fine balance of the two. This balance may perhaps be regarded as the ideal of the system.

Factors entering into the balance

Among the factors entering into the balancing of plant and animal cultivation are relation to the central market and the status of the cultivator. Generally the emphasis on animal cultivation *within this system* is found nearer to the central market than is the emphasis on plant cultivation,[9] other things being equal. When the occupier or cultivator is also the owner, he is more likely to stress livestock in order to conserve the fertility of the soil, than is the tenant farmer, unless, of course, the latter is impelled not only by market conditions but by the terms of the lease, to go into animal husbandry. The tenant farmer, ambitious to rise to the position of owner, and careless of the fertility of the land, is more likely to see quick profits in cereals than in animals. He wishes to get most out of the soil and then buy some farm of his own. The permanent tenant farmer will, on the other hand, tend to put much of his capital into good livestock. The temporary tenant farmer will raise hogs and chickens; the permanent tenant farmer may invest in graded or pure-bred livestock.

Scientific rotation as latest extensive system

The scientific rotation is the last, certainly the latest, system that can be called extensive. Anything beyond has been regarded as intensive. The scientific system that has spread with some degree of uniformity, as a type at least, was developed in the Agricultural Revolution in England, elsewhere considered.[10]   Its rise and progress in America is presented later.[11]   At this point it is instructive to stop to consider the special case of Ireland, which has known the scientific rotation for over 150 years, and yet has not adopted it nationally.   Ireland is the land of calamity and bad agriculture; we may well speculate as to the possible correlation.

54. IRISH AGRICULTURE IN THE EIGHTEENTH CENTURY. **All four types in Ireland** As one agricultural system arises after another, the older ones survive here and there, usually to meet local needs that once were more or less common.   The new system, in fact, more usually wins a position of novelty than of dominance, at least at first.   When Arthur Young visited Ireland, **1776** he found there all the leading methods of agriculture practised in England and on the Continent.   The most noteworthy was the most primitive, the system of natural husbandry followed chiefly by the cottars.

The cottagers, though essentially agricultural laborers, **Cultivation by Irish cottars** rented small plots of ground of a half acre or thereabouts. On these small holdings, they planted potatoes year after year.[12]   The potatoes were quite commonly left in the ground until needed for consumption.   In years of frost this practice led to sore distress.   And when excessive rain or blight injured this staff of life, there was famine, and also disease from undernourishment.   The most unfortunate died; many of the others migrated.   It is a commonplace that much of the economic history of some countries can be written in terms of one crop.   In case of southern China, it is rice; in the southern part of the United States, cotton; in the northern part and in Canada, wheat; and in Ireland, potatoes.   These palatable tubers, America's gift to Europe, proved to be the curse of Ireland.   And curiously enough those Irishmen who were undone by the unfortunate gift, perhaps to the number of more than a million, at once sought the land from which the fatal **1847-52** benefaction had come.   It is the accepted view that the great increase in Ireland's population was due in large part to the cheap food provided by the potato crop.   It is equally well accepted that the decrease was caused at first chiefly by the failure of that crop.   Of course much of the trouble was that the potato was rather fragile; but part of the danger lay in the fact that it was a single dependence. No potatoes, no solid food. The effect of such a system on the soil, especially in the absence of careful cultivation and the application of plenty of manure, would in the long run prove disastrous in itself. The same persistence of effort to exhaust the soil [13] and to make the land crop-sick, is seen in the case of other commodities, notably oats. After many crops of oats, the land was left to weeds and rubbish, to recuperate as best it could. Prominent among the offenders in this respect were the linen weavers of the north of Ireland.[14] Engaged in the weaving of cloth and the cultivation of the soil, they were successes in neither. And yet from the standpoint of quantity and security of income, there is much to be said for such a hybrid system.

General condition of Irish cottars

The Irish cottar class, interesting not so much because it is Irish as because typical of all or many peoples at certain times in their history, had not only potatoes (and sometimes a little oats and barley) but milk. This came from the family cow pastured on land rented from a near-by farmer. The rent for both pasture and potato land was paid for by labor. Thus prices might fall or rise; the cottar was all but exempt from their influence. But such security was accompanied by squalor and filth. The cabin was damp from its mud floor and walls and from its water-soaked roof. The small windows let in little light and no air. The smoke escaped through a hole in the roof, but not till it had impaired the eyesight of the cottager and his family. This was not a family in any narrow sense, such as we are familiar with to-day, for it included the dog, the cat, the chickens, and even the cow, all at times said to have eaten out of the same common platter. And yet, barring years of misfortune, the simple fare of potatoes and milk seems to have nourished a strong and virile population, at the very time when the English agricultural laborer, superior in his money wage but deprived of milk, lived poorly on bread and cheese with some sprinkling of butter, meat, and tea.

The other agricultural systems in Ireland were accompanied by no such picturesque scenes. They all displayed somewhat more efficiency and probably less of the rustic romance of the cottar. The naked-fallow system was common enough,[15] and on poorer soils almost necessary. Legume rotations were also found, both the partial legume [16] and the fully developed legume rotation.[17] Field-grass husbandry likewise existed.[18] Some landlords were reading agricultural treatises and generally looking to Flanders and especially to England for better methods. They experimented with clover and turnips, but Arthur Young still found it worth while and necessary to be very explicit in his recommendations as to the scientific system which they contemplated and which he urged.

Other Irish cultivators

In spite of Arthur Young's instructions Ireland went on from bad to worse. All types of agriculture existed in that island but the scientific rotation prospered least. The rich landlords who were in a position to introduce better methods did not do so. Whether it was because they feared to dispossess the Irish holders or whether they preferred the easier life of the landlord, we do not know. Certainly the Irish tenants competed strongly for holdings and cottages, thereby raising the rental beyond what they really could afford to pay. All this led to the famine and the changes consequent upon that event.

Irish agriculture about 1750–1850

The famine involved, as we have seen, a loss of population through death and migration. This in itself was shock enough. It was accompanied, however, by the repeal of the corn laws and the consequent opening of the British markets to the corn of all nations on a free competitive basis. At once Irish landlords began to plan to meet the new situation, which, however, was not to be so embarrassing, as had been expected, until much later, when American grain and livestock began to come in. To prepare for the expected, the landlord carried through the clearances or enclosures which have been awarded the usual denunciations that accompany any effort at economic reform. In about seven years, 50,000 families were evicted.[19] Death and migration were doing a somewhat similar work.

Irish agriculture since About 1850

About 1875 f.

They were righting the balance which potatoes seem to have disturbed. They were creating a larger unit of farm than had prevailed. They were also ousting men so that cattle might occupy the fields. They were turning arable into pasture. As the adjustments were made, there came to be less wheat grown and less land plowed. There was but little barley, rye, vetches, rape, beans, peas, mangel-wurzel, beets, carrots, parsnips, or cabbages, but a good deal of oats, potatoes, hay, and **1917** grass.[20] Over 60% of the land is in pasture, largely permanent pasture. Much of the rest is in permanent meadow.[21] Thus we may perhaps say that while Ireland was practising natural husbandry up to 1846, it has since that time combined elements of the fallow [22] and the field-grass systems. Permanent pasture and meadow are characteristic of the medieval fallow system, while the alternation of a three-year cropping of hay with cereals and green stuffs is evidence of the field-grass husbandry. Scientific rotation is still an insignificant system. Irish agriculture needs more turnips, stall-feeding of cattle, and more labor, capital, and management.

Animal husbandry The Irish are recognized as poor livestock men. They succeed at present in raising large numbers of cattle, but they sell them young. They do not increase their dairying very much; nor do they fatten the young cattle they breed. Some ascribe this simply to laziness; others set it down to the reign of old tradition. The fact is undisputed. Ireland's livestock industry, such as it is, however, is growing. With fewer persons engaged in agriculture there are many more cattle, sheep, and pigs raised.[23] Quantitatively Ireland compares favorably with Denmark and Holland.[24] It is an old view that Ireland is essentially a grazing country, but this is earnestly disputed. It has been stated that 81% of Irish pasture land could be used for arable.[25] Much of it could be better used for tillage, if the land was properly drained, especially in the south and west.

Reasons for bad technique The tangled web of causes is hard to unravel. Ignorance or the following of tradition bears its share. Laziness is accepted, being emphasised by some, minimized by others. Too much moisture is another factor. Rains have caused failures of potatoes and grain in Ireland and England, but that is hardly a reason for swinging to the extremes of a pasture-meadow system. Political and religious difficulties have certainly been disturbing, but perhaps not the chief factor. Tenancy and the small size of the holdings are also to be considered. All in all, it is hard to explain why Ireland's agriculture is at least three hundred years behind England's.

From the standpoint of agricultural technique, the curse of Ireland has been its small holdings. Since the famine, the average size has been increasing.[26] This means that the lazy beds (potato patches) and mud cottages are fewer in number. One statement is that the array of such very small holdings declined from half a million to hardly 20,000.[27] However that may be, there are many small estates still, especially on the poor soil of the west. About 200,000 of such tiny farms are said to be uneconomical.[28] *Size of holdings* *1841–91*

Until the famine, the Irish landlord occupied a favored position. He provided the land, the tenant the improvements. Except in Ulster, the tenant had little chance to derive any advantage from any improvement he might make. After the famine, the landlord took drastic action in consolidating his holdings, as we have seen; and until 1870 his general position was not seriously challenged. Since that year, however, public opinion has turned against him. Laws have been enacted helping the tenant as a tenant and also assisting him to rise to the position of land owner. At present Ireland is fast becoming a land of peasant proprietors. Whether this will result in agricultural progress or decline will depend on the development of knowledge, thrift, and industry. Much is being done to help co-operation in milk production, credit, and home manufactures by the Irish Agricultural Organization Society. The Department of Agriculture and Technical Instruction is active in promoting a better system of cultivation. The native Irish writers have emphasised the problems of political and religious freedom and land tenancy. These have now been largely solved. Henceforth the emphasis of many English and some Continental writers must receive attention, namely the system of cultivation and the application of more capital *Land holding in Ireland* *1885 f.* *Since 1889* *Since 1898* and labor to the soil. Ireland is free and no longer over-crowded. The negative work is done; the constructive tasks lie ahead.

Intensive agriculture and increasing population

55. SPECIALIZED INTENSIVE AGRICULTURE. The hope of Ireland, and many other countries agriculturally backward, lies in the scientific rotation of crops. The hope of the old Ireland of increasing population would have lain only in a very intensive system of agriculture which would have normally produced a surplus for export and in lean years enough for home consumption.

Plant and animal cultivation

Up to this point the history of agriculture is the development of plant and animal cultivation. In natural husbandry, the fallow system, and legume rotation, the two met only in the use of beasts of burden in plowing and the like, and in the pasturing of the livestock on the stubble. In field-grass husbandry, the two were dovetailed in a very real way, by being given alternately the use of the soil. In the scientific rotation of crops, the animals were taken from the fields, but their needs were as carefully provided for in the planning of the crops as were man's. In the sixth and latest stage of agriculture, however, there is a partial return to the conditions of the first. Again animal and plant culture are separated, and the land is used indefinitely for one purpose. This stage may be called specialized intensive agriculture. In the last two or three decades it has had a remarkable development in England. The back-to-the-land movement, facilitated by the Small Holdings Acts which aid people with little capital to procure small farms, has furthered the introduction of specialized agriculture. As we have seen,[29] the new system has shown great strength elsewhere, especially in the more densely settled parts of Europe and America, and near large towns and cities pretty generally. In France, where there has been a large number of small holdings since at least the eighteenth century, this new system has been a godsend, though even there—from ignorance or poverty—too little progress has been made, except, as stated, near large towns and cities.

1892 and especially 1908

Types of specialization

The agricultural specialist may devote all his attention to one field crop, such as truck-garden stuff. Or, he may be a dairy farmer whose ultimate product is exclusively milk. Indeed, specialization seems to shade off into horticulture, bee culture, fancy animal breeding, and the like. In probably all cases it is the logical ultimate development in the direction of a more intensive system.

In intensive agriculture there are large amounts of labor, *Intensive* capital, and management applied to the land.[30] The holding *agriculture* is small and brings a high price, if sold. The cultivator devotes his energies, resources, and intelligence to this small bit of land. His own labor is rarely sufficient. Capital in the form of manure, irrigation, machinery, seed, and fodder, is required in relatively large amounts. And a day-to-day oversight of growing crops is necessary, if the venture is to succeed. It is a matter of common observation that, generally speaking, the soil has been more and more intensively cultivated as one stage follows another.[31] But the pressure of population and general ignorance may lead to a very marked development in the direction of intensive cultivation *before* a new stage of agriculture arises and spreads. In such cases, however, the intensity of cultivation is perhaps generally found to be a matter of labor, rather than capital and management. In China, legume rotation is more intensive from the standpoint of labor than European truck gardening, but not generally from the standpoint of capital—to say nothing of management—for the poor Chinese peasants know nothing of commercial fertilizers.[32]

On irrigated lands, in China or elsewhere, an exceptional *Agricul-* situation is found. Intensive agriculture occurs without being specialized. The construction of trenches, canals, and *tion* dykes, together with their upkeep, involves much use of labor, capital, and enterprise. In Babylonia (Mesopotamia) and Egypt such systems of waterways had to be contrived, not only to lead the water to distant fields but to drain it off into reservoirs, so that the land would not be flooded in the early growing season. These irrigation systems served not only to carry the waters to distant sections and then back to the river, but also to distribute the fertilizing river mud more or less evenly over the fields.[33] In Mesopotamia where the calcareous soil is fathoms deep, there was a yield of 200-fold,[34] and probably without exhaustion or impairment as long as the waters of the Euphrates and Tigris were kept in control and properly distributed. It is thought that Mesopotamia in the hands of the British may again blossom forth as in the days of Herodotus and become the granary of the eastern world. Britain would then control not only the cotton grown in the Nile valley but the wheat of the Euphrates and the Tigris district. Such instances of irrigation as these occur elsewhere, but no others are known to have been so fruitful in cultural results. General agriculture by irrigation [35] is a very special type and does not really belong to our present interest. Agriculture by means of irrigation, it is true, is analogous to our specialized intensive system in so far as it is intensive; but in so far as it is general and not specialized, devoted to crops of many kinds rather than to one, it deserves no more than passing notice here.

Possibilities of intensive agriculture

The physical possibilities of intensive agriculture, as found in the sixth stage, are astonishingly great. By watering, fertilizing, and heating the ground, by soil pulverization, seed selection, treating seed chemically or bacteriologically, transplanting, protection by glass, and intertillage, enormous crops can be attained.[36] Perhaps most reliance has been and will be placed upon fertilizers, both commercial and barn-yard. In every stage of agriculture we find the use of fertilizers, though some peoples and individuals may have neglected them. The Indians of New England used fish heads to plant along with their corn in natural husbandry, and the English used marl as an ameliorator and barn-yard manure as a fertilizer in the Middle Ages when practising the naked-fallow system. And, of course, in succeeding stages, more fertilizers and manures were applied than before, especially at the hands of able cultivators. But the amount and variety put upon the soil in the stage of agricultural specialization are beyond all precedent. And yet there comes a point at which the returns are not proportionate to the labor, capital, and managerial skill expended.[37] This is in accordance with the law of diminishing returns,[38] which is applicable to all stages and systems of agriculture. A people experiencing diminishing returns in one system, has either to seek new lands (by peace or war), or has to change its system. Following the first course of action has led to great migrations and military conquests; following the second course means staying at home and peacefully improving the system of cultivation. It is an interesting reflection that most peoples have found it easier (psychologically) to migrate or fight than to improve their agriculture. They are the frontier peoples of the world, moving westward both in Europe and America, sweeping on and on with a vicious system of agriculture, reducing the fertility of the soil and making imperative sooner or later a more intensive system than they themselves were capable of.

In some of the older countries of the world, notably in those that are centrally located for commerce, agricultural progress seems to approach no immediately threatening limit. Denmark offers an illustration of specialized intensive agriculture that seems almost to transcend the type. The farmers have taken to cattle raising for beef, to dairying for butter, to hog raising for bacon, and to poultry raising for eggs. The beef has been sent largely to Germany; the other products to Britain; and butter even to America. The great success of the Danish farmers has been due to a number of circumstances. The climate of Denmark is favorable to the growth of grass and fodder crops generally. The country is conveniently located for export to Germany and Britain, and ships can readily land at its ports raw materials from distant parts: oil cakes from America, maize from Argentina, barley from the Black Sea, and so on. Cheap labor supplies the indispensable means of carefully handling the livestock and marketing the product. Co-operative societies aid in selling the output, in supplying credit, and disseminating information necessary for careful management. Such large amounts of labor, capital, and management are applied to the relatively small area of Denmark that we must regard the resulting agriculture as very intensive indeed. So much of the food-stuffs, the raw materials, are imported, that Danish cultivation has sometimes been called an industry rather than a system of agriculture.

Danish agriculture

Belgium

1900

1880

Belgium's population is over three times as dense as Denmark's, and nearly five times as dense as Ireland's. Almost as many of the Belgian people are engaged in agriculture as in industry. The holdings are remarkably small. Nearly two generations ago about 95½% of the farms contained below twenty-five acres [39] on the average; more recent statistics are not available. In late years there has been some diminution in the relative importance of small holdings.[40] Nevertheless, Belgium is one of the lands of intensive agriculture. Its people are little given to livestock; they are developing hog raising more than cattle raising; dogs and men do much of the work of horses; sheep are negligible and decreasing.[41] Such are common earmarks of an intensive system.

Japan

1922

In Japan about 60% of the people are engaged in agriculture, though many of the cultivators also have industrial occupations. About half the farming takes place on the uplands, the rest on the lower levels under a system of irrigation. The chief products are rice, cocoons, rye, barley, and wheat. Animal husbandry is little practised. There are even few pigs in Japan.[42] Dairying is almost non-existent. The government is doing something to assist animal raising, but progress is necessarily slow in a country that has no developed taste for flesh or milk and but little land for grazing purposes. Farming is intensive from the standpoint of both labor and capital. Long hours of patient toil are spent on tiny fields of rice. The cultivators, both men and women, often spend the whole day knee-deep in mud and water, tramping in the grass from the hillside for fertilizer or transplanting the rice. Capital in the form of manure is applied in large quantities. Night soil, barn-yard manure (not in great plenty), weeds, special leguminous crops, and commercial fertilizers are all used. A double system of cropping is common. That is, rice and barley, or rice and soy beans, or some other such combination, are grown in the same field in one year. Some elaborate rotations are recommended by agricultural institutions, and occasionally practised, but the system in vogue is the specialized intensive. Near the cities as many as three crops a year are taken by the gardeners, the plants being arranged so as to occupy the minimum space and to interfere least one with another. Out of it all the farmers get a living but on a rather low plane. Rice and barley are their food. About 32% of 1912 them own their land; 28% are tenant farmers; and 40% cultivate their own small holdings and some rented land in addition. The most significant summary is that the average farm in Japan consists of a little less than three acres.[43]

56. CROP FAILURES IN THE OLD WORLD. In all of the The sweep of dearths and famines stages of agriculture, early or late, scientific rotation or specialized intensive, failures of crops may occur. The old world of Europe, Africa, and especially Asia, has been particularly cursed by seasonal disasters which have at times wrought great havoc to health of mind and body. The long list [44] of dearths and famines that history has recorded is a staggering tale of human misery. At plowing time there has been great promise; at harvest despair has settled over the fields. If the failure is light, the problem is simply to pay the landlord or the money lender; if it is complete, the task is to keep even body and soul together. No period of recorded history, ancient, medieval, modern, or recent, has escaped the buffetings of agricultural fortune. No wonder some peoples have sacrificed to the spirit of the corn, and others erected statues to the goddess of agriculture. In real disaster the helplessness of man has been all but complete.

In India,[45] from earliest times, famine has been the child Immediate causes of drought.[46] Soil deterioration, over-population especially under British rule, and great poverty, have accentuated the trouble in India. North China has similarly suffered, and periodically millions of people die, because no rain falls. In such recent times as 1877–78, 1887–89, and 1920–21, vast armies of Chinese have died. Men have sold their wives, women their children. Some have slain their dear ones and then themselves, to escape the slow death of starvation. In the latest of these famines some westerners even refused to 1920–21 contribute to the relief, on the ground that the population was too numerous for such a dry area. Nature, giving too little rain to some lands, gives too much to others. England [47] and Ireland [48] have frequently experienced dearths and occasionally severe famines, because of too much moisture, which makes the plants grow but does not allow the grain or vegetables to ripen. When famines occurred in the times of Abraham and Isaac, the Jews turned to Egypt where the Nile had not failed to yield a crop. In the time of Jacob and again in the period of Moses, Egypt itself suffered. On the former occasion, it is said, the famine lasted seven years and was not confined to Egypt, though, because of that country's granary system, there was enough and to spare in the land of the pharaohs.[49] In all probability the cause of the trouble was both drought and pest. In the time of Moses the havoc of flies, locusts, and other insects is clear enough.[50] Storms have laid their heavy toll in lives snuffed out immediately and in more lives slowly ground out by famine. In South China the river floods rise up to prove what a puny thing is man. Foreign war and civic disturbance have curtailed agriculture to the point of disaster for the cultivators. Recently Russian farmers planted so little grain that when the weather was unfavorable great numbers were threatened with starvation. The peasants refused to produce a surplus for the use of the Soviet Government, and so planted a minimum of crops. With the drought came the famine.

1921–22

Ultimate causes

The great question of causation is, what lies behind the physical changes that recur so disastrously? It may be that terrestrial conditions are solely responsible. It is considered more likely, however, that planetary disturbances lie behind the scene. Whether it is one planet, such as the sun or Venus,[51] or a combination, is a matter of speculation. The tides reflect the influence of the moon; so may crop failures prove to be decided in heaven. Certainly they recur, but with what precise rhythm, has not yet been discovered.

Relation to agriculture

Famines happen in all stages of agriculture, as has been observed. Probably the later stages of agriculture provide more assurance against dearth or famine than any of those preceding. Scientific rotation produces a large surplus for sale in normal years and therefore enough for subsistence in times of dearth and perhaps enough for survival in periods of famine. Specialized intensive, when well balanced between the elements of labor, capital, and management, promises even more. With its drainage system the excess of moisture can be mitigated. With its irrigation possibilities the extremes of drought can be alleviated. With its system of warming by fires the evils of frosts can be combatted. With the accumulation of knowledge of biology, the insects, fungi, and other pests and parasites, can be battled with more or less successfully.

Of course, the worst evil of local famines, suffering to the point of starvation, can be eliminated by charity and commerce. India, China, and Russia have had assurances already. But the problem of moment here is how crop failures themselves, rather than their worst results, can be eliminated or lessened. The development of a commercial agriculture looking to a surplus helps. The discovery of drought-resisting varieties of grain would be of great assistance to the dry sections. But in these, as in other instances, one suspects that the immediate result would be such an increase in population, at any rate in the three countries mentioned above, that there would again be no great surplus, and that the margin of safety, indeed, would once more soon be passed. Although the problem of crop failure is primarily a matter of climate which lies beyond man's present control, the degree of the failure and disaster often depends on the long-time pressure of population upon the productive capacities of the soil, a situation which is coming to lie within man's power to guide and master. *Preventative measures*

57. POPULATION AND SUBSISTENCE. While the subject of crop failure has to do essentially with temporary distress, the question of the ratio of population to the means of subsistence is related to continuous conditions of wealth or illth, well-being or misery, as the case may be. *Compared with crop failure*

The problem with which we are at present concerned arises out of the (apparent) fact that man can reproduce faster than he can produce. The human species can double its number in a period of about seventeen years. This is a physiological possibility, not a situation found anywhere, at least not for long. The crux of the problem is to feed, clothe, and shelter a population experiencing such rapid growth. It may be pos- *The problem* sible to go on providing the manufactured goods needed for such an increase, but it is a vastly different problem to get the raw materials and the foodstuffs. In the production of cereals, vegetables, fruits, flesh, milk, and eggs, there comes a point beyond which added efforts bring diminishing returns, as we have already seen. Greater labor, more capital, and even more efficient management would fail to increase the yield of the soil indefinitely. Certain countries have given us proof of the difficulty, and many scholars, peering into the future, have thought that some day it would apply to the whole world.

Population increase

In the United States the increase in 130 years (1790–1920) has been from under four million to over 105 million. The increase has slackened from 36% in the decade, 1800–1810, to 15% in the decade, 1910–1920, but already people fear further

1921, 1924 additions. Immigration has been curbed for various reasons. Already prophets foretell a time that will be less favorable than past days, partly because of the pressure of population on subsistence. Ireland is a classic instance of rapid increase of population. In 1700 there were hardly two million people on the island. By 1800 there were probably over five million, and by 1841 over eight million. Then came the great famine

1846 and subsequent emigration so that to-day the population is

1911 somewhat under four million and a half. Japan contained

1920 about twenty-seven million in 1846 and now Japan (proper) has a population of about fifty-six million. In 1872 India supported at least 186 million people;[52] now the population is

1921 about 320 million, some of the increase being due to the addition of territory. The people of Great Britain increased from ten and one-half million in 1801 to nearly forty-three million in 1921. It has been estimated that just before the Great War, it produced only 20% of the wheat and cheese consumed, 25% of the butter and oleomargarine, and 58% of the meat.[53] Early estimates placed the population of Europe at 107 million in 1700 and 130 million in 1761. By 1801 it was about 200 million and in 1914 about 452 million.[54] The population of the world is thought to have doubled in the period 1830–1920, being at the present about 1700 million.[55]

It is held that if the increase of the period 1906–11 prevails for sixty years, the numbers will have again doubled.[56]

From the sixteenth century to about 1790 a common attitude (of mercantilists especially) was to think of an increasing population with enthusiasm. During this period war and disease kept down the increase and national strength required a numerous body of fighters and producers. Then for a period, as population grew rapidly, writers thought of the increase as a possible danger. A common explanation of the increase was the greater economic production, both in agricultural and in industrial products. The writings of Malthus dominated during the period. Then as both agriculture and manufacture appeared to keep ahead of demand in the world as a whole and in Europe in particular, a period of optimism ensued, which was not blanched even by the famines of India and China. But again there seems to be a turn in the tide. Pessimism is rising high, whether set off by post-war burdens or by fears based purely on considerations of production. The issue now is whether population pressed on subsistence before or after the late war.[57]

The diversity of opinion as to the causes of an increase in population is considerable. The history of Ireland and England indicates that as production increases population grows.[58] In the case of Ireland it was an increase in potatoes, at least in large part. In the case of England it was an increase in industrial production which gave the producers a greater command over raw materials and foodstuffs—imported from abroad. The establishment of peace is a second factor of great significance, as is illustrated by both Java under the Dutch and India under the British. Improved sanitation everywhere tends to have the same effect. It is the growing hope of the world that peace will be more and more our privilege, and it is the assurance of science that preventative medicine has even greater blessings for the future. All in all, apart from considerations of production, the world seems to be assured of more people than it has ever known before, unless other forces set in to prevent the continuation of the increase.

Views concerning population

1790–1880

1798

1880–1915

1915 f.

Causes of increase of population

199

Checks
to popu-
lation

We are told that the birth rate is falling off. Decline began long ago in France, and has followed in England, Germany, and among the native-born of America. It is a strong argument that, as increased production brings about greater well-being, as men and women tasting higher things seek even greater cultural heights, there will be everywhere a decline in birth rate. Civilization gives man, and notably woman, a feeling of individualism. Woman can not realize a very high personal destiny by sacrificing her life for a numerous progeny. Accordingly in the highly civilized countries of the world birth control has made rapid strides. By the prevention of conception, or by abortion, the birth of children is kept down. Optimists see in this condition stronger children and happier mothers. Fighting against this new emancipation are the potent forces of religion, nationalism, and industrialism. Circumstances will alone determine the issue. Another great

1918–19

epidemic such as the influenza of a few years ago would create a powerful movement away from birth control, because of renewed religious sentiment and on grounds of national expediency. Such is the issue, and such are the uncertainties that lie right ahead of us.

Effect of
the pres-
sure on
subsist
ence

How far birth control will go, we do not know. The increase of population is a fact of the present and therefore a possible danger for the future. It is, of course, obvious that the ultimate effect of an unlimited increase in population would be the starvation of the extra persons, as in North China in recent times. But this surely lies a long way ahead. The immediate effect is more complicated. If the demand for farm products should outrun the supply, the price of those products would rise. More people would enter agriculture, leaving the towns and metropolitan centers. Capital would accompany labor. Poorer land would be cultivated but at increased cost. Food and raw materials would be raised in sufficient quantities but at a greater effort. In other words man would get less for his labor and planning. Animal husbandry would decline and rice and potatoes would tend to push out wheat and rye. The plane of well-being would sink.[59] Already economists are scanning the level of real wages for a sign of the anticipated development,[60] the passing of the halcyon days of the nineteenth century. France is pointed out as the one nation that has staved off the inevitable by birth control,[61] while other nations have temporarily met the difficulty by emigration.

It is misleading to assume that agriculture can do nothing for itself to provide for a population twice as large as the present one. It is also not certain at what point diminishing returns will set in, though logically and ultimately they seem to be inevitable. There are many suggestions of improvements in cultivation to meet the threatened pressure. Some of them seem practical, some remote. The use of commercial fertilizers is at present limited by the cost of production. Already the extraction of nitrogen from the air promises a limitless and cheap supply of the chief mineral required by crops. Plant diseases are not yet well understood, but may some day be mastered. We may reasonably expect to have under control the chief insect pests of agriculture. More crops for the dry districts—already we have proso (millet) and kaoliang (sorghum)—will extend the area of profitable plant cultivation. The stimulation of plant seeds by the use of cheap chemicals will hasten the growth of crops and extend northward the zone of cultivation. More and cheaper power would, of course, enable man to irrigate the deserts of the earth. Some scientists expect to get this from the sun's rays, others by harnessing the atom. Therein would lie the solution of our problem of food and raw materials, and stave off diminishing returns or indeed entirely prevent them. Control over animal, as well as human, growth and performance is on the horizon of possibilities, as clearly as is unlimited mechanical power. The stimulus of animals by glandular control, or some other such means, promises—though rather remotely—cattle that will yield more milk and sheep that will produce more wool. It may be along such lines that the agricultural revolution of the future will take place. When we contemplate the remarkable accomplishments of the last agricultural revolution, outlined in the next chapter, the preceding speculations may not seem quite so fantastic.

Possible agricultural adjustments

58. Suggestions for Further Study

1. Go through the six stages in the history of agriculture as outlined in Chapters II and VIII in order to get clearly in mind the leading characteristics of each.

2. Where will agriculture improve most rapidly, in fertile lands of slight demand, fertile lands of great demand, or barren land of great demand? Consider West Flanders in the sixteenth century, Ireland in the twentieth century, and land around Aberdeen (Scotland) at the present time.

3. If you were leasing to someone else a farm of 100 acres, what clauses dealing with cultivation, would you include in the lease?

4. Can a free-trade country establish any kind of agricultural technique that it wishes? What was the effect of the French and German tariffs upon the types of agriculture since about 1880? See, for example, J. H. Clapham, *The Economic Development of France and Germany* (1921), pp. 178–183, 209–214.

5. Farmers are urged to vary their crops according to the market or demand. What is the bearing of crop rotation on the problem of commercial agriculture?

6. High farming is a term sometimes employed in England to describe the use of roots for cattle, cattle for manure, and manure for grain. With which stage do you identify it?

7. Do you regard the scientific rotation of crops as a fixed and narrow system, or does it allow for variations of intensity and emphasis?

8. What is the difference between a garden crop and a field crop? Which wins in the specialized intensive system?

9. Why is it necessary to consider capital and management as well as labor in studying the specialized intensive system?

10. What system of agriculture is being followed by the Japanese cultivator of a few acres when he alternates rice with barley in two fields, rice with soy beans in another field, and rice with clover in a fourth?

11. Was the agriculture of the old Virginian plantation, producing chiefly tobacco, in the stage of natural husbandry or specialized intensive? Consider also cotton in Texas at the present time.

12. With what stage of agriculture are the various articles of your breakfast table to be most closely identified—grapefruit, butter, ham, cereal?

13. Correlate the following with the stages of agricultural development: (1) subsistence cultivation, (2) commercial agricul-

ture with sale of surplus crop, and (3) wholly commercial agriculture.

14. Can you say in a very general way that it tends to be true that the farther you go from the nucleus the earlier the type of agriculture in the metropolitan marketing unit?

15. Can you work out the average yield of grain per acre in the various systems of agriculture? Is this really as important as the yield in its relation to the maintenance of soil fertility?

16. Have there been any famines in American history? Explain.

17. If specially interested in the subject of the pressure of population on subsistence, see T. R. Malthus, *An Essay on the Principle of Population* (1798, 1803, etc.).

18. For diminishing returns in American agriculture, see W. S. Thompson, *Population: A Study in Malthusianism*, Columbia Studies in History, Political Science and Public Law, vol. LXIII (1915), pp. 138, 143–144.

19. Study the recent history of Java for a significant instance of increase of population and subsistence.

20. Study a number of countries of the world to find out whether their population is increasing, whether they have a surplus for export, and whether they are developing manufactures with which to pay for future imports of raw materials and food. Consult *The Statesman's Year-Book*.

For further references, see the notes below.

59. Notes to Chapter VIII

1. See above, ch. II.

2. Some such stage as this has been designated by various terms: alternate husbandry, rotation of crops (*Fruchtwechsel-wirtschaft*), and diversified agriculture. Alternate husbandry had special reference to the alternation of green-leaf crops (clover, turnips, cabbage) and white-straw crops (wheat, barley, rye, oats). Diversified agriculture is not a happy expression, because it applies more or less to all stages of agriculture, and is well illustrated by one type of the natural husbandry of ancient Egypt, for example, about 1198–1167, B. C. J. H. Breasted, *Ancient Egyptian Records* (1906), vol. IV, pp. 122–123. The term convertible husbandry was applied to this stage, Sir John Sinclair, *Code of Agriculture* (1818), pp. 269, 293; R. W. Dickson, *Practical Agriculture*, vol. I (1805), p. 531; Sir H. Davy, *Elements of Agricultural Chemistry* (1813, 1839), p. 399; *The Penny Cyclopædia*, vol. II (1833), pp. 227–228. I do not know whether

I have coined the phrase scientific rotation of crops or borrowed it from someone else.

3. Cf. Sir H. Davy, *Elements of Agricultural Chemistry* (1813, 1839), p. 349.

4. Cf. A. C. Wiprud, *The Federal Farm-Loan System in Operation* (1921), pp. 96–97.

5. M. P.-H. Lee, *The Economic History of China, with Special Reference to Agriculture* (1921), pp. 150–155.

6. W. Roscher, *Nationalökonomik des Ackerbaues* (1858, 1903), pp. 127–128, 130.

7. It is an interesting thought that a good deal of agricultural knowledge may have come down in unbroken descent somewhat as follows: Carthaginians, Romans, Nabatheans, Moors, Spaniards, Flemings, English.

8. *Wages and Conditions of Employment in Agriculture, Board of Agriculture and Fisheries,* vol. IX (Great Britain, Parliament, 1919), p. 221.

9. See above, ch. VI, sect. 42, p. 146.

10. See below, ch. IX, sect. 60, pp. 208 f.

11. See below, ch. XII, sect. 87, pp. 294 f.

12. A. Young, *A Tour in Ireland . . . in the Years 1776,1777, and 1778* (1780), vol. II, pt. I, pp. 133, 137, 221; pt. II, p. 33.

13. Cf. a quotation from an English traveller (1818), in G. O'Brien, *The Economic History of Ireland in the Eighteenth Century* (1918), p. 135.

14. A. Young, *A Tour in Ireland . . . in the Years 1776, 1777, and 1778* (1780), vol. II, pt. II, p. 163; Cf. vol. II, pt. I, p. 244.

15. *Ibid.,* vol. I, pp. 8, 17, 25, 32, 58; vol. II, pt. I, pp. 26, 158; vol. II, pt. II, p. 139.

16. *Ibid.,* vol. I, pp. 8, 32, 71.

17. *Ibid.,* vol. I, p. 29; vol. II, pt. I, pp. 23, 241.

18. *Ibid.,* vol. II, pt. I, pp. 39, 58–59, 78, 126, 130, 135, 141, 148, 158, 191, 228.

19. Ernest Barker, *Ireland in the Last Fifty Years, 1866–1916* (1917), p. 45.

20. See *Agricultural Statistics of Ireland with Detailed Report for the Year 1917.* Department of Agriculture and Technical Instruction for Ireland (Dublin, 1921), p. 23.

21. In 1911 the statistics are as follows (acres):

Grain	1,254,431
Green crops	1,013,727
Flax	66,618
Rotation hay	939,223
Permanent meadow	1,573,180
Pasture	9,846,584

Agricultural Statistics of Ireland with Detailed Report for the Year 1917 (1921), p. 3.

22. The fallow itself, however, has gone.

23. See *Agricultural Statistics of Ireland with Detailed Report for the Year 1917* (1921), p. 10.

24. *Ibid.,* p. 11.

25. Cf. Ernest Barker, *Ireland in the Last Fifty Years, 1866–1916* (1917), pp. 41, 43 n.

26. *Agricultural Statistics of Ireland with Detailed Report for the Year 1917* (1921), p. XIV.

27. L. Smith-Gordon and L. C. Staples, *Rural Reconstruction in Ireland* (1919), p. 27.

28. Ernest Barker, *Ireland in the Last Fifty Years, 1866–1916* (1917), p. 46.

29. See above, ch. VI, sect. 42, pp. 41–42.

30. H. C. Taylor, *An Introduction to the Study of Agricultural Economics* (1905), p. 88; *ibid.* (1921), pp. 132 f.

31. Professor V. G. Simkhovitch, however, suggests that agriculture probably passes from intensive to extensive, because of soil exhaustion. Rome's Fall Reconsidered. *Political Science Quarterly,* vol. XXXI (1916), p. 221.

32. M. P.-H. Lee, *The Economic History of China, with Special Reference to Agriculture* (1921), p. 65.

33. Much of the history of Egyptian cultivation is conjectural, especially the pre-Ptolemaic agriculture. By the time of the Greeks, great progress had probably been made, though it is really a matter of uncertainty to what extent the Greeks found an advanced agriculture and to what extent they themselves advanced it. There is little question that at least a naked-fallow system had been attained and probably a legume rotation, possibly the scientific rotation of crops. See M. Rostovtzeff, *A Large Estate in Egypt in the Third Century, B. C.* (1922), pp. 82, 83, 90, 96, 107, 113, 144. For irrigation, see W. L. Westermann's articles in *Classical Philology,* vol. XII (1917), pp. 237–243, 426–430; vol. XIV (1919), pp. 158–164.

34. John A. Scott, Herodotus and the Fertility of Babylonia. *The Classical Journal,* vol. XV, pp. 370–372 (March, 1920).

35. For irrigation in America, see below, ch. XIV, sect. 100, pp. 5–6.

36. See P. Kropotkin, *Fields, Factories, and Workshops* (1898, 1913), chs. III, IV, V.

37. Cf. F. W. Taussig, *Principles of Economics* (1911, 1920), vol. I, p. 187.

38. Cf. A. Marshall, *Principles of Economics* (1890, 1907), p. 153.

39. A. von Chlapowo Chlapowski, *Die Belgische Landwirtschaft im 19. Jahrhundert.* Münchener Volkswirtschaftliche Studien (1900), p. 62.

40. Size of Agricultural holdings in Belgium:

Size	1846	1866	1880	1895
Up to 5 acres	400,514	527,915	710,563	634,353
5 to 25 acres	126,120	163,503	158,261	150,586
25 to 124 acres	41,583	42,062	38,169	41,102
124 acres up	4,333	5,527	3,403	3,584
Total . . .	572,550	744,007	910,396	829,625

A. von Chlapowo Chlapowski, *Die Belgische Landwirtschaft im 19. Jahrhundert,* Münchener Volkswirtschaftliche Studien (1900), pp. 60–61; *Annuaire Statistique de la Belgique,* vol. XLV (1920), p. 373.

41. *Annuaire Statistique de la Belgique,* vol. XLV (1920), p. 384.

42. The number of pigs increased from nearly 299,000 in 1911 to over 499,000 in 1921. There are practically no sheep in Japan. *Résumé Statisque de l'Empire du Japon* (1923), p. 22.

43. For brief accounts of Japanese agriculture see F. H. King, *Farmers of Forty Centuries* (1911), pp. 27, 29, 31, 35, 208, 378–380; *Outlines of Agriculture in Japan,* Published by Agricultural Bureau, Department of Agriculture and Commerce (Tokyo, 1914), pp. 3–8, 17; *The Recent Economic Development of Japan* compiled by the Bank of Japan (1915), pp. 17–19, 27, 43, 52–53, 56–57; D. H. Buchanan, The Rural Economy of Japan, *Quarterly Journal of Economics,* vol. xxxvii (1923), pp. 545–578.

44. C. Walford, Famines of the World: Past and Present, *Journal of the [Royal] Statistical Society,* vol. XLI (1878), pp. 434–449; F. Curschmann, *Hungersnöte im Mittelalter* (1900), pp. 89–217.

45. Noteworthy famines occurred in India in the following years: 650, 941, 1023, 1033, 1148 f., 1344 f., 1396 f., 1661–62, 1769, 1790–92, 1876–78, 1899–1901.

46. E. W. Hopkins, *India, Old and New* (1902), p. 232.

47. Severe dearths occurred in 1005, 1315–16, 1586–87, and 1594–98. For medieval England, see J. E. T. Rogers, *A History of Agriculture and Prices in England,* vol. I (1866), ch. XIII; vol. IV (1882), ch. VIII; and vol. V (1887), ch. VII; F. Curschmann, *Hungersnöte im Mittelalter* (1900), pp. 108, 208–217; N. S. B. Gras, *Evolution of the English Corn Market* (1915), index under "Dearth."

48. E. g. 1727, 1740, 1800, 1846, 1879.
49. The Bible, Genesis, ch. XLI, verses 48, 54–57.
50. *Ibid.,* Exodus, chs. VII–X. Compare the Hessian fly, chinch bug, and locust in the United States of America.
51. See below, ch. XV, sect. 109, p. 14.
52. W. F. Willcox, The Expansion of Europe in Population, *American Economic Review,* vol. V (1915), p. 748.
53. See H. Cox, *The Problem of Population* (1922), p. 36.
54. W. F. Willcox, The Expansion of Europe in Population, *American Economic Review,* vol. V (1915), pp. 741–742.
55. See E. B. Reuter, *Population Problems* (1923), p. 93.
56. H. Wright, *Population* (1923), p. 59.
57. J. M. Keynes (*The Economic Consequences of the Peace,* 1919, pp. 21–22, 277) thought that the pressure began before the war. Sir William Beveridge (*Economica,* Feb., 1924, pp. 1–20) thinks that it did not begin so soon.
58. Whether this is due to physiological or more likely to psychological influences is, of course, a matter of uncertainty.
59. Cf. H. Wright, *Population* (1923), p. 60.
60. For example, W. S. Thompson, *Population: A Study in Malthusianism,* Columbia Studies in History, Political Science and Public Law, vol. LXIII (1915), pp. 45, 146, 159.
61. *Ibid.,* pp. 157–158.

CHAPTER IX

THE AGRICULTURAL REVOLUTION, CHIEFLY IN ENGLAND

Economic revolutions

60. NATURE OF THE REVOLUTION. The economic historian is accustomed to revolutions in the modern period. The commercial revolution began in the sixteenth century with the growth of a distant over-sea trade, the formation of trading companies, and the concentration of commerce in large cities. Then came the agrarian and the agricultural revolutions, the former in land holding, the latter in technique of cultivation. Somewhat contemporary with these two were the industrial revolution (the one best known and most far-reaching in social results), and the revolutions in transportation, economic thinking, and national economic policy. The changes involved in these revolutions constitute a large part of modern European economic history and, with a few modifications, of American history as well.

New stage in agriculture

The revolution with which we are concerned, involved changes in the methods of carrying on agriculture. It saw the decline of legume rotation and probably field-grass husbandry in some of the coast counties and in the Midlands of England, as well as the disappearance of the naked-fallow system in much of the rest of England and of what remained of natural husbandry in Scotland and Ireland. Expressed more positively, it brought in the stage of agriculture, here called the scientific rotation of crops.[1] No earlier change in agricultural technique displayed such a rare combination of speed of development, extent of improvement, and degree of acceptance. And to us to-day it has a peculiar significance, for, generally speaking, we can say that its lessons are still the ideals of good cultivation, and will doubtless remain so, till a more intensive system is necessary.

AGRICULTURAL REVOLUTION IN ENGLAND

The new system of agriculture, the scientific rotation of crops, was, in the restricted sense, just the careful cropping of the land with a view to the largest returns. But this formula is too narrow, unless one comprehends in it all the ramifications involved. It implied strict attention to field crops, **Items of** also to cattle. It meant the careful choice of seed and the **improvement** selective breeding of cattle. More machinery for field use and more stalls for feeding were required. More use was made of capital and management. And management involved, not only careful oversight of crops and beasts but of marketing conditions. A new balance was struck in things agricultural between attention to cultivation and to marketing, field and stall, crops for man and crops for beast, labor and management, practice and theory, dirt farming and book farming.

The agricultural revolution was made in England out of **English** Continental materials: Spanish clover, Burgundian and French **and** grasses, the Dutch plow, the horse-hoe of Languedoc, and the **contri-** Flemish method of cultivating turnips in fields. It was about **butions** as indigenous or national as Scotch marmalade made out of foreign sugar and oranges, or the English cotton industry which subsists on foreign and colonial cotton. But as in these instances so in the agricultural revolution, the important general background was native. England experienced the revolution herself rather than just learned it from abroad, though much of it might conceivably have been taken whole cloth from across the Channel. It has generally been the lot of England to develop in this way. Such a course has meant experimentation, error, and temporary loss but also strength, ultimate success, and power for further expansion.

From a distance we regard the agricultural revolution as a **Phases** movement covering about two generations at the end of the **of the** eighteenth century. As we study it more intensively, the revolution seems to widen out into an *avolution,* a turning away **lution** from the old and into the new. Instead of one chapter or division we find several. Perhaps the period about 1650–1700, we may call the incubation, when English travellers were curiously interested in Flemish agriculture, when experiments were made in England with clover and turnips, and when writers were telling a little, a very little, about the new system. We remember both Weston and Blythe of this time. Later from about 1700 to about 1770, we have the period of experimentation when innovators, most of them unknown to us to-day, were perfecting the system by adding English to Continental elements. The period from about 1770 to about 1850, we may regard as the time when the new agriculture spread at home and abroad. And during the generation 1850–1880, the new system reached its height in England, for it was at this time that the finest balance was struck between tillage and cattle breeding. The older system had emphasised the growing of cereals. Now, following the repeal of the corn laws, came a period of more or less free competition, as far as the tariff was concerned. English farmers found it profitable to go farther with cattle raising than ever before.[2] About 1880 American wheat began to spoil the balance. English cultivators saw that it paid better either to go into grass farming or to occupy smaller holdings for truck gardening or fruit farming. In other words, at this point the scientific rotation begins to lose to specialized intensive agriculture. Whether this loss is permanent or temporary remains to be seen. Some think that, when the soil of America no longer produces cheap wheat, the scientific rotation of balanced rations of tillage and cattle raising will again come into its own in England.

1846

Peak of the revolution

It is a reasonable question at this point to inquire about the portion of the period since 1650 that we regard as most revolutionary. Unquestionably from a quantitative standpoint (the extent of adoption of the new system), the answer must be 1770–1850, but from a qualitative standpoint (the discovery of the methods and factors), the emphasis must be put upon the earlier period 1700–1770. If we are anxious to discover the peak of the revolution—travellers tell us the quest for peaks is elusive—we might choose 1780 but at the risk of being disputed.

The revolution spreads

When we are studying English history, we speak about *the* agricultural revolution. In dealing with the similar development of agriculture elsewhere, we find only *an* agricultural

revolution, in this country or in that. England was the first
to make much of the scientific rotation of crops. Irishmen,
Scotchmen, Frenchmen, Americans,[3] even Germans and Flemings, came before the end of the eighteenth century to regard
England as the agricultural teacher of the western world. No
other introduction of the scientific rotation could be so revolutionary as England's.

61. HEROES OF THE AGRICULTURAL REVOLUTION. Eng- **Leaders
land's agricultural revolution was unique, not only in its well
priority and in the attention it attracted, but in the prominence known**
of its leaders. Although these leaders have not received
the widespread consideration given to the standard-bearers
of the French and American revolutions, still, the lives of
many of them are carefully chronicled and their contributions adequately appraised by contemporaries and by subsequent generations. Although only a few of them can be dealt
with here, nevertheless, the ones considered cover a wide period of time and comprehend all possible interests. The earliest was born in 1674 and the last died in 1842. Some were
interested primarily in tillage; others stressed livestock; and
still others included both.

Although Jethro Tull can hardly be called the morning star **Tull,
of the revolution, he lived and played his part not long after 1674–
the dawn of the movement. He was educated at Oxford, and 1741**
for the law at Gray's Inn; and inherited land in the southern
part of England. After the fashion of the gentlemen of his
day, he made the *grand tour* on the Continent, learning much
about agricultural practices. Before going, he had invented
the drill; on his return, he practised pulverizing the soil. By
the former he did away with the broadcasting of seed; by the
latter he hoped to keep his fields fertile without manure. His
main aim was to get the most out of the soil. Sowing seed
by scattering it to the wind was wasteful of seed and of hand
labor. To obviate these, he invented, or re-invented, a machine that would sow seed in uniform rows and cover up the
seed in the rows. Accordingly each plant would have more
space to grow, and although there would be fewer plants, the
net yield would be greater. Aware that manure implanted

the seeds of unwelcome weeds, he thought he had found a substitute in pulverizing the soil. Such pulverization as was necessary he did by frequent hoeing, not by hand but by horse. The result was that planting was so delayed by long-drawn-out cultivation that the crop matured very late, in the case of wheat, so late that it was subject to rusts. Tull's methods were not at once adopted, but ultimately the drill was almost universally used, and frequent cultivation by horse power, especially of turnips, was found to put the land in good condition by breaking up the clumps of earth and eliminating weeds. Tull was an innovator and he made the mistakes of a pioneer. He seems to have thought that plants lived on fine particles of soil, instead of minerals in solution. But he set the example of inquiry, investigation, and invention, which ultimately led to victory. His life was sad. With poor health, stupid laborers, inadequate equipment, he tried to make headway in the face of prejudiced and perhaps malicious compatriots. At the end of his life he could take pride neither in his family affairs nor in the acceptance of his principles of cultivation. But his writings preserved his efforts, and taken up in France, they were translated, discussed, and approved; and finally, indeed, they were appreciated even in his native land.[4]

Towns-hend, 1674–1738

At the same time that Tull was horse-hoeing the soil and drilling his seeds, Charles Townshend was growing turnips and earning for himself the sobriquet, "Turnip" Townshend. Educated at Eton and Cambridge, and a member of a distinguished family, he made the usual foreign tour. Returning, he entered not agriculture but politics. Handsome, well connected, confident in himself, and industrious, he was given one post after another, ambassador, secretary, and virtually prime minister. Losing his position of political prominence, he retired to his Norfolk estate to engage in agriculture, during the last eight years of his life. Not only turnips but clover occupied his interest. He practised marling and furthered enclosures. In short, he was one of the pioneers in raising the level of cultivation in his county and, through it, in all England.[5] The agricultural revolution began in one of the poorest districts in the country, and this beginning was closely connected with the humble turnip. A century earlier similar progress had taken place in the poor and sandy country between Ghent and Antwerp, where turnips also played a part.[6] Before the movement was over, almost all England had been revolutionized and alongside of the turnip, occupying positions of prominence in crop rotations, were the swede, the mangelwurzel, the sugar-beet, and the potato.

Like Tull and Townshend, Arthur Young was interested in tillage rather than livestock, though little that was agricultural escaped his attention. He was in a sense the prophet of the revolution. He sought not so much to be a farmer as to lead his people out of the land of ignorance, naked fallows, and small estates. It is the lot of few private citizens to be personally so interesting and nationally so important. Precocious in youth, vivacious, restless, and bold, he commanded attention wherever he went. Imaginative and racy, fond of gossip, he found many readers for his numerous writings. His autobiography and his travels occupy a place at once in literature and in history. It was his greatest contribution, however, to have written the declaration of independence of English agriculture, and to have preached it as long as health and strength served: independence of ancient methods that were both wasteful and unprogressive. We may forgive him, as we forgive Jefferson, if he overstepped the mark. The enemy was strong, the cause good, and zeal abounding. Though he went too far in denouncing commons, small holdings, and naked fallows (on certain soils), he did knightly service in inviting experiments, recording observations, and arousing an interest in the soil without parallel either before his time or since. What did it matter if he failed as a practical cultivator, provided his books stimulating others, were a success? We can forget the gloom of his last years of religious contemplation and fervor, when we remember the brilliant society of English friends, Pitt, Priestly, and Coke of Holkham, and the distinguished strangers, the Empress Catherine, Lafayette, and Washington, who honored him by their correspondence or presents. When we think of those who went from Poland, France, Sicily, and

Arthur Young, 1741–1820

America to visit him, when we recall his wide interest in his home country, in Ireland, the United States, Canada, and French India, and when we realize how he engendered enthusiasm for a great cause,[7] we can think of but one parallel in our time, Theodore Roosevelt and the conservation of natural resources.

William Marshall, 1745–1818

Not unlike Young in his interest and approach, was William Marshall, whose life span was almost coterminous with Young's. While Young was born in London, Marshall was born in Yorkshire. While Young was a theorist, Marshall was practical, with four centuries of farming experience in his blood. While Young was the Moses of his people, Marshall was the Jeremiah, a prophet but with a touch of pessimism and fear of uncritical book learning. And yet, like Young, he not only farmed but published many agricultural treatises. And when Marshall suggested the establishment of a Board of Agriculture,[8] Young was appointed secretary.

Bakewell, 1725–1790

The heroes of the revolution so far mentioned have been in part responsible for the emphasis on tillage. Others did much that would have righted the balance, had general economic conditions been favorable. Distinguished among these, alike by his priority as by his accomplishment, was Robert Bakewell of Leicestershire. He took over his father's farm of 440 acres but not his father's methods. Choosing good stock, he bred within the flock and herd, selecting those qualities desired. Thus he doubled the weight of his sheep and cattle and made their flesh suitable for roasting, whereas boiling had hitherto been wiser. All animals were kept clean and warm and were kindly treated—they were his only children. A local farmer's club was started to maintain purity of breed; and the hiring of select rams was begun. One ram rented out for breeding purposes brought in a handsome income each year. And yet, so great were the expenses of breeding, digging ditches, and building stables, that he was bankrupt toward the end of his life. But Leicestershire sheep and Leicestershire long-horn cattle had become established, and the possibilities of livestock breeding demonstrated.[9] As we have seen, England borrowed many elements of the new tillage from the Continent, but in cattle breeding she was not only supreme but, at the time, apparently unique. Horse (and dog) breeding had been known before and practised widely— Bakewell bred some army horses—but conscious cattle breeding was England's own contribution.

So great was the contagion of the revolution that not only commoners but nobles participated. Although Bakewell had more immediate pupils, he had no more distinguished follower than the Duke of Bedford. An ancestor of the house had drained the famous Bedford level for tillage; this member of the family gave most attention to animal husbandry. He was president of the famous Smithfield Club and host of the sheep-shearings held on his model farm at Woburn Abbey. Here were invited all farmers who were interested. Plowing contests took place; cattle and sheep were exhibited; and prizes were awarded. And then like the tournaments of old, the assembly came to an end with a grand banquet.[10] Thus under private auspices the results of a public exhibition were attained. This is suggestive of the nature of the whole movement and illustrative of the individualism that put it through.

Duke of Bedford, 1765-1802

Lord Somerville, a friend of the Duke of Bedford, and a graduate of Cambridge, attended the sheep-shearings at Woburn. Along with the Duke, he was a member of the Board of Agriculture. And like him he devoted much time to animal breeding on his estates. Merino sheep were the object of his special interest, and it is said that, barring the king, he was the largest fancier and owner of the famous Spanish breed in England. Some of them he sold at fabulous prices. He annotated one of Bakewell's books and wrote several of his own. Vigorous, practical, and patriotic, he did much to further the cause of animal husbandry in England.[11] Happy the land with leaders who serve the general good in their private affairs!

Somerville, 1765-1819

Somewhat more balanced in his emphasis on both tillage and livestock was Sir John Sinclair. When a mere boy, he inherited his father's estate in Scotland. He abolished old servile tenancy, introduced improved rotations, brought in better sheep, and planted trees. He became president of the

Sinclair, 1745-1835

Highland Society of agriculture. And in 1791, he started a sheep-shearing festival, after the fashion of those in the southern kingdom. Few have had so varied a career—in the navy, army, writing, finance, in medicine, law, agriculture, and politics. He became a parliamentary advocate of enclosures and persuaded Pitt to establish the Board of Agriculture. As president of this Board, he embarked on such colossal schemes of inquiry and publication that he embarrassed the whole enterprise and had to give way for a time to Lord Somerville.[12] It is hard to refrain from comparing him with Alexander Hamilton. Both were Scotch, very confident in their own abilities, industrious, and apt to emphasise statistical information. Both left behind volumes of writings, in the one case memorials of the agricultural revolution, in the other of the American revolution. One organized the government's activity on behalf of the new husbandry; the other on behalf of the new political system.

Coke of Holkham, 1752–1842 The prince of the gentleman farmers, himself a member of the nobility, was Coke of Holkham. With the usual background of education at home and travel abroad, he divided his time between agriculture and politics. By long service in parliament, he earned the name of father of the House of Commons. Though he favored mild reform, he believed that agriculture should be protected by a tariff. To his country he gave over fifty years of service as a legislator and over sixty years as a cultivator. Although none surpassed him in practical success, he became an agriculturist by accident. Two of his tenants had refused leases of land at ridiculously low figures. Then he tried his own hand, and by experimentation and observation, gathering around him practical farmers, he transformed the appearance and methods of western Norfolk. He found it open-field; he left it enclosed. He found rotations antiquated; he left them modernized. He found the livestock mere scrubs; he left them of good breed. His lands came to him with forests of no special distinction; he lived to develop them to a point where he realized a handsome annual profit from his timber. He was not only a cultivator but a landlord; and in this capacity, his accomplishments were hardly less distinguished. By giving his tenants good advice, long leases, and favorable terms, he enriched both himself and them. By his annual sheep-shearings, the most noted in England, he spread the fame of his methods beyond the county and beyond England. Coke's clippings, or semi-public sheep-shearings, became a convention of agriculturists from far and near, interested in livestock and tillage. They were practical short-courses such as are provided in American agricultural colleges to-day. But they were entertainments, too, long to be remembered by the participants.[13] Without much exaggeration, we may regard Coke of Holkham as the Washington of the revolution. Both were handsome men, moderate in policy, farmers, practical rather than theoretical. By inclination Coke was a politician; by circumstances a cultivator. By choice Washington would have been a farmer; by necessity he became a statesman. Coke favored American independence; Washington won it. Each might have envied the career of the other.

For the most part the heroes of the agricultural revolution were distinguished amateurs. They were gentlemen first and farmers second. They were dabblers and adventurers in cultivation, brilliant speculators in stocks and crops. They were enthusiastic, restless spirits, the leaders of a new system of land exploitation. It was not just their plan or purpose; it was in part the contagion of the time. Agriculture was a fad. Voltaire said that all but laborers were reading about farming. Arthur Young remarked that London citizens who breathed the smoke of the metropolis for five days a week drank in the air of cultivation for the other two.[14] Catherine II of Russia, Joseph II of Austria, Gustavus II of Sweden, Leopold II of Tuscany, Stanislaus II of Poland, and George III of Britain, lent their support to agriculture. Thinkers in France erected agriculture into an economic system. It was not hard to become a hero in such a popular revolution.

Enthusiasts and faddists

62. CAPITALISTIC AGRICULTURE. The leaders in the agricultural revolution had plenty of enterprise, indeed many of

Capitalistic spirit

the psychological traits of the capitalist. Willingness to venture, desire for profit, eagerness for efficiency marked their efforts.

Livestock   The material basis of the new technique, however, was capital itself, expended in large amounts upon the various ventures. It is not difficult to discover the uses of such capital, though it would be tedious to enumerate them all. The carefully selected, specially bred, and occasionally imported animals, were very expensive. Such stock received treatment corresponding to its value. It was housed in the best stables and fed in carefully prepared enclosures. It required about £5 of capital per acre to cultivate an arable farm, about £8 for a mixed arable and pasture, and about £20 for a pasture farm.[15] A large part of this difference was doubtless due to the animals required.

Fertilizers   The capital needed for equipment was large, that is, for barns, stables, fences, drains, and laborers' cottages. All of these came in for special consideration in England; and in parts of Scotland, landlords had to put out not a little in improved roads and in bridges. Fertilizers, too, received their share of the new investment, animal manure from the barnyard and later guano from overseas. Some zealots looked with anxious eyes upon the waste of fertilizer, liquid and solid, incurred by towns and cities everywhere. All seemed to recognize the situation, but either through prejudice against the source or through fear of pollution and infection, little was done to utilize urban waste, without the use of which the Chinese would starve.

Agricultural machinery   The capital put into the invention, perfection, and manufacture of machinery, was large but beyond present calculation. Although in ancient times there had been machines for raising water for irrigation purposes, machines for drill cultivation, and mowers, nevertheless, these had been lost or forgotten, so that when the agricultural revolution began, the common instruments of husbandry were the hand-hoe, the horse-plow, the hand-rake, the wooden harrow, the sickle and scythe, the spade, fork, and flail. Inventive activity, however, left the position of none of these undisputed by the end of

the eighteenth century, though satisfactory improvements in some had to wait till after the middle of the nineteenth century. Apart from the horse-hoe and drill of Tull, already considered, the most interesting were the reaper and the threshing machine. From the offer of a prize for a reaping machine by the Society of Arts to the invention of the Bell reaper, **1780** many men tried their hand. Some reapers attracted considerable attention, but none before Bell's seems to have **1826** been widely used. Although there were several English reapers invented after Bell's, none was so satisfactory as the improved McCormick machines made in the United States. Indeed it has been a significant general fact that after two or three generations, leadership in agricultural machinery passed from Britain to America.[16] And after Thaer had called the **1803–** attention of Germans and others to English machinery, there **1806** was not a little activity on the Continent.[17] It is noteworthy that a large part of the inventive work was done in the in- **About** dustrial northern section of England and in Scotland. The **1784** threshing machine came from the hand, if not the brain, of the Scotchman, Andrew Meikle.[18] A generation after its invention, it was more in use in the north of England than in the south, and more popular in Scotland than in England.[19] Various explanations of this situation have been given, but the most probable one is that in the northern parts labor was scarce and the machines most needed. In southern England, the ancient flail was still in use in the early part of the present century. The new machines came in slowly. Used at first on large estates, they gradually have been applied to small ones.[20] The latter development has been made possible partly by the lowering of the price of the machines and partly by the co-operative purchase and use of machines by small farmers. **Source**
The source of the new capital that went into machines, stock, **of the** and buildings, is a subject of significant inquiry. Undoubt- **capital** edly much came from accumulations of rent hitherto consumed or turned into commerce. Some was probably the profit of improved methods turned back into the business of agriculture. And not a little may have come from commerce through merchants and small tradesmen who invested in farms, large and

small, in some cases for renting to others and in some cases for cultivation directly. That there actually was a considerable surplus of capital for agricultural improvements is a noteworthy fact in itself.

Surplus
for the
market

63. CAUSES OF THE AGRICULTURAL REVOLUTION. A movement such as the agricultural revolution, men like the leaders who brought it about, and the development of capitalistic agriculture have undoubted interest as well as value, but no such fascination or importance as is attached to the explanation or the causal factors. The most general expression of the cause of the agricultural revolution is that it was due to the desire (and opportunity) of cultivators to secure a larger surplus for sale without exhausting the fertility of the soil. It seems that there had been no actual impoverishment of agricultural lands on any large scale, though the poorer and lighter soils had already suffered. And as has before been pointed out, the most prominent locality in which early improvement took place was Norfolk, much of the soil of which is far from fertile. On the whole it seems that the issue was not so much to restore fertility as to maintain it; not to replenish lands worked out by earlier and cruder methods, but to keep them fit while heavier demands were being put upon them.

The heavier demands upon agriculture arose out of the increasing commercialization of production. This was due partly to the continued growth of towns and partly to the development of metropolitan economy, notably in England. The demand upon agriculture is strikingly illustrated by the

Foreign
trade

great increase in grain exportation during the early part of the agricultural revolution.[21] It is difficult, or impossible, to say to what extent this demand was due to the general ex-

1673 f.,
1689 f.

pansion of the market and to what extent to the bounty paid by the government on English grain exported abroad. It is at least a plausible view that, while the bounty may have helped not a little, nevertheless, the main factor was the general growth of commerce, as is indicated by the following arguments. The progress in agriculture leading to the revolution began before the bounty was paid, and continued after it had ceased to be available. And on the analogy of developments in other countries, the expansion of general commerce tends to bring in the scientific rotation system.

Not only foreign but also domestic opportunities presented themselves. At home there was apparently an absolute increase of population of over two millions in the eighteenth century. There was likewise a rising standard of living that demanded fresh meat where formerly salted meat had been sufficient. This higher standard and new taste were doubtless due to the development of trade with its increasing opportunities and profits. And bound up with the new commercialism of growing towns and metropolitan economy, was the industrial revolution, which produced a larger surplus of manufactures than had been possible under the earlier industrial systems. This industrial revolution in turn put demands upon agriculture. It required raw materials in increasing amounts, notably wool and hides. *Domestic demand*

After the agricultural revolution had got under way, other factors emerged. Some small cultivators perceived that the industrial revolution was taking away their by-occupation of manufacture. During the summer months they had been cultivators, in the winter, handicraftsmen marketing their wares either in the wholesale or the retail trade. Having lost industry, they had only agriculture to rely upon. The smallness of their holdings made such reliance precarious or impossible. The new agriculture was beyond their scant means. Accordingly they had either to become laborers on the larger estates of others, or to go off to the towns to work in the factories. If they went to the towns, they increased the market for agricultural products. If they became agricultural laborers, they helped produce the needed supply and gave up their scant acres for cultivation according to new and improved methods. *Cultivators lose their handicraft*

It is likely that the rise in the price of agricultural products, particularly during the Revolutionary and Napoleonic wars, exerted some influence upon agriculture. Cultivators and landlords were stimulated to produce a larger surplus in order to enjoy the larger profits. This could be safely done only by cultivating the soil scientifically, that is, by effective rota- *Rise of prices 1793–1815*

221

tion and by feeding the cattle in the stalls. At best, however, this was but a temporary factor, inducing the farmer to grow as much grain as possible, whilst the logical development of the

new system would have suggested somewhat more attention to livestock than was given during the period of high wheat prices.

The government, too, may have had its influence. The effect of corn bounties has already been mentioned. The existence of protective corn laws for a whole generation may have been at least a minor factor. The favor shown to enclosers of land, at first by private act, and then by general statute, was

doubtless of much greater moment, because without the large units of enclosed lands the new agriculture would not have come in, at least not so early and not so rapidly. The preachings of the Board of Agriculture and the fine example of George III, "Farmer George," should not be forgotten as contributing factors.

When we have set forth the causes of the agricultural revolution we have in part explained why the revolution began in England and not on the Continent. England had developed a metropolitan economy more completely than any other nation. This involved the careful organization of both foreign and domestic demand, the development of improved systems of transportation, and the industrial revolution. It meant available capital for improvements with assured returns. Apparently England alone had an effective corn bounty.[22] And Englishmen stood preëminent among Europeans as applied scientists and practical philosophers. Those who emphasise the materialistic interpretation of history will stress metropolitan economy; those who hold to the idealistic interpretation will make more of the traditional capacity of the English for applying knowledge to practical purposes.

64. RESULTS OF THE AGRICULTURAL REVOLUTION. In trying to determine the results of the far-reaching agricultural changes, we encounter the same general difficulty as in trying to ascertain the causes. And in addition we find here as elsewhere that some results themselves become secondary causes.

Out of the agricultural revolution came greater economic efficiency. Labor marched with a quickened step. Formerly, lazy squatters and cottars with their tiny holdings had done just enough to keep them in the barest necessities. They had let the cow, the geese, and the hens work; they had gleaned in the harvest fields of others; and they had pilfered where they dared.[23] Now when these people lost their holdings, they were compelled to rely upon their labor exclusively. They were forced to work with unwonted effort. The steady continuous effective work of an increasingly large number of men may be put down as one of the greatest contributions of the agricultural revolution. The conditions under which they were for a time to labor in town and country were pitiable, it is true, but the discipline of effort was brought into play to bring about the more complete utilization of labor power. It was doing much, to uproot men from a miserable existence in idleness, ignorance, and dependence on alms and theft. They might object, and unreasoning sentimentalists may weep tears of pity, but the fact remains that at last these people were being compelled to play a part—a humble one but the only one for which they were fitted—in the general economic order of the day. They had sojourned on the fringes of the antiquated village community, whilst they should have been joining the newly developing metropolitan organization. They slumbered right through the stage of town dominance, only to awake sleepy-eyed in the morning of metropolitan economy. **Greater labor efficiency**

As agricultural methods have changed, in answer to the varying needs of general economic organization, the size of the unit of cultivation has increased, at least up to the stage of specialized intensive agriculture. Legume rotation had tended that way but scientific rotation in England much more.[24] The opportunities offered by the new system of agriculture were open chiefly to those who had capital available for machinery, livestock, and improvements generally. These same persons could find no interest in small holdings or small enterprise. Their object was gain, their spirit bold, their methods ruthless. **Larger farms**

Accordingly estates leased to several cultivators were thrown together to make one good-sized farm. And holdings long in the possession of small people, such as customary tenants (descendants of villeins) and yeomen, came into the possession of landlords either to be operated directly or indirectly through tenant farmers. Those who worship the god of efficiency will observe only the material victory, closing their vision to the offerings of the human victims that the god demanded. England could not fail to observe, though she seemed powerless to prevent, the loss of an agricultural middle class that had shown stability in peace and tenacity in war. These victims of change had done "yeoman service," but they could not hold their own in the economic contest, when the general trend was against them. Some of them became laborers in the towns, some in the country, while others migrated to the new world to become Americans but without ceasing to be yeomen. At a later date the descendants of some who had remained at home crept back to the land, when those who had crossed the Atlantic made the scientific rotation no longer profitable in England, because of the low-priced American grain they were exporting abroad. Again the small estate had a chance under a more intensive system of agriculture, but long years will doubtless elapse before a body of men so strong in will and limb, with traditions of religious faith and political independence, again people the countryside of England. The economic mills grind continuously, at times rapidly, often ruthlessly, as in this agricultural revolution.

About 1880 f.

Sometimes the owners of large estates cultivated their lands in whole or in part, by means of agents, foremen, and laborers. Such were many of the heroes of the agricultural revolution. More often, however, they rented their lands to farmers at the highest rent practicable. Some of the renters were gentleman farmers who employed overseers and laborers, while they themselves gave general directions, dabbled in politics, and spent a season each year in London or abroad. Whether rising from the ranks in agriculture or in trade, or with the blood of generations of gentlemen in their veins, they were determined to enjoy life. While their men carried on the

Gentleman farmers

routine of cultivation, they dined and wined with their friends, rode with them to the hunt, and proudly displayed their broad acres and luxurious dwellings.[25] Their neighbor might be a **Working** working farmer, a tenant like themselves but laboring with **farmers** his servants in the fields and stables. This man's mode of living might not be so pretentious, but his economic function was essentially the same. Although he worked with his hands, nevertheless his chief business was to manage his estate and to provide the necessary capital.

Now, none of these cultivators was entirely new. In a sense, the farming landlord was the manorial lord working the demesne through the bailiff. The gentleman and working farmers existed since the fifteenth and sixteenth centuries. The agricultural revolution, however, led them all into new ways and to new enterprises. They experimented, studied, **Their** travelled; in short, used their mental faculties as these had **new** never before been used in agriculture. They were the business **enter-** men of agriculture. They provided large amounts of capital **prise** where formerly it had been scant; they determined the best technique where formerly superstitious routine had often prevailed; they directed the purchase of abundance of supplies and the sale of large surpluses where formerly the ideal had been a meagre commercialized system.

Out of the movement, with which we are dealing, came **Threefold** the entrenchment of the threefold type of managerial sys- **class** tem, for which England is famous.[26] The landlord pro- **system** vided the land and such permanent improvement as buildings, lanes, and bridges; the farmer provided management and capital for machinery, seed, livestock, and temporary improvements; and the laborer provided all he had, the work of his own hands. Once a system held in high esteem because of the revolution in methods it introduced, it is now seriously questioned, largely because the laborer fares badly. He lives in an unsatisfactory cottage and receives low wages.

Such a system of landlord, tenant farmer, and laborer involved a change in the tenure of land. The old manorial system left in its wake the landlordship of the lord holding the ancient demesne on the one hand and on the other the

225

proprietorship of the peasant paying a quit rent to the lord. The agricultural revolution dealt a heavy blow to this peasant proprietorship, for, as has been noted, the peasants (yeomen and customary tenants) lost their lands almost everywhere in England,[27] in marked contrast to France. These lands went to the landlords in large part, and the particular means of bringing this about was called the enclosure movement.

The enclosure of land meant, as we have seen, the erecting of fences or hedges around pieces of land formerly open, arable, meadow, pasture, and waste. There have been three such movements in English history. The first was started by lords and tenants under town economy, to provide for better cultivation, possibly for legume rotation or for field-grass husbandry in some southern and coast districts.[28] The second was instituted by the lords to get rid of tenants engaging in unprofitable agriculture and paying only nominal rents. The land enclosed was used either for pasture or for field-grass husbandry. The third, with which we are most concerned, was carried through by the rich and greedy, the enterprising and the ambitious. The reason for it was that the new agriculture—scientific rotation—might be practised. The enclosure itself was the result of the new agriculture and the profits it offered to landlords and farmers. In the process of enclosure the small holders of lands suffered, sometimes through the highhandedness of rich enclosers, sometimes through the cost of enclosing, and sometimes because of their inability to change their methods. The government of the day being in the hands of the noble and rich, facilitated the process of enclosure.[29] The result was agricultural efficiency and human suffering, the usual two chapters in the book of economic revolution.

Agricultural education, which had hitherto been largely confined to apprenticeship in practical work, now became somewhat professionalized. Although treatises had been written on agriculture in England since the thirteenth century, they were not numerous until after 1650. In Scotland formal education for agriculture had been recommended at least as early as 1729;[30] and a professorship of agriculture was established at Edinborough in 1790.[31] Societies for the improvement of cultivation had been founded, in Scotland in 1723, in the west of England in 1777, and the Smithfield Club in London in 1793. *The Farmer's Magazine,* a monthly, was established in 1776, and *The Farmer's Journal,* a newspaper, in 1808,[32] *The Journal of the Royal Agricultural Society* began to appear in 1840. Books of travel had neglected agriculture, but henceforth agriculture was to have its own descriptive literature based on the tours of its devotees.[33]

Agriculture was not content with gaining a literature of its own: it might almost be thought of as setting out to conquer the literature of England. The declining village plays a part in English prose from Goldsmith's *Vicar of Wakefield* (1766) to Julia Patton's *The English Village* (1919). Scores of poems in eighteenth and early nineteenth centuries bore the name village in their titles, and at least one poem was devoted to the methods of agriculture.[34] Goldsmith saw nothing but beauty and repose in rural life, and regarded the revolution as a calamity:

Literary conquests

> "A bold peasantry, their country's pride,
> When once destroyed, can never be supplied." [35]

Robert Burns enlists our sympathy for the poor but manly peasant, who has no ambition for culture and is satisfied with his lot:

> "Gie me ae spark o' nature's fire,
> That's a' the learning I desire." [36]

It remained for George Crabbe consciously to set out to analyse, and to depict in verse, the real situation in agriculture and rural life. In an attitude of scorn and contempt, he condemns what he saw as unlovely, uncultured, and degraded. The farmer is a "creature no more enliven'd than a clod," [37] and the country scene a "vile prospect." [38] Both attitudes, idealistic and realistic, have many early prototypes, but their rôle in literature was somewhat new and quite significant. Thus do letters reflect the economic system of the times and in some measure are to be interpreted economically.

**Well-
being**

To many students of our day, the most significant result of the agricultural revolution was not economic efficiency, not change in land tenure, and not literary culture, but the loss of well-being by the rank and file of country people. The proletarianizing of the yeomen and the customary tenants seems a great social set-back. Where they had been masters, they now became laborers, at least in many instances. And then the cottars and squatters, the traditional poor and laboring class of the village, suffered greatly when their holdings were enclosed for the new agriculture. They lost their cow, pig, and geese when the commons were enclosed, and instead of milk, pork, and fowl, they lived on bread and tea. They lost their fuel when the waste land was enclosed; and if they wanted to keep warm, they were invited to use the stables. Truly it was but slight compensation for such losses to have plenty of work offered to them and to be compelled to accept it to keep body and soul together. Industrial discipline is one of our modern acquisitions, but the price in this case and commonly is a very heavy one. The usual escape from this sad dilemma is to regard the economic gain as permanent and the human suffering as temporary. But the unescapable reflection is that the sufferers have but one life to live, and when that is gone, civilization is gone—for them. They have helped to furnish the elegant home of the gentleman farmer and they have submitted to the new discipline. They have built the poet's palace of art but they dwell not in it.

65. Suggestions for Further Study

1. A scholarly and detailed account of English agriculture from 1660 to 1874 is to be found in R. E. Prothero's *English Farming, Past and Present* (1888, 1912), chs. VI–XVII. Briefer treatment is given in W. H. R. Curtler's *Short History of English Agriculture* (1909), chs. XI–XX.

2. W. E. H. Lecky (*History of England in the Eighteenth Century* vol. VII, ch. XXI, 1887), has described social conditions generally, including agricultural changes.

3. For the agricultural laborer in England, see W. Hasbach, *A History of the English Agricultural Labourer* (1894, 1908), chs. II–IV.

4. A very interesting and sympathetic story of the sufferings of the poor people during the period of agricultural changes has been written by J. L. and B. Hammond, in *The Village Labourer, 1760–1832* (1911, 1920).

5. For a more detailed study of enclosures, the works of the following should be read—Leadam, Gay, Tawney, Gray, Johnson, Slater, and Gonner. A recent book on the subject is by W. H. R. Curtler, *The Enclosure and Redistribution of our Land* (1920). See above, ch. VII.

6. For a list of contemporary publications for the period 1640–1840, see W. Cunningham, *Growth of English Industry and Commerce*, vol. III, *Laissez-faire* (1903, 1912), pp. 976–998.

7. Which peoples have not yet experienced an agricultural revolution?

8. Which countries have had agricultural revolutions? Place these revolutions in their chronological order.

9. Did agricultural revolutions introducing scientific rotations of crops, have as far-reaching results in other countries as in England?

10. What do we mean when we say that the agricultural revolution introduced a balanced agriculture?

11. Do you regard the agricultural revolution as social or personal, as the work of many or a few, as the result of general forces or of the will and intellect of a limited number of men?

12. Which class contributed most to (a) experimentation, (b) financing, and (c) supervision?

13. Do you regard the heroes of the agricultural revolution as the only innovators, or only the few that happen to be known?

14. Was the agricultural revolution primarily economic or technological?

15. Work out as many connections as possible between the agricultural and the industrial revolutions.

16. Why did the agricultural revolution not begin in the sixteenth or earlier centuries?

17. Work out the connection between the agricultural revolution and metropolitan economy.

18. Was the agricultural revolution the work primarily of individuals or of the government?

19. Consider the effect of the government bounties (1673, 1689) on the exportation of corn. Did it encourage or otherwise affect agriculture? See the divergent views of Adam Smith, *Wealth of Nations* (1776), bk. IV, ch. V; and W. Cunningham, *Growth of English Industry and Commerce*, vol. II, *Mercantile System* (1903), pp. 540–545.

Study the general political situation in 18th century England to discover wherein and why it furthered the agricultural changes.

21. How did the prevailing doctrine of *laissez-faire* affect the agricultural revolution?

22. Why did agriculture and rural life receive so much attention in English prose and poetry in the period 1760–1840?

For further references, see the notes below.

66. NOTES TO CHAPTER IX

1. See above, ch. VIII, sect. 53, pp. 181 f.
2. H. Levy, *Large and Small Holdings* (1904, 1911), pp. 60–61, 168.
3. See below, ch. XII, sect. 87, pp. 295–297.
4. See Sir Ernest Clark, Jethro Tull in the *Dictionary of National Biography,* vol. LVII (1899), pp. 304–306; W. Cobbett's edition of Tull's *Horse-Hoeing Husbandry* (1822, 1829), pp. xiii, 7; A. Young, *Rural Œconomy* (1770), p. 315.
5. J. M. Rigg, Charles Townshend in the *Dictionary of National Biography,* vol. LVII (1899), pp. 109–117.
6. Sir Richard Weston, *A Discourse of Husbandrie used in Brabant and Flanders* (3rd ed., 1654), pp. 6–7. For turnips in the scientific rotation, see above, ch. VIII, sect. 53, p. 4.
7. Henry Higgs, Arthur Young, in the *Dictionary of National Biography,* vol. LXIII (1900), pp. 357–363.
8. T. Cooper, William Marshall, *ibid.,* vol. XXXVI (1893), pp. 251–252.
9. J. Humphreys, Robert Bakewell, *ibid.,* vol. III (1885), pp. 22–23.
10. Mrs. Radford, Francis Russell, Fifth Duke of Bedford, *ibid.,* vol. XLIX (1897), pp. 435–437.
11. Miss Clerke, Lord Somerville, *ibid.,* vol. LIII (1898), pp. 253–254.
12. Ernest Clark, Sir John Sinclair, *ibid.,* vol. LII (1897), pp. 301–305.
13. G. F. Russell Baker, Coke of Holkham, *ibid.,* vol. XI (1887), pp. 249–251; R. E. Prothero, *English Farming, Past and Present* (1912), pp. 217–221.
14. A. Young, *Rural Œconomy* (1770), p. 175.
15. Cf. Sir John Sinclair, *The Code of Agriculture* (1818), pp. 37–38; *An Encyclopædia of Agriculture* (ed. J. C. Loudon, 1825, 1857), p. 781.
16. M. F. Miller, *The Evolution of Reaping Machines,* U. S. Department of Agriculture (1902), pp. 12 f.
17. Thaer's work was written in German, Hanover 1803–1806, and translated into French, Paris, 1821. See A. Meitzen, *Der*

Boden . . . des Preussischen Staates, vol. II (1869), p. 66.

18. J. Mackinnon, *The Social and Industrial History of Scotland* (1921), p. 7.

19. E. W. Dickson, *Practical Agriculture,* vol. I (1805), pp. 28–31; *An Encyclopædia of Agriculture* (1834, 1857), pp. 1319, 1322–1323.

20. Cf. G. Fischer, *Die sociale Bedeutung der Maschinen in der Landwirtschaft* (1902), p. 65.

21. Total corn exported from England:

1697–1731	12,367,357	quarters
1732–1766	23,627,671	"
1767–1801	7,254,086	"

R. E. Prothero, *English Farming, Past and Present* (1912), p. 452.

22. See N. S. B. Gras, *Evolution of the English Corn Market* (1915), p. 144. See also W. Naudé, *Die Getreidehandelspolitik der Europäischen Staaten (Acta Borussica,* 1896), pp. 102 f.

23. Manorial documents show the tenants stealing the grain and livestock of the lord and poaching on his preserves. The lord had taken some of their land; they snatched some of his products. For the modern period see J. L. and B. Hammond, *The Village Labourer, 1760–1832* (1911, 1920), pp. 64–65, 84–85.

24. In America the scientific rotation has led to smaller farms. See H. C. Taylor's *Agricultural Economics* (1920), ch. XIV, The Size of Farms.

25. For an interesting picture of the farmer who became a gentleman and the gentleman who became a farmer, see George Crabbe's The Gentleman Farmer (1812), in *Poems* (Cambridge English Classics, 1905), vol. II, pp. 42–43.

26. For an account of this system see Sir James Caird, *English Agriculture in 1850–51* (1852), chs. LIII, LIV, LV.

27. Cf. below, ch. XI, sect. 81, p. 268.

28. See above, ch. VII, sect. 47, p. 160.

29. See J. L. and B. Hammond, *The Village Labourer, 1760–1832* (1911, 1920), pp. 21 f. See also the works of G. Slater and E. C. K. Gonner.

30. *An Essay on Ways and Means for Inclosing, Fallowing, Planting, . . . Scotland* (1729), p. 199.

31. *An Encyclopædia of Agriculture* (ed. J. C. Loudon, 5th ed. 1857), p. 131.

32. *Ibid.,* 131. I have been unable to find this newspaper.

33. Cf. A. Young, *The Farmer's Letters to the People of England* (1767, 1768), pp. 460–461.

HISTORY OF AGRICULTURE

34. T. Batchelor's *Progress of Agriculture* (1804).
35. Oliver Goldsmith, *The Deserted Village* (1770).
36. Robert Burns, Epistle to J. Lapraik (1785), *Cambridge Edition of the Poets* (1897), pp. 44–46.
37. George Crabbe, The Gentleman Farmer, *Poems* (Cambridge English Classics, 1905), vol. II, p. 42.
38. George Crabbe, The Lover's Journey, *ibid.*, 142.

CHAPTER X

THE PHYSIOCRATS

AGRICULTURE ENTHRONED IN FRANCE

67. THE BACKGROUND OF FRENCH AGRICULTURE. The **English** English put agriculture upon a scientific basis when they rev- **and** olutionized their methods. The French put agriculture upon a **attain-** high theoretical pedestal when their writers glorified the farmer **ments** and his work. The English had reason to be proud of their accomplishments in fact, but, in their thinking and writing, they did not emphasise agriculture so much as manufacture. The French had little cause for enthusiasm about their actual practices, but they saw in agriculture a great opportunity for national advance. The English agricultural revolution and the French physiocratic doctrines gave the cultivator a position in fact and theory, in the deeds and thoughts of men, for which there was no precedent.

The physiocrats were a group of French economists who **Who the** for a time directed the attention of thinkers in France to the **physio-** deplorable condition of French agriculture and to the impor- **crats** tance of the cultivators' work at all times and in all states. **were** Although the movement was short-lived, it was of vast import- **1756–** ance, partly for what it accomplished and partly for what it **1770** signified. Similar movements have occurred in other countries, notably in America. Before we can understand what the physiocrats stood for and particularly the reasons for their position, we must consider the background of French agriculture.

While the population of England was increasing fairly **Popula-** rapidly, that of France was said to be decreasing. It was **tion of** thought to have been about twenty-four millions in 1650, **France** about nineteen millions in 1700, and sixteen millions about 1750.[1] Although the last figure seems too low, when we re-

First census, 1801

member that in 1800, after several years of warfare, the population was about twenty-seven millions, still it is probable that in the century preceding the activities of the physiocrats, there was some decline in population. We may infer that this was due to the numerous wars, to the expulsion of the Protestants (Huguenots), and to local dearths and resulting diseases. A large proportion of the people was engaged in agriculture.

1921

1840

About 56% of the French nation is resident in rural districts to-day, and a little less than half is at present engaged in agriculture.[2] Three generations ago about 75% lived in the country. At the time of the physiocrats it was variously estimated that from one-half to four-fifths lived in rural parts.[3] Having in mind the later and more exact figures, we may infer that four-fifths or 80% was a conservative estimate of the agricultural population of France. As is to be expected, such a population exported chiefly agricultural products. Prominent among these were grain (when export was allowed), wine, brandy, leather, salted meat, butter, cheese, fats, and tallow.[4]

France and England compared (early 18th century)

While France was losing in population, England was gaining. While France was remaining rural, England was slowly becoming urban. While France lost wars, England won them. While France had difficulty in avoiding bankruptcy, England was gaining in financial strength. While France was frequently experiencing dearths, England had a large surplus of grain for export abroad.

French agricultural technique

French agriculture was still medieval. It smacked of town economy. The prime consideration was subsistence with a small surplus to pay rents and taxes. There was little accumulation of capital and therefore slight improvement. The internal trade in agricultural products was restricted, and export to foreign countries was often prohibited. The fallow system of cultivation prevailed in almost pristine strength. The only question is whether the cruder two-field or the more advanced three-field type was the more common. In both, there was a permanent separation of arable, meadow, and pasture. But in the two-field system one half of the arable was left fallow, while in the three-field system only one third was so used. In the two-field system oxen were probably commonly used as beasts of burden, while in the three-field system horses were more feasible. In the two-field system, the chief crop was wheat for men with little cereal or other planted crop for animals. The oxen and other beasts were pastured in the summer and fed hay in the winter. In the three-field system, crops for men could be planted on one-third of the land, and crops for animals on another third, while the rest was left fallow.[5] Accordingly there were wheat for bread and oats for fodder. All this, of course, is in marked contrast to the agriculture of England where the issue was not between types of the fallow system, but between the fallow system and the scientific rotation of crops. In France the question was not the enclosure of land for better methods, but rearranging the fields with their scattered strips so as to get more spring, and less winter, grain.

In France much more of the manor survived than in England. In a few parts even bailiff-farming prevailed. Although personal serfdom had largely disappeared, tenurial serfdom was common. At the top of the rural hierarchy was the lord, lay or ecclesiastical, who collected many dues and rents from his servile tenants. Although the great mass of the tenants were probably descended from the old-time holders of servile land, there was an increasing number of farmers. The farmers were either small metayers, paying a share of their crops (usually one-half) to the lord, or the cash farmers, the *fermiers* (farmers *par excellence*) who paid a money rent. The metayers had little capital or skill; the cash farmers had a great deal of capital and were promising cultivators. The lord supplied to the metayers not only land and permanent improvements but capital in the form of oxen and sometimes seed and machinery. The cash farmers on the other hand furnished everything but the land and the more permanent improvements. It was estimated that while the cash farmers, located chiefly in northern France, held as much as six or seven million arpents (the size of an arpent varied greatly according to the locality, being here less, there more, than an acre), the small-scale tenants, both the old-time holders of servile lands and the metayers, occupied about thirty million.[6]

French agrarian conditions

The hope of the future, from the standpoint of efficiency, rested with the cash farmers, aided by the agricultural laborers, and the newly developing class of lords who were not noble at all but came from the towns, the bourgeois who wished to introduce the same efficiency into their agricultural holdings that had given them wealth in their urban business. These two classes of capitalists were in the minority, in the face of the serried ranks of king, dukes, marquesses, counts, viscounts, barons, archbishops, bishops, and abbots on the one hand and the serfs (by tenure or by tenure and status) on the other.

The French government and agriculture

The government of France in its most enlightened moments could not fail to view with alarm the retrograded condition of agriculture. There were many local dearths; Paris was nearly always on edge for fear of a deficiency.[7] The taxes were paid with difficulty. After the old religious civil war of the sixteenth century much had been done to restore agriculture by the king's minister, the Duc de Sully. Something might now be done to repair the damages of foreign wars and mistaken commercial policies. What was done was the work of two

1759–63
1774–77

outstanding controllers-general, Bertin and Turgot. What they and other government officials accomplished can be understood only when the leaders of thought and the schools to which they belonged, have been considered.

School of economists

There were three groups of political economists in France in the eighteenth century. The first, the financial economists such as Boisguillebert and Vauban, were modified mercantilists. They emphasised the need of building up the various productive agencies, notably agriculture, in order that the national revenue might be increased. They were inclined to stress money. The commercial school (half physiocratic) of Gournay and Turgot, stood for more free trade than had been enjoyed, sought to improve agriculture in order that commerce might flourish, and in general put the emphasis on industrial and commercial capitalism. It has been called a school of liberal mercantilism. The third group was the school of the physiocrats who put all their emphasis on agriculture. Commerce should be improved,[8] they thought, but it was in order to benefit agriculture and to increase taxes. The way in which this was to be done was by applying more and more capital to agriculture. In a sense, all three schools emphasised capital, the first in the form of money, the second commercial and industrial capital, and the third agricultural capital.

68. PERSONNEL OF THE PHYSIOCRATIC GROUP. Publicists **Contem-** in France were for a time divided into groups, the physiocrats, **porary** the half-physiocrats (for example, Turgot), and the opponents **groups** of the physiocrats (Voltaire, Grimm, Linguet, and Rousseau). And what a galaxy of stars they were, potent in their influence on succeeding generations of men! Some were brilliant, some keen and penetrating. Bold speculators in the field of the social sciences, they blazed the trails since followed by better equipped investigators.

The master builder was Quesnay, father of the physiocratic **Quesnay,** school. Born on a farm near Paris, he came to know in- **1694–** timately the tasks of the cultivator. As a young man he went **1774** to the metropolis where he studied languages, medicine, surgery, botany, philosophy, and mathematics. Not content to practise his profession of medicine, he wrote learned treatises on science and philosophy. As court physician he had leisure and influence. At the age of sixty-two he wrote his first **1756–57** treatises on economics for the new Encyclopedia which was to have so much influence on the course of French history. These articles, one on Grain and the other on Farmers, indicate his absorption in agriculture. This interest was not alone theoretical, for the year previously he had purchased a farm on **1755** which he put his children. From this learned doctor radiated enthusiasm and suggestion. Princes and courtiers, lawyers and administrators, sought his company. By conversation as by pen he roused his fellows to talk, write, and act. What Luther did for the Protestant revolution, Voltaire for enlightenment, and Rousseau for political revolution, Quesnay did for the development of French agriculture and economics. How far he was brought to action by his experience as a cultivator, or by his realization of the need of regenerating agriculture in order to support the Court at which he resided, or by his studies of medicine which suggested and emphasised the physical basis of social affairs, is hard to say. It is not unlikely that all three influences constituted the personal background of his action.

Followers of Quesnay

Quesnay spoke in laconics, his followers in arguments and action, books and royal edicts, reforms and propagandist societies. The most brilliant of the disciples was the Marquis de Mirabeau.

Mirabeau, 1715–89

At first an advocate of a large population, he came, under Quesnay's influence, to emphasise the possession of capital, especially in agriculture. Without much power of formulation or sustained argument, he called attention to the new doctrines, not only by his social position but by his very peculiarities of style and wealth of figures. Bertin and Turgot, the two ministers of great influence, did what they could to put the doctrines into practice.

Du Pont de Nemours, 1739–1817

Although there were many other physiocrats and half-physiocrats, only one more need be dealt with here. Du Pont was the son of an aristocratic mother and a bourgeois father. As a youth he was a learned prodigy. Though he studied medicine, he never practised it, preferring to serve the public cause at home and abroad. He became interested in economic

1763

questions at the end of the Seven Years' War, when the French government was hard put to it to meet its financial obligations. He contributed his own ideas on the subject and came to know Quesnay and Mirabeau.[9] Falling under the influence of Quesnay, he became the propagandist of the physiocratic school. He played a part in negotiating the treaty between France and England, that led to the recognition of the independence of the United States. Indeed the latter part of his life was spent in America, where his descendants have been prominent in war and manufacturing munitions of war.

Du Pont and the word physiocrat

The word physiocracy was apparently first used in 1767 and physiocrat in 1799, in both cases by Du Pont. Physiocracy means the rule of nature. Nature rules in accordance with certain unalterable laws which lead to the increase, progress, and good-fortune of mankind. The laws of man should be in harmony with the laws of nature. In short, society should be governed by the natural order of things. To the physiocrats this meant the use of nature in agricultural production, making trade free like the winds and waters, and the acceptance of private property and monarchical government. Up to 1767 the physiocratic school had been known as the school of "the economists"; now it was for a short time called physiocratic. But this term was soon given up, to be revived later when economist and economics came to have a more general meaning.[10]

69. ORIGIN OF THE SCHOOL. The roots of the present lie both in the surface soil of the present and the subsoil of the past. The mercantilistic system of Colbert had furthered the interests of manufacturers and of merchants handling manufactured wares. The export of grain had been frequently prohibited by Colbert and his successors, and the freedom of internal trade in agricultural products had been only partly established by Colbert.[11] The result, as might be expected, was unfavorable to agricultural progress. Without an assured market at home or abroad, the cultivator planted the minimum of crops. Accordingly in years of plenty there was enough and some, occasionally a great deal, to spare; in years of crop failure there were local dearths, distress, and disease. France needed an agricultural revival and no school of economists could get a hearing without including agricultural regeneration in its program. The physiocrats were unique largely in the emphasis which they gave to the cultivation of the soil.

Reaction from mercantilism

The fact that Quesnay was a physician may account in part for his emphasis upon physical production, such as agriculture. But there is a social aspect to the school. France had a brilliant Court and a distinguished aristocracy. The king and the nobles were the age-long leaders of France. They were deriving much of the benefit of taxation. In the regeneration of France they should play a part. They were traditionally debarred from trade (or most of it) and of course from manufacture. Agriculture was open to them; in fact they were already engaged in it as landlords and as landed capitalists putting at least a part of their income back into the soil in the form of permanent improvements. In the theories of the physiocrats, the lords had a genuine rôle to play as rent takers

Social considerations

and tax payers. They were even to put themselves out a bit by staying at home a little more in order to look after their estates and by curtailing their expenditure on luxuries so as to reinvest more of their income in permanent improvements. Thus the physiocratic policy was to renew the vigor of a dying manorial system. The noble protagonists would readily appreciate such an ambition, and the conservative lawyers and administrators would and did fall in with a plan that was based on the essentials of existing conditions. The physiocrats were hopeless optimists in thinking that there was any economic vigor in the ease-loving and highly cultured aristocracy and Court.

Influence of England

1756–63

1760

1758

Reaction from mercantilism, personal tendencies, and social consideration would not in themselves have brought about so sharp a turn in thought and action as actually occurred. The precipitating event was the Seven Years' War with England. During the early years of the war, France lost her hold on both India and Canada. It is no accident that Anglomania and Agromania occurred at the same time. Frenchmen had long been looking across the Channel at English economic changes and progress. In 1750 Duhamel published the first volume of his treatise on the methods of Jethro Tull. Patullo in his essay on agriculture [12] noted that France did not have such sheep as England possessed. The Marquis de Turbilly, the distinguished agronomist, suggested that France follow the example of England in importing rams and ewes from abroad.[13] Voltaire, Forbonnais, and Quesnay set up the rich English farmer as a model for France.[14] A writer in an economic journal said that most of the stimulus in the direction of improvement came from England.[15] An opponent of the physiocrats asserted that the agronomic pest came from England.[16] It is perfectly clear that the English agricultural revolution in its early phase was having a potent effect upon France. Simple imitation, however, does not furnish the sole clue. England's victories over France at Plassey in 1757, at Louisburg in 1758, and at Quebec in 1759 called for action. It is an old practice to learn from one's enemies. The French saw England exporting manufactured wares and raw products;

they saw the English merchants dominating in the state through their control of London in which the trade of the nation and the empire was concentrated.[17] France could hardly hope to equal England in the exportation of staple manufactures, and possibly because of this fact, at least in part, it turned to the other alternative, the export of raw products and foodstuffs. A regenerated and progressive agriculture would make France the equal of England in economic strength. As we now see, this was no more practical than the attempt to infuse vigor into the nobility. But the enthusiasm for the cause went on. It was said that one recalcitrant writer was so bold as to publish a preservative against the mania for agriculture, but in the end he himself, like Mirabeau, succumbed to the malady.[18] Many treatises were written and foreign works, both ancient and contemporary, pertinent to the new interest, were translated and printed.

70. GENERAL ECONOMIC DOCTRINES OF THE PHYSIOCRATS. **Production** The physiocrats had a theory that the only kind of production was physical. They emphasised agriculture and possibly included mining, quarrying, and fishing. Manufacture and commerce were held to be unproductive, or, as they said, sterile. These were both useful but yielded no surplus, because they consumed as much material, directly or indirectly, as they brought forth. The chief criticism of this doctrine is that the physical aspects of goods are emphasised to the exclusion of other utilities. Of the five kinds of production now commonly accepted, the physiocrats recognized only one, the first of the following list: commodity (chiefly agriculture), form (manufacture), place (transportation), time (storage), and exchange (merchandising and banking).

The second general economic theory of the physiocrats **Distribution** explained the distribution of wealth among the classes.[19] Agriculture yielded an income which was divided, part going to the cultivators and part to the landlords. That going to the landlord is the surplus, or net product; or, as we may call it, rent. Out of this net product the landlord pays taxes to the government, and buys food from the cultivators, manufactured goods from the artisans, and various commodities from the merchants. The artisan, in turn, spends his income in buying raw products and foodstuffs from the cultivators and the merchants. In this way there is a circulation of goods and advantages. In general, the theory is sound enough, and constituted a great contribution, but it is faulty in detail of expression.

Single tax

If agriculture was the only kind of production and if the only net product went to the landlord, it followed that he should (and did) pay all taxes. The landlord no longer led armies, no longer ruled the state, but was to constitute the great tax-paying class. He did not produce the surplus out of which the tax was paid, but he did actually pay the tax to the government. Here at least was a useful job for the aristocracy. The tenants of land, the occupants of houses, the manufacturers of goods, and the merchants of wares were to pay no taxes. The rich colonial planter and the money lender and speculator were to go scot-free. In more recent times the single-tax idea has been extended to the point where the government is to claim more and more of the surplus, perhaps leaving to the landlord little over the cost of collecting the rent. Such we often find is the view held to-day in America, Canada, and elsewhere. But the physiocrats had no such confiscatory idea. The great protagonist of the single tax in America was Henry George, but he did not owe his theory to the physiocrats. The single tax in America was born afresh and in a somewhat novel form to meet the feeling of the landless, the oppressed, and the dispossessed.[20] Under a single-tax plan it would probably be easier for a cultivator to buy a farm, because the value of land would be lower when it was heavily taxed. It would be easier to get started in owning a farm; it would, in other words, reduce tenancy. It would tend to make the size of holdings smaller and cultivation more intensive. Accordingly we would expect to find the friends of the single tax in America among tenants ambitious of ownership and among small owners seeking more land; while the opponents would be speculators in land, landlords, and the owner-operators of large estates.

1839-97

1871

71. AGRICULTURAL POLICY OF THE PHYSIOCRATS AND **Glorifi-**
THEIR CONTEMPORARIES IN FRANCE. Even before the time **cation of**
of the physiocrats there had been developing an interest in rural **ture**
life. Watteau's pictures of the seasons, garden scenes, and
village characters display a rare gift of poetic realism. The
fairs and village scenes of Lancret more popular in his day then
in ours, are significant of contemporary interest. In many
literary pieces the setting came to be rural. Thomson's "Seasons" (1730) was translated from English into French. In **1759**
the sessions of the Society of Agriculture of Paris one could
see the cultivator, the dirt farmer, seated alongside of peers,
nobles, and magistrates.[21] Quesnay lamented the unjust plac-
ing of agricultural workers below the common people of the
town.[22] Another physiocrat regarded the peasant as the most
neglected but still, as was held by many, the most necessary
in the state.[23] Agriculture was looked upon as the seat of
the virtues of honor and liberty, the nursery of soldiers, the
source of perpetual creation on which other activities and
civilization itself depend. We may well raise the question
whether there was any precedent for such extreme laudation
Certainly there was some justification for it. Agriculture
if carefully managed, is an inexhaustible and unending source
of raw materials and food. It is adapted to a relatively high
mental, moral, and physical existence. It produces the prime
necessities of life, though it is not alone in doing so. It produces enough of them to enable civilization to go on to greater
heights.

France was not content with the recognition and praise of **Technical**
agriculture. To many writers, both physiocratic and non- **improve-**
physiocratic, agriculture was capable of improvement. The **ments**
English plan of compulsory enclosure, where the majority favored it, was advocated.[24] A royal edict authorized the en- **1769**
closure of common pastures. The preamble, indeed, says that
many communities have demanded enclosures. It is to be
noted that reference is made to pasture lands, not to arable.
In Béarn, located in southern France, the enclosure of common **1767**
pastures took place. In the same province the right of the lord

243

1770

1767-74

1763

to pasture his livestock along with that of the tenants on the stubble fields was taken away. Within a short period of seven years, it was said, a remarkable agricultural revival followed these enclosures.[25] But, unfortunately, not all France moved with Béarn. The unenclosed field system prevailed, with its provision for leaving one-half or one-third of the arable lying fallow. In a few local districts the fallows had, indeed, become a thing of the past. In a large part of Caux, in northwestern France, there had been no fallows for about two generations.[26] In the place of the old fallow system the rural economists advocated either field-grass husbandry [27] or the scientific rotation of crops,[28] though, of course, without employing these terms. The progress of England in using artificial pastures, turnips, and potatoes was noted, and Frenchmen were invited to follow. Quesnay advocated the general increase of livestock in order to provide more manure.[29] It was laid down by an ordinance of 1761 that no cow fit for calving should be sold. Next year it was likewise decreed that no butcher should kill a cow less than ten years old. Veterinary schools were established, one at Lyon in 1761 and one at Alfort in 1765. Foreign breeds were introduced.[30]

Approach to an agricultural revolution

1773

France experienced many agricultural improvements, but they were local. There was a veritable furor for utilizing waste land by clearing, draining, and enclosing. There was much talk of English technique. There were noble lords who experimented with crops and animals. Tull's horse-hoe was used locally. The chemist Parmentier wrote a book exposing the unreasonable prejudice against the potato. And yet in spite of all these promising circumstances France remained a land of fallows and scattered strips, of scrub animals and clumsy machinery.

Arthur Young's observations, 1787-89

Arthur Young travelled through France as a pioneer investigator. Frenchmen marvelled at his journey undertaken on horseback and alone to investigate not historic ruins but agricultural technique. Young found much to record. In Picardy he saw only villages, no scattered farmsteads as in England. He observed that French women worked hard, plowing in the fields and filling the dung carts. On the other hand he met gentlemen of culture who were interested in the management of their estates and found one that had nearly as good a library on agriculture as his own. But the estates were generally small and even where enclosure had taken place the old fallow practice was followed. The metayers he condemned as unprogressive. There was a great lack of gentlemen and farm tenants, the agricultural middle class so characteristic of English agriculture and so dominant in his own land.[31]

A physiocrat provides us with an illustration of a poor estate. It contained 360 arpents (perhaps about 300 acres), of which one-third was waste land given over to pasture and chestnut trees. There were four or five thatched cottages for the metayers, about twenty oxen, some hectic cows, about 100 wretched sheep, some rye, black corn, maize, large turnips, and little or no wheat sown or harvested. The best lands were used as meadows for growing hay, which, like the oxen, was to be sold to near-by tenant-farmers.[32]

An example of a poor estate, 1767

The physiocrats condemned such poor technique but were primarily interested in the more general questions of increasing the size of the farming unit and the amount of capital applied to the farm, and in furthering the trade in the products of the cultivator. Since the seventeenth century there had been restraint of trade within France itself. Even before the physiocratic school had been born, a measure of relief had been granted. Under the influence of the physiocrats the freedom of internal trade in grain was extended and nobles were permitted to engage in buying and selling grain. The edict making these changes was soon suspended, but when Turgot (a half-physiocrat) came into power, the trade in grain both within France and over the borders was again made free. As before, however, this freedom was short lived, and with it went many of the hopes for a new agriculture.

Emphasis of the physiocrats

1754
1763

1770

1774

Some of the heralds of progress did their work as individuals. The Marquis de Turbilly was a beacon light in his district, though the light went out all too soon. The well-to-do botanist and agronomist, Duhamel du Monceau, wrote many books on technical aspects of agriculture. The physiocrats

Agencies of agricultural improvement 1700–1782

245

supported two journals [33] which had much influence upon the leaders of thought, though little on the rank and file of cultivators. Agricultural societies, such as those of Paris and Tours, formed under physiocratic auspices, offered prizes for products of high quality and for treatises on agricultural methods. The physiocrats had a tower of strength in Henri Bertin, the controller-general of France. It was he who translated many of the policies of his fellow economists into official action, from the establishment of agricultural societies to the freeing of the grain trade, from the draining of swamps to the building of canals. But Bertin, like Turgot at a little later time, did not hold office long enough to execute many of the things he himself advocated. And in both cases those who came after were either lukewarm in reform or reactionary.

1759–63

An agricultural policy

72. CONTRIBUTIONS OF THE PHYSIOCRATS. The physiocrats called attention to the importance of agriculture and the danger involved in neglecting it. In the nineteenth century England did not heed the warning, though it has recently; in other words not until it is (perhaps) too late. Germany on the other hand has had an agrarian as well as an industrial policy. The result has been a struggle between the two, which has ended in the victory of neither. Indeed, we may now almost re-define physiocracy as a policy which rises ghost-like to warn the unfortunate nation whose agriculture is languishing, that decay and death may lie ahead. Whether this is to be actually the case will depend much on the continuation of the geographical division of labor and the development of international peace which will allow Belgium and England for example to manufacture goods and import raw products and foodstuffs.

Theoretical contributions

The physiocrats started modern rural economy, or agricultural economics, though it must be confessed this study was not put on a scientific basis. They began the theoretical study of political economy, though some of their leading concepts were false. They called attention to the distribution of wealth from class to class, though they built on the single foundation of physical or agricultural production. They set forth a theory of free trade, such as had been advocated

246

for internal commerce by the mercantilists, and for internal and external commerce by the financial economists and the commercial school. They called attention to the rôle played by capital, but others had performed a similar task, not for capital in agriculture but in manufacture and commerce.

As a school the physiocrats did not last long. Unity soon disappeared. There were physiocratic edicts and laws until the time of Napoleon, but these were of little practical importance. Agriculture did not progress very far in France. Free trade did not come as a general policy until 1860.

Survival after 1770

In Europe generally there were isolated devotees, more distinguished in position than actually influential in practice. In Germany, Poland, and Russia, the physiocrats had some vogue and a little influence. In England they found no exact reflexion, but they helped to produce Adam Smith, the generally accepted founder of political economy. America has always been a fertile soil for new ideas and immature doctrines. The physiocrats had their followers at first along the coast and then inland. While abroad, Benjamin Franklin drank deeply of the physiocratic beverage.[34] Thomas Jefferson obtained his economics as he did his political philosophy from France. To him the cultivators were the salt of the earth, the most virtuous citizens a state can possess, the most loyal to the government and yet the most wedded to liberty. If the cultivator cannot continue on the soil, it is better for him to become a sailor or a manufacturer.[35] A striking lithograph published in an American agricultural journal shows eight persons, each of whom performs a special service. The clergyman prays for all, the merchant trades for all, the lawyer pleads for all, the representative legislates for all, the physician prescribes for all, the railroad man carries for all, the soldier fights for all, but the central figure, the cultivator, pays for all.[36] Later another agricultural journal became eloquent with similar thoughts. We depend upon the farmer for everything. Were it not for the farmer, the ship would not sail, the train would not start, the factory would not open, the city would not grow, the skyscraper would not rise, and fortunes would not be amassed. When this farmer class is

Spread abroad

1869

1892

dissatisfied, real statesmen and publicists, it was said, will take careful note and govern themselves accordingly.[37]   Such a doctrine is preached at country fairs, but is also echoed in Congress.   It is the meat and drink of some rural politicians, but it is also the stock in trade of some representatives and senators.[38]   Whether townsmen or big business men like it or not, they must realize that agriculture is fundamentally important.   It is not the precise theory of the physiocrats but their general emphasis that has enduring value.

73. Suggestions for Further Study

1. See the article on The Physiocrats by G. Schelle in the *Dictionary of Political Economy* (ed. by Sir Robert H. I. Palgrave), vol. III (1899, 1918), pp. 102–108.
2. Read H. Higgs, *The Physiocrats* (1897).
3. Read C. Gide and C. Rist, *A History of Economic Doctrines from the Time of the Physiocrats to the Present Day* (1909, translation 1915), pp. 1–50.
4. Read Turgot's *Reflections on the Formation and the Distribution of Riches* (1770, ed. by Sir W. J. Ashley, 1898), pp. 7–17, 17–25, 54–58, 95–98.
5. What is the meaning of physiocracy?
6. What are the cardinal beliefs of the physiocratic school?
7. What part of the doctrines of the physiocrats do you accept, what part reject?
8. Do you agree with the author of the article on the physiocratic school in the Encyclopædia Britannica that Gournay was one of the founders of the school, and with Alfred Marshall that the physiocrats sought to "diminish the suffering and degradation which was caused by extreme poverty."
9. Read Arthur Young's *Travels in France during the Years 1787, 1788, 1789* (1792 and many later editions).
10. Describe agricultural conditions in France at the time when the physiocratic school began.
11. Was there an agricultural revolution in France?
12. For a vivid realistic picture of the life of the metayer in France, read Emile Guillaumin's masterpiece, *The Life of a Simple Man* (1904, trans. into English, 1919).   It pictures the toil of the peasant not unlike that of the time of the physiocrats and the grouping of several families into one household.   Perhaps the dominant notes are (1) family animosities, (2) hard work and niggard living, and (3) disagreement with landlords who

feared to be cheated of their half or sought to raise the money rent.

13. Is there any connection between the failure of the physiocrats' efforts to reform France on the one hand and the French Revolution on the other?

14. What are the social aspects of the physiocratic school? Which class was to be the driving power, which was to benefit most, and which did not have its welfare considered very seriously?

15. What was the relative position of France and England in economic theory in 1770? In economic development? Explain.

16. Distinguish between the following: physiocrat in the strict sense, half-physiocrat, and physiocrat such as we find here and there growing up out of the soil without reference to the French school.

17. If specially interested in the physiocrats, consult the works of Adam Smith (in English), August Oncken (in German), and G. Schelle (in French).

18. If interested in economic theory, trace the progression in the following systems: patristic economics, scholastic economics, canonist economics, mercantilism, physiocracy, classical economics, historical economics, neo-classicism, and social economics. See the works of J. K. Ingram, L. H. Haney, and C. Gide and C. Rist.

19. Is it true that the physiocratic doctrine has been more studied in Europe but more believed in America?

20. Do you know of any physiocrats in your district at the present time?

21. Is there any real contribution that a study of the physiocratic school can make in the formulation of an agricultural policy for America?

22. Study the attitude of American farmers toward the single tax. See for example, A. N. Young's *Single Tax Movement in the United States* (1916), pp. 191–197.

For further references, see the notes below.

74. Notes to Chapter X

1. Quesnay, "Grains" in *Physiocrates* (ed. by E. Daire), pt. I (1846), p. 299. See also L. Schöne, *Histoire de la Population Française* (1893), chs. x and xii.

2. H. Busson, J. Fèvre, and H. Hauser, *La France d'Aujourd'hui et ses Colonies* (1924), pp. 420, 434.

3. G. Weulersse, *Le Mouvement Physiocratique en France*, vol. I (1910), p. 248.

4. Quesnay, "Fermiers," *Physiocrates* (ed. by E. Daire), pt. I (1846), p. 244.

5. See Quesnay, *ibid.*, pp. 220 f.

6. Cf. *ibid.*, p. 230. For kinds of farmers, see Olivier de Serres, *Le Théâtre d'Agriculture et Mesnage des Champs* (1600), p. 61.

7. See H. Carré, in Lavisse, *Histoire de France*, vol. VIII, pt. II (1911), p. 360.

8. Cf. the *Maximes Générales* of Quesnay, *Physiocrates* (ed. by E. Daire), pt. I (1846), p. 98.

9. G. Schelle, *Du Pont de Nemours et l'École Physiocratique* (1888), pp. 9–11.

10. C. Gide and C. Rist, *A History of Economic Doctrines* (1909, translated 1915), pp. 3–4.

11. See above, ch. VI, sect. 43, p. 150.

12. *Essai sur l'Amélioration des Terres* (1758).

13. G. Weulersse, *Le Mouvement Physiocratique en France*, vol. I (1910), pp. 341–342.

14. *Ibid.*, pp. 360–361.

15. *Ibid.*, vol. II, p. 152.

16. *Ibid.*, p. 706.

17. See the article of Quesnay (1766) quoted in G. Weulersse, *Le Mouvement Physiocratique en France*, vol. II (1910), p. 709.

18. G. Weulersse, *Le Mouvement Physiocratique en France*, vol. II (1910), p. 152.

19. See the *Tableau Economique* (1758), by Quesnay, in *Physiocrates* (ed. by E. Daire), pt. I (1846), pp. 57–78.

20. See The Single Tax Platform of 1890 in A. N. Young, *The Single Tax Movement in the United States* (1916), pp. 321–323. Cf. H. G. Brown, The Single-Tax Complex, *The Journal of Political Economy*, vol. xxxii (1924), pp. 164–190.

21. G. Weulersse, *Le Mouvement Physiocratique en France*, vol. II (1910), p. 156.

22. *Ibid.*, vol. I (1910), pp. 367, 369.

23. Baudeau in the *Physiocrates* (ed. by E. Daire), pt. II (1846), pp. 701–702.

24. G. Weulersse, *Le Mouvement Physiocratique en France*, vol. I (1910), pp. 364–365.

25. *Ibid.*, vol. II (1910), pp. 172–175.

26. *Ibid.*, vol. I, p. 344, n. 5.

27. *Ibid.*, p. 366.

28. *Ibid.*, p. 343.

29. Quesnay, *Maximes Générales, Physiocrates* (ed. by E. Daire), pt. I (1846), pp. 94–95.

30. G. Weulersse, *Le Mouvement Physiocratique en France,* vol. II, pp. 196–197.

31. Arthur Young, *Travels in France during the Years 1787, 1788, 1789* (ed. by Betham-Edwards, 1900), pp. 8–9, 23–24, 64, 193, 198, 258.

32. G. Weulersse, *Le Mouvement Physiocratique en France,* vol. I (1910), pp. 331–332, n. 7.

33. *Journal de l'agriculture, du commerce et des finances,* and the *Ephémérides du Citoyen.*

34. See the *Works of Benjamin Franklin* (ed. by Jared Sparks), vol. VI (1840), p. 279 (letter of 1768).

35. See the *Writings of Thomas Jefferson* (ed. by H. A. Washington), vol. I (1871), p. 403 (letter of 1785).

36. S. J. Buck, *The Agrarian Crusade* (1920, 1921), frontispiece.

37. *Farm, Stock and Home,* vol. VIII (15 Aug., 1892), p. 322.

38. In 1922 one of the leaders of The Agricultural Bloc in the United States Senate wrote: "we cannot allow the balance of real production which comes only from the land to get out of balance with the dependent manufacturing industries, commerce, banking and government." Arthur Capper [of Kansas], *The Agricultural Bloc* (1922), p. 4.

CHAPTER XI

HISTORY OF PROPERTY IN LAND

Transition from Europe to America

75. ORIGIN OF PROPERTY IN LAND. The Atlantic is broad but there is no ocean of difference between the social development of Europe and that of America. In the preceding chapters on the old world we have had occasion to look at the new world. So in the present chapter on property in land we can make no true beginning without following the long lane of European experience and early American inheritance down to recent changes in the new world, which, while not unique, are at least independently arrived at.

Criteria of property

It seems impossible to define property in such a way as to satisfy either the lawyer or the economic historian. Just as soon as we set forth some criterion or test, we think of an exception. Nevertheless there are three attributes that property, or ownership, tends to possess. The owner has undisputed possession as against the claims of other individuals or groups of individuals. He is free to dispose of what is his own as he will. And for the use of what is his, he makes no payment whatever.

Ownership of personalty

Applying these criteria we see that personal property, such as jewels, weapons, and clothing, existed from the earliest times. So personal were some of these things that they were buried with the owner when he died. On the other hand, other personal property, such as cattle, was in the cultural nomadic stage the property of the kinship group.

Property in land before the settled village

Before men settled down to live in permanent villages there seems to have been no property in land at all. That is, there was no thought of one individual, or a group of individuals, owning land to the exclusion of others. To be sure, there was political control by whatever kind of government existed. One clan might regard this or that stretch of territory as its hunting preserves at a certain time of year, or this or that bit of land as its field for cultivating grain, but such control seems to have been all that existed. The actual cultivation of such ground was a common task, chiefly for women, and the crops were regarded as more or less common property, shared freely within the clan and even with needy strangers. It has often been pointed out that when Americans purchased land from the (nomadic) Indians they bought one thing, while the Indians sold another. The American purchased undisputed continuous possession. The Indian sold casual hunting rights and the privilege of taking a crop now and again. Therein lay the source of at least some of the trouble that led to bloodshed.

Property in land originated, so far as evidence is available, in the settled village. It arose after men had located permanently in one spot and become aware of the possibilities and the limitations of their position. The great issue is whether the ownership was first vested in the village group or in the large undivided family. The third possibility, namely that the individual owned land, is ruled out at once, because it runs counter to all we know about early conditions.

Origin in the village or in the family?

A large number of able scholars have held to the view that property in land originated in the village group, which was ordinarily made up, of course, of a number of families. The theory has been developed from and applied to Germany, India, Greece, Rome, and other countries. The most notable of the early protagonists of the view are Kemble [1] (1849), Von Maurer [2] (1854), Maine [3] (1861 and 1871), and Laveleye [4] (1874). Many later writers accepted their theory,[5] and, of course, it is a good analogy for "socialists." If originally land was owned by the village group, they might argue that it should be so owned again.

Communal village theory

The village communal theory was ably challenged by Ross in 1883 [6] and by Coulanges in 1889.[7] Other writers [8] have more recently followed the doubts of Coulanges, or they have gone even farther in evidence or argument in favor of the theory that property originated in the family holding. It is very doubtful whether a single case of early village ownership

Family ownership theory

of all kinds of land has ever been adduced. The co-operation in agricultural labor, so well worked out in the early village, has been mistakenly taken to mean the common ownership of land.

Two kinds of land

An understanding of the issue and the solution of the problem probably lies in a distinction between two kinds of lands. On the one hand there were the arable and meadow and on the other the pasture, wood (waste) lands, and, we may add, ponds and streams. On the former a great deal of labor was expended. To the latter but little attention was given. The supply of the former was necessarily limited, of the latter usually indefinite and beyond the needs of the community. The former, the arable and meadow fields, were typically new, characteristic of the settled village; while the latter, the pasture and wood lands, were reminiscent of earlier conditions of hunting and pasturing. It seems that we can find most argument for the family ownership of arable and meadow, and most argument for the communal ownership (or at least something that might grow into it) for pasture and woodland.

Stages of ownership

Thinking only of the arable and pasture, we can find four stages of ownership: the allodial, manorial-feudal tenure, semi-manorial tenure, and free ownership. This subject is highly controversial. The above classification allows us to gain an elementary notion of the issues and probabilities. It is a significant fact that while all of these stages developed in Europe, they are all reflected in American conditions, some of them being deeply entrenched.

Historical emphasis, inheritance

76. ALLODIAL OWNERSHIP. At various times from the sixth century [9] to the present, we find the word allod. The etymology of the term is quite unknown. The early emphasis is on inheritance.[10] The allod was land that was not acquired from some outsider, either by purchase or gift from a lord, but was inherited within the family, according to the particular customs of each people.

Other attributes

By inference we arrive at various conclusions concerning the allod. It was probably a pre-feudal method of holding land. It seemingly existed in ancient Rome [11] as well as in medieval Europe.[12] Alienation of the allod was free from

254

feudal rules but not free from the family custom.[13]   It was free from service to a lord, but was probably not free from service to the state.[14]   Both the arable and the meadow were owned jointly, just as the depositors in a bank have a joint claim on the bank, not for certain coins or notes but for so much money.   A family had so many *jugera* in ancient Rome [15] or so many acres in medieval England.   At times, may be more or less irregularly, the holdings were changed so that a family would come to have a quite different set of strips of land from what it had possessed before.   This co-ownership is, of course, not to be confused with common ownership in which the *amount* of land held by the family might change from time to time.

This early form of land holding has been regarded as so admirable that modern people have desired to restore it or have maintained that their own land was allodial.   The state of New York has declared that its land is held allodially.[16]   Land has been declared to have always been allodial in Louisiana.[17]   Excellent as American land tenure may now be, it is not allodial, unless we extend the meaning of that term.   To-day it is not an undivided family (parents and children with their wives or husbands and children), but individuals who own land.   The American state of our day not only has the right of escheat but the right of eminent domain.   This is becoming more far-reaching as the social point of view grows.   Modern states even seize land, with or without compensation, in order to distribute land among the poor.   It has often been said that the allodial owner held his land under God; certainly the American owner holds his under the state, subject to the right of eminent domain, strict police regulation, and taxes which, some think, threaten to become confiscatory.

Is there an allod in America?

1846

77. MANORIAL-FEUDAL TENURE.   In marked contrast to the allod was the manorial-feudal tenement which succeeded it.   In this system the occupiers of the land did not own it.   Ownership was logically and legally vested in the sovereign.   There was a grand feudal hierarchy in which the sovereign political power was legal owner of all the land (except the allods), the people merely holding in various

The feudal hierarchy

degrees of remoteness from the throne. Roughly speaking, there was the sovereign, the tenant-in-chief, and the operating tenant. All three, and sometimes other ranks, were held together by customs and laws of obligations and rights. Thus the state was a real social contract, in which the individuals contracted to do certain things, each class having its duties to perform and its rights to claim. Possibly state socialism is the nearest modern concept, in a general way, with which we can compare the feudal state.

Position of the lord

Apart from the king, the manorial lord, commonly the tenant-in-chief, had the strongest claim to ownership. Sometimes he is loosely called owner, but theoretically and actually he was not. His position was one of great advantage. He was responsible to the state for his land and for the tenants occupying it. He had residuary rights of great importance. When a lower tenant (such as a simple freeman, a villein, or a cottar) died without an heir, the land escheated to him. When such a tenant was outlawed, the holding went to him. Property on the manor, with some exceptions, when not claimed rightfully by the tenants, belonged to the lord. Of course, all the tenants owed to him something for the use of their land, while he in turn owed something to the state.

Kinds of tenure

There were five kinds of manorial-feudal tenures in medieval England that merit consideration, one of which is of vast importance at the present time. (1) Military tenure involved the holding of land under an agreement to supply soldiers, that is, fully equipped knights. The tenants-in-chief, such as a duke, an earl, a baron, an archbishop, and a bishop, ordinarily held by this tenure. Such a tenure was legally abol-

1660

ished in England only in modern times, though it had long ceased to have any real military significance. (2) Tenure by

1924

grand and petty sergeanty, still existing in England, involved some special service such as carrying the king's banner, holding the king's head when he crossed the Channel, or some other real or nominal obligation. (3) Free alms was a tenure enjoyed by the Church. Under this term land could be held without rendering any material service. A penitent man might give a manor to a monastery to be held by free alms on the condition that the monastery would say prayers for the donor. Thus the service was spiritual and virtually nominal. The next (4) tenure is the one that has become the most important. It is the free and common socage tenure of the free man [18] who in the Middle Ages paid money and gave a little agricultural service to the manorial land. Here we have the middle class of the county districts in the medieval period. Such a holding was more manorial than feudal, constituting just a part of the manorial fief or unit. Numerically the last (5) kind was of greatest importance. This is the villein or customary tenure [19] of the lowest landholding class. The service was ordinarily fixed in amount but not in kind, and was the most burdensome in the whole manorial-feudal régime.

The tenant had to pay to his superior at least one kind of rent, commonly two or three kinds, along with other dues and obligations. These we must note, at least briefly, because in any consideration of land holding, rents are important. Some of them were, as we have seen, service rents, military, official, spiritual, or agricultural. Some were payments in kind, others in money. Besides these there were the heriot,[20] the relief, and the fine. There were the three feudal aids, paid directly by the higher tenant class, though the burden fell in the last instance on all classes. There were also wardship and marriage, escheat, and forfeiture. The enumeration of these rents and obligations seems to point to an excessive burden involved in land holding. Heavy it was, but we must remember that many of the dues enumerated above, were collected only once in a tenant's or a lord's life time. *Rents and other obligations*

Some such system, with local variations, has existed in the great states of history, eastern and western. It was found in ancient Egypt and China, in medieval states generally, in modern Russia,[21] and in present-day Syria. Probably it existed in ancient [22] as well as medieval [23] Italy. Though it never existed in the Anglo-American colonies, it was found in both Spanish and French dependencies in America. In Mexico a manorial-feudal system developed in the sixteenth and seventeenth centuries. It was legally abolished at the revolt from Spanish dominion, but the subordination of ten- *Extent of this system* *1821*

1924
1917
About
1634 to
1854

ants to lords or landlords has remained in the form of peonage,[24] such indeed as we find in the United States of America to-day and in Russia up to the proletarian revolution. In French Canada, that is, the Province of Quebec, a manorial-feudal system was early established and long maintained. Although the service rents on the lord's demesne were not extensive, they existed and were exacted. The other feudal incidents were numerous and objectionable. They were finally abolished by the popular vote of the Province.[25] To the United States of America such a manorial-feudal system is of interest, not simply as an historical institution, and not simply as an antiquity existing on the southern and northern borders until well into the last century, but in so far as it is the soil out of which early American tenure has itself sprung.

Manorial tenure gone

78. SEMI-MANORIAL TENURE. When the agricultural services on the lord's demesne ceased to be performed, a change took place of great importance. Various non-service incidents or obligations of manorial existence might continue to be exacted, but the manor in its most essential aspect disappeared.[26] We may speak of a semi-manorial existence and a semi-manorial tenure.

Name for this new stage

Such a system might be called a quit-rent system, if it were not for the fact that such a term is ambiguous.[27] Nevertheless rents were paid to be quit, or free, of one or more incidents. A tenant paid a rent to be quit of some objectionable service. He paid a penny, for example, to be free from the necessity of plowing the lord's land, a penny for each day of plowing due the lord. Or he paid several shillings, or bushels of grain, to be free from a great many obligations. This might be called a "free and common socage" system (legal term), if such a designation were not equally applicable to other tenures.[28] It seems best to call it by a rather loose term, the semi-manorial system of tenure.

Origin

In England and France such a system grew up slowly in the fourteenth and following centuries. In Quebec it was established by law when manorial-feudal tenure was abolished. The holder of land was given the option of handing over a lump sum to his former lord or paying a quit-rent each year

1854

Probably even now there are few of the smaller holders in Quebec who are free from quit-rent.[29]

In the Anglo-American colonies the semi-manorial system existed from the first. Theoretically it had existed in all parts, actually in all but New England. While in Quebec it was the Custom of Paris that was to prevail, in the English colonies the various grantees were to hold their section of America according to the custom of some English fief, the manor of East Greenwich, the castle of Windsor, the honor of Hampton Court, or the palatinate of Durham.[30] When the king of England made a grant to an individual or a company, about to colonize some part of America, he made a fairly liberal donation of rights to induce men to venture for profit in the new enterprise. The system was not accompanied by any agricultural service, but it did involve fealty, escheat, and relief.[31] The most important manorial incident, however, was quit-rent. On the eve of the Revolution this varied a good deal, for instance in Pennsylvania from two beaver skins for 60,000 acres and a red rose for 10,000 acres to four shillings for 100 acres.[32]

In America, since 1607

Quit-rents constituted one of the sore spots in the several colonies in which they existed, New York, Pennsylvania, Maryland, and the Carolinas. They were paid technically to be free, or quit, from agricultural and other services, which were slowly dying out in England. The colonists had come to America to be free from old-world disabilities. They disliked dues of all kinds. When such rents were used as a source of private income instead of for public purposes, a further cause of complaint existed. The drift was obviously toward public uses, but even then they had been appropriated for the support of the royal side in the struggle for constitutional liberty, as in New York and North Carolina where they were used to pay royal officials when the popular party had refused to make the grants desired.[33]

Quit-rent and the American Revolution

79. FREE PROPRIETORSHIP. The development of free proprietorship was a great innovation. At last landed property was put on substantially the same basis as personal property (some of which had been on this basis apparently since

What it is

259

the beginning of human society). The owner was an individual. No family, village, or lord stood in between the owner and the state. There was, of course, free alienation. No rents were due to anyone. The owner was a proprietor free in all these respects. This is the kind of ownership now so familiar. It does not go unchallenged by socialists, communists, and anarchists, but the owners themselves are supremely satisfied, except for the increasing burden of taxes, that smacks of the weight of old-time rent.

Historical development

It would be very difficult to write the history of free proprietorship because of the lack of precise information. It seems to rise gradually as individualism develops, as the same ideas of purchase and sale are applied to land as are used in ordinary commerce; in short, in the stages of town and metropolitan economy. Doubtless the Roman plebeians received their grants of public lands to hold as free proprietors,[34] though they gradually lost them as the large estate engulfed the small and as free men lost their freedom.[35] Here and there an allodial holding, escaping the manorial-feudal system, say in southern France or Frisia, may have become a free proprietorship.[36] Some of the British colonies, such as those in New England, really had free proprietorship from the first.

1620 f.

We are so accustomed to the idea of the newness and importance of the Puritan's contributions that we need to put no emphasis upon them now. But along with notions of religious liberty (halting and imperfect), the theory of popular sovereignty, the practice of maintaining a balance between central and local institutions, and the appreciation of the vital place of education in public affairs, must be written down the birth of free proprietorship in America. If we were trying to explain the factors giving rise to the birth, or rebirth, of free proprietorship in the Modern World, and with special reference to New England, we should have to consider both ideals and facts. The ideal of freedom from external control, whether of bishop or lord, was strong in the Puritan's make-up. It is doubtful, however, whether this ideal would have developed into a reality, if New England had possessed land of great fertility and a climate of semi-tropical mildness with the resulting demand for large estates.

The chief development, in Europe as in America, was out of the semi-manorial system. In England it developed in the sixteenth and seventeenth centuries. Freemen who had commuted their services to a money rent in the two preceding centuries found themselves by a set of happy circumstances enjoying a new kind of land system. The small money payment due to their lord was compounded for or dropped. The fall in the value of money had made the old fixed rentals and other fixed dues insignificant. Military obligations were soon abolished. The amount of semi-manorial incidents or obligations that remained, such as the attendance on court and the payment of a few dues, was so slight that virtual free proprietorship was imperceptibly established. The enclosure of lands cut off the freeman's holdings from those of the lord and the other (customary) tenants. But all this is somewhat misleading because of two outstanding facts. Very few of these freemen actually survived the process that made them free. The "statesmen" of Yorkshire, the men with estates, have been among the last survivors, but their number is not great if indeed any at all survive. The other fact is that legally the semi-manorial system still exists in England. Recently an act was passed to abolish the remaining manorial incidents, but its enforcement has been postponed. The customary tenant in England, now represented by the copyholder (actually or nominally the descendant of the medieval villein), lives in a larger measure of semi-manorial system than the freeholder. The new law promises to abolish copyhold and all other customary tenures. The quit-rents and the other surviving manorial incidents are to be done away with,[37] but, as said above, the enforcement of the act has been postponed. Legally and actually, the customary tenants of England are still in an attenuated semi-manorial system; while actually, but not legally, the freeholders are substantially free proprietors.

America, that is the United States of America, did not gain

Genesis from semi-manorial tenure

1660

1922 Until 1 Jan., 1926

In America

free proprietorship until the time of the Revolution. As we have seen, New England had enjoyed this advanced system from the first, but the other colonies gained it by the Revolution. Although the revolutionists might claim the new system from the beginning of the Revolution, it could hardly have had any legal standing until the individual states acted in the matter. Virginia and Pennsylvania abolished quit-rents in 1779. New York State virtually did the same in 1786.[38] Other states followed, either by formal act or by ignoring the quit-rents and other manorial incidents. The Northwest Ordinance established, in the territory northwest of the Ohio and east of the Mississippi, free proprietorship without using any special term to cover it. It also provided that in case of no will or testament, land should descend equally to all the children.[39]

France set up free proprietorship as a national land system only at the time of the French Revolution. Prussia made a beginning not long afterwards. Eastern European countries during and after the Great War have turned either in the direction of village communism or free proprietorship, as is indicated in the sections that follow.

80. MODERN VILLAGE COMMUNISM. By communism we mean, not co-operation nor co-ownership but common ownership. Under this system there is no inheritance of land but just a succession of right to a share, according to the custom of the people. Such a system can be managed only by more or less frequent redistribution of the amount available for the individual or family.

As has been seen,[40] in the early settled villages, pasture and wood lands, ponds and streams, and wastes generally, were held for common use. In so far as there was any notion of ownership, it was doubtless of common ownership.[41] This may be regarded as the lineal descendant of political control over land in collectional and cultural nomadic economy. When the free village became a manor, the lord made claim to some of these possessions. He secured rights in the common pasture, and arrogated to himself special hunting privileges in the woods. The more wild the waste land, the easier it was for

1776

Establishment elsewhere 1811

Meaning

Early settled villages

262

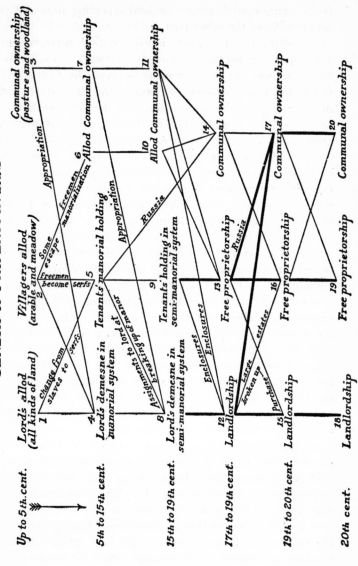

HYPOTHETICAL AND TENTATIVE EXPOSITION OF THE GENESIS OF PROPERTY IN LAND

Up to 5th cent.

5th to 15th cent.

15th to 19th cent.

17th to 19th cent.

19th to 20th cent.

20th cent.

Communal ownership (pasture and woodland) 3

Villagers allod (arable and meadow) 2

Lord's allod (all kinds of land) 1

Appropriation

Freemen

Some escape

Freemen become serfs 5

Change from slaves to serfs

manorialization

Allod Communal ownership 7

Tenant's manorial holding

Lord's demesne in manorial system 4

Assignments to lord at breaking up of manor

Appropriation

Allod Communal ownership 11

Allod Communal ownership 10

Tenant's holding in semi-manorial system 9

Lord's demesne in semi-manorial system 8

Appropriation

Russia

Enclosures Enclosures

Communal ownership 14

Russia

Communal ownership 13

Free proprietorship 13

Landlordship 12

Large estates broken up

Communal ownership 17

Free proprietorship 16

Purchase

Landlordship 15

Communal ownership 20

Free proprietorship 19

Landlordship 18

(The heavy lines show developments among whites in America)

263

him to establish a claim. In the enclosure movements the final partition took place, the lord receiving part and the manorial villages the other part.

Misleading arguments

In literature of various kinds we find reference to early community ownership of land in general. Usually the ideas of the writers are very vague as to ownership; little or no distinction is made between the family and the village, and none at all between arable and meadow on the one hand and pasture and wood land on the other. Sometimes it is argued back from a modern state to an early condition, as in Mexico and Russia. Certainly after the abolition of the manorial-feudal system in these countries, we find a village communism either established or taking form. But, of course, to argue backward to the beginning or village settlement from such recent information is always without justification and generally misleading.

Case of Russia

Russia provides one of the most illuminating instances of modern communism. It has been often stated that village communism in Russia is very ancient, but careful research has practically proved that it is quite modern.[42] This village commune is called the mir, a word which means several things but most significantly stands for the world and the village. It is at once the world of affairs for the Russian peasant and the organization controlling and owning the land that he cultivates. The history of the mir is somewhat as follows. Up to the sixteenth century it was a free village of families holding the arable and meadow in co-ownership[43] and the pastures and forests undivided, unallotted, and in common ownership.

Allod

Manor

From the sixteenth century until 1719, it was a manor with co-ownership and re-allotment of arable and meadow but with no *redistribution* of arable and meadow, at least with none on a wide basis. Then for about 150 years the mir was a manor with rights to the arable and meadow as well as the pasture and woodland redistributed among the families according to the number of persons in each family. This redistribution, which was to take place not oftener than every third year and at least every nineteenth year, was an innovation of Peter the Great. In the year 1719 a new law made the individual rather

1719–1861

264

than the family holding the unit of taxation. In order to enable each community of individuals to pay the tax, the land had to be divided among the families according to their productive or labor power. When the emancipation came another period was ushered in, the period of the free commune. The lords were given part of the lands and some money compensation. The title to the rest of the land was vested in the mir which had the right to redistribute land as it was required. As a matter of fact, the redistribution proceeded very unevenly, taking place in some villages but being ignored in others. A short period in the affairs of the mir was brought about by a reactionary imperial edict making it easy for the individual peasant family to withdraw from the village organization. Of course, he could not take his land out of the village, but he could get out of the co-operative and common ownership group and avoid all subsequent redistributions. In case there had been no redistribution for about twenty years, the peasant might withdraw, keeping what land he already held. In case such a redistribution had actually taken place within this time, special provision was made for getting out. The result was that millions left the mir, many of the most ambitious and most able of the peasants.[44] Clearly the communal aspect of the institution was doomed to early extinction. This was partially avoided, at least temporarily, by the proletarian revolution which offered the peasants a chance to gain, if they re-embarked on the communist or socialist ship. Not only were the communist villages to have the land of the peasants but also that of the Czar, nobles, monasteries, and churches. These were put at the disposal of the mirs.[45] In the following year all private property in land was abolished, the land passing to the use of those who would work it. It was to be so divided that the family of the cultivator would escape want. Although the title is vested in the Soviet Republic, the use and management are entrusted to the mir, or more strictly to the Soviet organization of the district.[46] There are some who think that, while the bribe has worked to the extent of enlisting the early support of the peasants for the new government, it has not succeeded to the extent of permanently establishing

1861
Commune

1906

1917

1918

socialistic or state ownership. That free proprietorship will emerge out of the welter, is indicated by the recent law which, while maintaining state ownership, establishes the right of the family to withdraw from mir control, and therefore to use their land somewhat as they will. The law provides for family succession to the land and for the hiring of labor during a period of temporary distress. If full legal private ownership finally emerges then the cycle in a sense will have been completed. State ownership will have been eliminated, but the allod nevertheless will not be restored. In a modern state it must be free proprietorship, that is, if it is not to be a communal (or socialistic) or a landlord system.

Special communities in America

In America there have been idealistic communities, a few of them founded by Russians, a great many by Germans. In general, there are two groups of such communities, those primarily religious and those primarily communistic. The latter is illustrated by New Harmony (Indiana), Owen's colony, broken up by the selfishness of its members. The religious communities were established by Shakers, Inspirationists, Rappists,[47] Huterian Brethren,[48] and so on. Generally, we find such groups hard working, cleanly, and pious. They stand isolated culturally and experience great difficulty in keeping the young people in the dull and monotonous fold. Although they usually have separate homesteads clustered together to form hamlets or villages, they use a common dining hall and own property in common. The communism can be said to be an economic success, if one can apply that term to a static community within a progressive nation.

Judgment on communism

Communism is one of the most important systems of land holding in human history. It has, however, never made unqualified conquests. It has persisted in one way or another in the large undivided family; it has applied to pasture and woodland; it has included all lands for a while; it has been tried by idealists; but it has never been both an economic and a cultural success. It is better suited to conservation than to progress. It holds a fort against an enemy, whether a near-by Russian lord or Mexican exploiter, or the American spirit of change. The fact is obvious that it is harder to move a group than an individual. It is difficult enough for a single free cultivator to make progress; under present conditions it seems impossible to push a whole rural community at anything but a snail's pace. This is a rather serious charge in the face of all the demonstrated improvements in agricultural technique, marketing, credit, and general culture that need to be made. It is hard to discover the means of the upward climb; it is disheartening to find a community so organized as to keep out or retard rural betterment.

81. LANDLORDISM. From one point of view there are just two land systems, the free proprietorship and the unfree. In the unfree systems the individual cultivator finds some group or individual standing in between him and the state, curtailing his freedom. In the case of the allod it was the undivided family. In communism it was the village group. In the case of manorial-feudal tenure it was the family, the village group, and particularly the lord. The family and the village, however, are no longer potent institutions in land tenure in the advanced countries of the present day. Thus we have as the only current serious rival of free proprietorship, the lord, or, in his modern form, the landlord. He no longer has the political or legal upperhand, but he possesses great economic strength. His persistence in one form or another through history and his promise of great vigor in the time to come, make us stop to consider him at some length. *One of the important systems*

Let us note some of the progressive moves of the landlord system through history, that is, the system wherein some person stands in between the state and the cultivator. There are some who think that coterminous with the settled village of freemen there was a private plantation (the lord's allod) worked by slaves at first and then by the labor of serfs or villeins. Such a plantation could grow into a manor, as seems historically to be demonstrated in the Roman Empire,[49] just as the free village grew into a manor. In other words, one of the origins of the manor seems to be the large private estate.[50] Then came the manor with its manorial-feudal lord and all his privileges. Such a lord had as his special property, the demesne, and those parts of the former communal prop- *Genesis of landlord system* erty arrogated to the demesne. When the manorial-feudal system decayed, the nature of the lordship changed somewhat. The lord lost the services of his tenants; but as long as the semi-manorial stage lasted, he enjoyed quit-rents and other manorial incidents, in addition to his own demesne. The demesne now grew apace. When a semi-manorial tenant died without heirs, his land escheated to the lord as in the manorial-feudal period. During the enclosure movements, tenants' land in one way or another, legally or illegally, came into the possession of the lord.[51] In some countries, notably in Prussia, when the manorial system was broken up, from one-half to one-third of the tenants' land went to the lord. When by evolution or by revolution, the tenants became free proprietors, the lords became landlords. Deprived of their overlordship of tenants' lands, the landlords kept on with their demesne holdings. By purchase, more lands were secured, to engage in cultivation on a large scale or, much more commonly, to rent out to tenant farmers.[52] Family intermarriages, which had long been potent factors in the situation, continued to build up huge estates of thousands, even hundreds of thousands, of acres in the old world. When the old aristocratic families decayed, new blood came in, as rich merchant, tax-gatherer, manufacturer, or other business man, purchased country estates for repose or more likely for social prestige. On the upward climb, it is proper to become a country gentleman before seeking a title of nobility.

In Quebec and Mexico, as we have seen, the manorial-feudal system was established. In most of the English colonies there was a semi-manorial system. Gradually even in the colonial period there developed a certain amount of landlordism. In New England, for example, we are told that some landlords worked part of their land and rented out the rest on lease.[53] Around Philadelphia there were tenant-farmers[54] and therefore landlords. How far the Fathers of Federation, such as Washington and Morris,[55] and many other rich people of no such public distinction, bought up western lands for speculation and how far for renting out to cultivators, cannot now be determined. Gradually, at least as early as the first

Margin notes: 1811, 1816 f.

In the new world

1775

268

part of the nineteenth century, large estates for renting to tenant-farmers arose and have, of course, been with us ever since. The Wadsworth estate in the Genesee Valley, New York, is a noteworthy example, as is the Scully estate in the middle west. The former has supported a family, not without distinction; [56] the later has gained fame from the popular opposition it has aroused.

The Scully estate, though located in America, was in a sense born in Ireland. It was there that the family of the Scullys combined the life of educated gentlemen of leisure and the oversight of landed estates. Such a combination has persisted down to the present day. Denis Scully was a lawyer, Catholic agitator, and landowner. William Scully, his son, was a lawyer as well as landowner. Finding that the lands he had inherited were in bad condition, he did his best to rehabilitate them. The establishment of free trade in corn probably did something to retard improvement, for it allowed foreign grain freely to enter the chief market that Ireland possessed, that is, England. To recoup his fortunes and get rid of the difficulties at home, William Scully came to America where he toured the middle west on horseback, finally locating in Logan County (Illinois). In that state his original purchase of 30,000 acres of fertile land was to constitute the nucleus of his total holding. At first he cultivated his land on a large scale, but soon turned to selling it off and then to renting what remained. Then, for over a generation, he purchased more land to rent to other persons. Agitation against him and his methods led to laws forcing him to become a citizen. He complied, but lived only a few years longer. His widow divided the estates, amounting to over 200,000 acres between her two sons. Thomas A. Scully received the lands in Illinois (about 41,000 acres) and in Missouri (about 46,000 acres) and Frederick Scully the holdings in Kansas (about 60,000 acres) and in Nebraska (about 64,000 acres). The two sons are American citizens, graduates of colleges, but not resident on their estates, probably not even in America. Although the Scully estate is now divided, the two parts are managed in substantially the same way. Some of the holdings are fertile

Side notes: Scully estate in America · 1773–1830 · 1853 · 1866–1900 · 1900 · 1906 · 1918

lands for general agriculture; others are semi-arid, fit only for grazing. According to a carefully worked out plan, the farms, which are larger or smaller than 160 acres depending on the soil, are leased on a yearly cash basis. Permanent improvements are provided by the owners, such as tiling, hedge fences, the brick for wells, and foundations for houses. A certain routine of agriculture which on the whole is quite superior, is stipulated in the leases. The Scullys require the tenants to follow an approved rotation of crops, such as corn, wheat, oats, and a legume (clover, alfalfa, etc.). When a clover crop is plowed in to fertilize the land, an allowance is made to the tenant. No hay or manure is to be sold off the farm. Drainage ditches are to be kept clean. The tenants

1920

must pay a stipulated rental, varying from two to ten dollars an acre when rents were high, lower since that time. The tenants must provide all buildings and other temporary improvements. The other capital, and labor of all kinds, are furnished by them. They pay the taxes directly to the state. Some of these tenants are squatters who by mistake located on the Scully lands in early days. Others own farms of their own. Many are on the way to become land owners. Only the sober, industrious, and capable cultivators, such as the district provides, are kept on the farms. Some of these tenants, however, aided by local politicians, have complained, held meetings, carried on local campaigns, and even engaged in "uprisings" against the system of which they were a part. They have objected to the amount of rental. They find themselves amassing capital but unable to buy the lands they cultivate, because the Scullys will not sell. They complain that the buildings and other temporary improvements, such as ordinary fences, are not provided by the landlord, and such repairs as they make, are the property of the landlord. Orchards planted by the tenants belong to the landlord. Some have objected to the agricultural routine, particularly to the necessity of having to plant so much clover.[57] In taking such a stand they show themselves more interested in harvesting a paying crop than in maintaining the fertility of the soil. When one considers both sides, he finds very much to be said for the Scully system of landlordism. The objections that can be raised are more or less commonly made against capitalistic enterprises managed under a perfected mechanism that allows the owners to live abroad without the daily cares of business. To offset this is the fact that the system of agriculture is probably better than the tenants would otherwise engage in.

The tenants of lords and landlords, as well as townsmen, have manifested their disapproval, even opposition to the system. There have been peasant revolts against manorial-feudal lords. Agitations and revolutions have threatened, even swept away semi-manorial lords. And laws, and revolutions have undermined or broken up the estates of landlords. It is the landlords rather than the lords who interest us most at this point. In England there was agitation against landlords (and semi-manorial lords) in both the seventeenth and eighteenth centuries. Thomas Spence, William Ogilvie, and Thomas Paine all advocated land reform or land redistribution in the name of natural law.[58] Ogilvie advocated the simple application of the law of eminent domain, then in use in Great Britain to provide land for new highways and canals, to the seizure of land for small cultivators.[59] Socialists and others maintained the demand, but little was really accomplished until the death duties and subsequent taxes dealt the landlords such staggering blows that many of them have had to sell large blocks of their estates in order to maintain the rest and to keep up their old-time position. Often the tenants on the land have been given preference in the sale of the estates. Thus a free landlord system is changed into a free peasant proprietorship. In America there has been agitation within the states against large landlords, notably in Nebraska, Kansas, and Illinois against William Scully.[60] But in America there has been no general demand for a change, because the landlord system has never been regarded as seriously widespread. In Mexico, on the other hand, the revolution that overthrew the harsh but peaceful régime of Díaz and began a whole series of disturbances,[61] was made possible by the promise of the re-

Movements against landlords

1781

1894 f.

1876–1900

1910–11

271

distribution of the land among those possessing little or no property.[62] When it is remembered that there are in Mexico eleven *haciendas* of 250,000 acres each, as well as many more estates of lesser magnitude,[63] the significance of the move is much clearer. The purpose is to substitute, at least for the non-Indian population, free proprietorship instead of landlordism. One of the Mexican states has limited the size of holdings according to the nature of the land.[64] In Czecho-Slovakia and other central and eastern European nations coming into existence after the Great War, land reforms of far-reaching importance have been started. In Czecho-Slovakia one law enunciated the ideal of the expropriation of the large estates and their distribution among small farmers, cottagers, tradesmen, landless peasants, and others. This was actually accomplished legislatively one year later, and since that time the task has been to execute the plan. The agrarian party wants free proprietorship; the socialists seek common ownership. The former undoubtedly has won but not completely.[65] The landlords have lost much but not all. They are fighting a losing battle for the present, but time and tide may have better things in store for them. The new changes may injure not only the forests and forest conservation (in spite of protective legislation) but high-class agriculture,[66] although in neither case need the injury be permanent.

The landlord system has gone through many changes. So has the system of small proprietorships. Communal holding came early and is still possessed of vigor. The issue lies between them.[67] Most people favor one or another for some social or political reason, although careful study from an economic standpoint shows that each has merits as well as demerits. If the history of the past means anything for the future, we may expect that all three will continue—in proportions determined by circumstances of time and place. They will all probably continue to exist, because they offer advantages, each in its own way. Together they provide the alternatives for the shifting sands of social change. They are the standards under which men do battle. Citizens may die for them, scholars must understand them.

Margin notes: 1920 · 1919 · 1920 · The tripartite struggle

82. AMERICAN LAND POLICY AND THE GROWTH OF LAND- **Four** LORDISM. As might be inferred from what has already been **periods** said, America has a preference for one kind of land system **ment** as against all others, and a corresponding policy for making that preference a reality. We may trace the development and working out of this policy in four periods. First there was the colonial period of divergence, when New England possessed the reality of free proprietorship, while much of the rest of the colonial population could do little more than hold to the ideal. Then came the period of federal experiments, when the nation took its first steps in **1785–** land legislation and slowly worked out a policy. It adopted **1841** a rectangular system of land demarcation that has been a great **1785** help in surveying, and in local government generally. The township was to consist of a block of thirty-six square miles, or thirty-six sections, following the lines of latitude and longitude. The land was to be sold for at least one dollar an acre.[68] Two years later came the Northwest Ordinance, al- **1787** ready considered.[69] The price of federal land was raised **1796** from one to two dollars an acre, but the purchasers were allowed time in which to pay the government.[70] On the whole this system favored the rich purchasers rather than the poor settlers. The division of sections into four parts, quarter **1805** sections,[71] helped to fix the standard for the normal American holding. The price of government land was reduced from **1820** two dollars to one dollar and a quarter an acre, so that the poor settler could more easily pay for his holding, but at the same time the credit system was abolished.[72] The government had found itself face to face with the necessity of displacing poor *bona fide* settlers who, largely because of the undeveloped condition of the country, had been unable to pay the required amount. It was at this time that the old agrarian **1829** policy of eastern town laborers demanded the equal distribution of land as well as of capital.[73] In the third period a policy of pre-emption was followed. The government went **1841–62** so far as to declare itself in favor of actual settlers as against land speculators and prospective landlords. Squatters were given the right to buy or pre-empt the land they held at one **1841**

273

dollar and a quarter an acre.[74] This law was not entirely new, for there had been numerous relief measures adopted from time to time, but now it was general and quite open to all. Moreover this law still left the speculator free to buy up as much unclaimed land as he wished and could pay for. During this third period there was a new agrarian policy which concentrated on the subject of the distribution of land (rather than capital) as of primary importance in social regeneration. A very definite demand arose for the distribution of the land without any payment and its allocation to only actual settlers.

1845

It was said that there was developing a system of landlordism that was ultimately to lower the American cultivator to the position of the European peasant. The land was held to be man's natural right.[75] Accordingly, the slogan became, "vote yourself a farm." [76] The result of such demands was the Homestead Act which introduced the fourth period.

**Home-
stead Act,
1862**

The Homestead Act is about as important as a law can ever be. On the one hand, it was the consummation of a modern ideal; on the other hand, it was the guide to millions of ambitious struggling settlers. There were to be given free to every real settler 160 acres of land, that is, a quarter section. Full title was to be granted only after five years of occupancy.[77] Such was the triumph of genuine settlement, the victory of the small estate, the enthronement of free proprietorship. It was really a war measure, passed by Congress after years of debate, only when the south had withdrawn. The south had wanted the soil sold in large blocks, so that planters with their slave system would dominate the new lands. The east had wanted the land sold, not given away, so that the burden of taxation would be lighter in the older settled regions. The west, of course, had long stood for free gift and small holdings, as had the town laborers of the east.

**Subse-
quent
laws**

Much as the Homestead Act met the needs of the times, it had later to be modified. It was found that a farm of 160 acres in the semi-arid sections was of no use. So a farm of

1909

320 acres was to be granted free to a genuine settler for the purpose of dry farming.[78] In the same year the residence re-

quirement was abolished on the desert lands of one single state, where there was no water at all. It is necessary for the cultivator to live somewhere near-by.[79] In the arid parts anyone intending to establish a stock-raising farm can now get 640 acres free, the smallest holding that will support a family.[80] Other laws have altered the residence in favor of the settler. In one half of the states there is still plenty of public land to be secured under these and other laws, in fact about 183 million acres, of which 126 million have been surveyed. It is perhaps needless to say that most of it is in Nevada, Utah, California, New Mexico, Oregon, and Arizona. Under present conditions it is of little use, being mountainous, desert, sand, burned over, cut over, swamp, peat bog, rough grazing land, or poor agricultural land, according to official designation.

Utah, 1909

1916

1912, 1919

1922

Under the various acts giving free homesteads to actual settlers, millions of acres have been taken up and a system of free peasant proprietorship established. Whether a farm of 160 acres in normal parts was the best size, is hard now to determine. Certainly it was large enough to attract settlers. The owner expected to gain by the increase in the value of the farm, partly due to his own efforts, partly due to general social progress. He expected to make a living by means of an extensive system of farming. So far so good, but what of the future? As agriculture becomes more intensive, some farmers are finding themselves with more land than they can carefully cultivate. But increased agricultural education, on the other hand, will tend to produce cultivators who can handle larger holdings than their fellows can. It is also to be noted that the laws did not for a time prevent mineral and forest land from getting into the hands of the rich. They did not actually prevent psuedo-settlers from proving claims and then selling these claims to the rich. However, it is probable that estates built up in that way were for direct exploitation, like ranches, bonanza farms, and the like, rather than for renting to small cultivators.

Success of Homestead Acts

There are no statistics at all, and no reliable estimates, of the extent of landlordism in the United States before 1880.[81]

Growth of land-lordism

275

Since that date there has been a progressive increase in the landlord system, as the following summary table shows.

TABLE SHOWING PERCENTAGE OF TOTAL FARMS RENTED BY LANDLORDS TO TENANTS:

1880	25
1890	28
1900	35
1910	37
1920	38

There is much of significance, however, that these figures do not disclose. An overwhelmingly large number of the landlords live in the same county and have but one farm to let out. Obviously they are largely retired farmers. Many of the tenants are really on the way to become owners,[82] being industrious agricultural laborers, the sons, or the sons-in-law of the farmers.[83]

Two kinds of landlords

It is vital to an understanding of the land situation in America to distinguish between two kinds of landlords. The one is permanent and professional, with a large holding, and more or less absentee. The other is temporary, amateur, with a small holding, and generally resident in the district, the farmer who has retired and moved to town. Now in so far as the second class is temporary, it looks to a future land-owning system. To it there are no objections, but we need not consider them here.

Professional landlordism

Professional landlordism is a fact in America especially in the south, and has been, in one form or another, from the earliest settlements. The aim of American policy, as we have noted, has been to check it. The great question is whether economic forces will or will not make it increase in spite of national ideals. Some factors there are that tend in the direction of the landlord system. The lack of good free land helps increase land values thereby making it increasingly difficult for cultivators to buy farms. The lack of managerial capacity on the part of cultivators, notably in the south among both whites and negroes, prevents them from amassing enough capital to buy farms. The same lack will reduce some cultivators from a position of ownership to one of tenancy. The lack of sufficient capital in our increasingly intensive system of agriculture will force tenant farmers to remain tenants, so that they may use all their capital for good livestock, machinery, and the like, rather than put some of it into land. As some cultivators gain in skill, both in agricultural technique and business management, they demand more than the 160 acres inherited from their fathers. At times they abandon their farms to others and rent land from larger owners. Such are found among the tenants of the Scully estate. Such able cultivators employ many agricultural laborers. It is to be expected that this will be one of the developments in America in the future. Some rich men will furnish the land. Other less well-to-do but able. enterprisers will provide the brains and the capital. Many incapable farmer-owners will have to sell their holdings to the landlords, becoming laborers at the command of the tenant-farmers. When Europeans flocked to America to take up farms, some able managers came and some who were of the type (agricultural laborers and artisans) that need guidance in a highly competitive society. Fortune gave them all 160 acres of land and crude economic conditions enabled them to hold on, taking their profit in the general advance of land values which has concealed from them the fact that they were not really successful profit-making farmers. The promise of the future is not so bright for them. Politics is one of their resorts, but the economic setting is not so favorable.

83. SUGGESTIONS FOR FURTHER STUDY

1. How would you define property in land? Consult the dictionaries under "property."
2. Define as exactly as possible the following terms: allod, manorial-feudal, semi-manorial, and free proprietorship.
3. Contrast the allod and the free proprietorship.
4. Contrast the position of the manorial-feudal lord with that of the landlord.
5. What were the pros and cons of the semi-manorial system (of quit-rents and other manorial incidents) in the Anglo-American colonies?

6. What is peonage? Where and why does it exist?

7. To-day the land-holding title in America is sometimes called allodial and sometimes free and common socage. Why are both objectionable? What is the advantage of the term free proprietorship?

8. Contrast co-ownership with common ownership.

9. What is the significance of the following dates for the history of land holding—1660, 1789, 1841, 1862, 1911, 1918?

10. Read the biography of W. A. Wadsworth in *Who's Who in America, 1918–1919,* for an example of an American gentleman farmer.

11. What are the arguments for and against (1) free (peasant) proprietorship, (2) common (communal) ownership, and (3) landlordism?

12. Enumerate the factors that make for landlordism. Will cheap credit help or hinder the growth of professional landlordism?

13. What are the advantages and disadvantages of the permanent landlord system? Re-read that part of the text describing the Scully estate.

14. Comment on the following: "Give a man the secure possession of a bleak rock, and he will turn it into a garden; give him a nine years lease of a garden, and he will convert it into a desert" (A. Young, *Travels in France during the Years 1787, 1788, 1789,* ed. of Betham-Edwards, 1905, p. 54).

15. What are the ideals of a permanent landlord system? See B. G. Bhatnagar, The Ideal System of Land Tenure, *Indian Journal of Economics,* vol. III, pt. 4 (1920), pp. 383–393.

16. What are the advantages and disadvantages of the temporary (or retired-farmer) landlord system?

17. It is said that the tenant-farmer is not a good livestock man. Is this more applicable to the permanent tenant or the tenant who is a prospective owner?

18. Which has usually the lower standard of living in the northern states, the permanent tenant or the tenant who is a prospective owner?

19. Comment: the tenant-farmer resembles the town laborer in his spirit of political unrest.

20. It is profitable to read G. M. Stephenson's *The Political History of the Public Lands from 1840 to 1862, from Pre-emption to Homestead* (1917), chs. IV, VII, XI.

21. What do you think of the following criticism of the Homestead Act of 1862? The unit of 160 acres was too large. A monopoly of land, as against the claims of future generations, was set up. The natural resources of mine and forest were sac-

rificed. Settlement became so rapid that overproduction and low prices resulted, thus discouraging and even injuring the settlers themselves. See the excerpts in *Agricultural Economics* (ed. by E. G. Nourse, 1916), pp. 674–679.

22. What is your opinion of the following policy adopted by The Third Party at its meeting in St. Paul, 18 June, 1924? "Land was created for all the people and we demand a system of land tenure which shall abolish landlordism and tenantry and will secure the land to the users thereof."

23. The volume entitled *Systems of Land Tenure in Various Countries* (ed. by J. W. Probyn, 1881), though out of date and in places inaccurate, is still of value. The chief essays deal with tenure in Ireland, England, India, France, Russia, Prussia, and Belgium and Holland.

For further references, consult the notes below.

84. Notes to Chapter XI

1. J. M. Kemble, *The Saxons in England* vol. I (1849), p. 40.

2. *Einleitung zur Geschichte der Mark-Hof-Dorf-und Stadt-verfassung* (1854), pp. 5 f.

3. *Ancient Law* (1861, 1870), pp. 257–262; *Village Communities in the East and West* (1871), Lecture I.

4. *Primitive Property* (1874, 1878), p. 4.

5. Such as E. Nasse, *On the Agricultural Community of the Middle Ages . . . in England* (1869, 1871, 1872), pp. 2–3.

6. D. W. Ross, *The Early History of Land-Holding among the Germans* (1883), pp. 40, 57–58.

7. *The Origin of Property in Land* (1889, introduction by Sir W. J. Ashley, Eng. trans. 1891). F. Seebohm (*The English Village Community,* 1883, 1896, p. 418), had already set up the villa in place of the free communal group.

8. Sir F. Pollock and F. W. Maitland, *The History of English Law before the Time of Edward I,* vol. I (1895, 1899), p. 630; R. Hildebrand, *Recht und Sitte auf den verschiedenen wirtschaftslichen Kulturstufen* (1896), pp. 140–189; E. W. Hopkins, *India, Old and New* (1902), pp. 226–229; Sir Paul Vinogradoff, *Growth of the Manor* (1905), pp. 18–19, 24, 92; J. S. Lewinski, *The Origin of Property* (1913), pp. 28–32.

9. See ch. 60 of the Salian Law (*Lex Salica Emendata* by A. Holder, 1879, p. 39).

10. See B. Guérard, *Polyptyque de l'Abbé Irminon* vol. I (1844), pp. 476–480; Fustel de Coulanges, *Histoire des Institutions Politiques de l'Ancienne France, L'Alleu et le Domaine Rural* (1889), pp. 155, 162, 163, 166.

11. See above, ch. III, sect. 16, p. 53.

12. Cf. above, ch. IV, sect. 24, pp. 79–80.

13. Gavelkind (in Kent, England) may have been a survival of the allod.

14. In England a very old non-feudal national obligation was placed upon the free man to serve in the militia, to maintain fortifications, and to build and repair bridges.

15. See above, ch. III, sect. 16, pp. 52–53.

16. "All lands within this State [of New York] are declared to be allodial, so that, subject only to the liability to escheat, the entire and absolute property is vested in the owners, according to the nature of their respective estates," Article I, sect. 13.

17. W. R. Vance, The Quest for Tenure in the United States, *Yale Law Journal*, vol. XXXIII (1924), p. 248 n., referring to M. O. Hudson, *Land Tenure and Conveyances in Missouri* (1915).

18. See above, ch. IV, sect. 26, p. 86.

19. See above, ch. IV, sect. 26, pp. 86–87.

20. These and the following terms are explained in most dictionaries and encyclopedias.

21. See for example, E. Schkaff, *La Question Agraire en Russie* (1922), pp. 23, 29.

22. See above, ch. III, sect. 16, p. 52, and sect. 21, pp. 72–73.

23. See above, ch. III, sect. 20, p. 69.

24. See G. M. McBride, *The Land System of Mexico* (1923), pp. 31, 33, 45, 50, 58. For peonage in the United States, see below ch. XV, sect. 110, p. 30.

25. W. B. Munro, *Documents Relating to the Seigniorial Tenure in Canada, 1598–1854* (1908), pp. xxvi, xxxi, xlvi, lxxxix, xc, cxiii.

26. Cf. above, ch. IV, sect. 30, pp. 94–96, and chs. V and VII.

27. The term quit-rent applies to (a) the commutation of labor services, as in England from the 14th century onwards, (b) the commutation of several of the manorial incidents, as in the Anglo-American colonies, 1607–1776, and (c) the commutation of *all* such incidents as in Quebec, 1854.

28. Free and common socage applies (a) to one form of manorial-feudal tenure, as we have seen, (b) to part of the semimanorial system now under consideration, and (c) to free proprietorship with the sovereign or state as the lord of the land.

29. W. B. Munro, *Documents Relating to the Seigniorial Tenure in Canada, 1598–1854* (1908), pp. cxiii, cxv.

30. See W. Macdonald, *Select Charters and other Documents illustrative of American History, 1606–1775* (1899, 1910), pp. 10, 28, 55, 122, 185, 242.

31. See E. Fraser, Future Interests in Property in Minnesota, *Minnesota Law Review,* vol. III (1919), p. 326 n.

Fealty is loyalty to feudal chief, king, or state, expressed by solemn oath.

Escheat is the reversion of estates, in feudal days to the lord, in modern times to the king or state. The reversion comes through failure of heirs or by conviction of a serious crime.

Relief is a payment made by an heir to a lord for the privilege of succeeding to property.

32. B. W. Bond, *The Quit-Rent System in the American Colonies* (1919), p. 134.

33. *Ibid.,* p. 444.

34. Cf. above, ch. III, sect. 17, p. 58.

35. See above, ch. III, sect. 20, pp. 65–66.

36. See the graphic illustration of the Genesis of Property in Land (below, p. 263), nos. 2–6–10–13–16–19 and 3–7–11–13–16–19.

37. The old fines (arbitrary and certain), the reliefs, the heriots, and the quit-rents, according to this act, are to be abolished, compensation being allowed to the lord. 12 and 13 Geo. V, ch. 16 (29 June, 1922), Thirteenth Schedule, pp. 270–274 of the printed act.

38. B. W. Bond, *The Quit-Rent System in the American Colonies* (1919), pp. 160, 252, 284. See W. R. Vance, The Quest for Tenure in the United States, *Yale Law Journal,* vol. XXXIII (1924), pp. 260–263.

39. *Laws of the United States of America,* vol. I (1815), pp. 475, 479.

40. See above, ch. XI, sect. 75, p. 254.

41. R. Hildebrand (*Recht und Sitte,* 1896, p. 187) doubts whether in such a case there really was any thought of ownership.

42. On this subject see M. Kovalevsky, *Modern Customs and Ancient Laws of Russia* (1891), pp. 93–95; J. S. Lewinski, *The Origin of Property* (1913), p. 29.

43. See above, ch. XI, sect. 77, p. 257.

44. Al. A. Tschuprow, The Break-up of the Village Community in Russia, *Economic Journal,* vol. XXII (1912), pp. 187–197.

45. See the decree in E. Schkaff, *La Question Agraire en Russie* (1922), p. 244.

46. *Ibid.,* pp. 301–302.

47. See Charles Nordhoff, *The Communistic Societies of the United States* (1875), pp. 25 f., 63 f., 117 f., 385 f.

48. Bertha W. Clark, The Huterian Communities, *Journal of Political Economy,* vol. XXXII (1924), pp. 357–374, especially pp. 361–369.

49. See above, ch. III, sects. 17, 18, 20, pp. 55-63, 65-69.
50. See above, ch. IV, sect. 24, p. 79.
51. See above, ch. VII, sect. 48, pp. 163–164.
52. See the graphic illustration of the Genesis of Property in Land (above, p. 263), nos. $1 < \genfrac{}{}{0pt}{}{4-8}{5-9} > 12-15-18$.

53. *American Husbandry* (1775), vol. I, p. 62.
54. *Ibid.*, p. 186.
55. Charles A. Beard, *An Economic Interpretation of the Constitution of the United States* (1913), pp. 102, 151.
56. See H. C. Taylor, *Agricultural Economics* (1919), pp. 246–249; *Who's Who in America, 1918–19* (W. A. and J. W. Wadsworth). For a bibliography of landlordism in America, see C. L. Stewart, *Land Tenure in the United States with special Reference to Illinois,* University of Illinois studies in the Social Sciences, vol. V (1916), pp. 127–133.
57. The above information has been gleaned from newspaper files, correspondence with editors and agronomists, and communication with the Scully representatives.
58. See *The Pioneers of Land Reform* (ed. by M. Beer, 1920), pp. v–ix.
59. *Ibid.*, p. 45.
60. See *The Lincoln* (Nebraska) *Sunday Star,* 11 Sept., 1921, pp. 3, 6.
61. Helen Phipps, The Agrarian Phase of the Mexican Revolution of 1910–1920. *Political Science Quarterly,* vol. XXXIX (1924), pp. 1–18.
62. G. M. McBride, *The Land System of Mexico* (1923), p. 157.
63. *Ibid.*, p. 25.
64. *Ibid.*, pp. 167–168.
65. Lucy E. Textor, *Land Reform in Czecho-slovakia* (1923), pp. 32, 68, 82, 139.
66. For the unfavorable effect of the break-up of large estates in Russia, Poland, and Roumania, see E. Dana Durand, Agriculture in Eastern Europe, *Quarterly Journal of Economics,* vol. XXXVI (1922), pp. 190–196.
67. For the long continued paralled development of the three kinds of land holding, see the graphic illustration of the Genesis of Property in Land (above, p. 263) ; the lord and landlord system, $1 < \genfrac{}{}{0pt}{}{4-8}{5-9} > 12-15-18$; the villager's allod and free proprietorship, 2–6–10–13–16–19; and the communal ownership, 3–7–11–14–17–20.
68. *Laws of the United States of America,* vol. I (1815), p. 563.

69. See above, ch. XI, sect, 79, p. 262.

70. *Laws of the United States of America,* vol. II (1815), pp. 536–537.

71. *Ibid.,* p. 638.

72. *Ibid.,* vol. VI (1822), pp. 486–487.

73. J. R. Commons and others, *History of Labour in the United States* (1918), vol. I, p. 522.

74. *Laws of the United States of America,* vol. X (1845), p. 158.

75. See E. Stanwood, *A History of the Presidency* (1898), p. 255. For later expressions of land policy, see *ibid.,* pp. 293, 347, 430–431, 461, 474, 500, 506, 553.

76. G. M. Stephenson, *The Political History of the Public Lands* (1917), pp. 106–110.

77. 37th Cong., sess. II, ch. LXXV. *The Statutes at Large of the United States of America,* vol. XII (1860–63), pp. 392–393.

78. 60th Cong., sess. II, ch. 160. *Ibid.,* vol. XXXV (1909), p. 639.

79. 60th Cong., sess. II, ch. 160, sect. 6. *Ibid.,* p. 640.

80. 64th Cong., sess. II, ch. 9. *Ibid.,* vol. XXXIX, pt. I (1917), pp. 862–865.

81. For a general statement, see H. C. Taylor, *Agricultural Economics* (1919, 1920), chs. XX and XXI.

82. W. J. Spillman, The Agricultural Ladder, pp., 170–179, and R. T. Ely and Charles J. Galpin, Tenancy in an Ideal System of Landownership, pp. 180–212, *The American Economic Review, Supplement,* vol. IX (1919).

83. Then on the other hand, these statistics do not disclose to what extent the owners of the land actually own it, that is, how far they are free from mortgages.

CHAPTER XII

STAGES IN AMERICAN AGRICULTURE

Property
and cul-
tivation
compared

85. EARLY STAGES OF AGRICULTURE IN AMERICA. In the preceding chapter we noted some of the chief changes in property or ownership of land. In this chapter we follow developments in actual farming. Property in land has to do with rights, long-time interests, relationships between man and man and man and the state; in short it is largely a matter of legal history. The cultivation of land is a matter of work, day-to-day business, dealing with nature as well as man; in short it is largely a matter of economic history. The two are distinct but not unconnected. Those who own land often tend to engage in a somewhat different kind of agriculture from that followed by those who rent. On the other hand, the cultivator who follows an approved up-to-date system of farming is more likely to become or remain an owner than one who is following antequated practices.

European
and
American
agricul-
ture
compared

The subject of actual agriculture, the tilling of the soil and the caring for animals, has here been studied so far almost wholly in its European aspects. Such emphasis, even from the American standpoint, is justified, because, not only have European skill but American practices grown out of the early experiences of the old world. In short, the study of European, and especially English, agriculture is a good introduction to American farming. The crops are essentially the same, except that Indian corn or maize has played a vital part in America, while it has been but little used as a field crop in Europe. Domesticated animals are almost identical, America having all that Europe has and only the relatively unimportant turkey in addition. On both continents, local peculiarities and variations occur in great plenty, according to climate, soil, and topography. In both, there have been a few agricultural leaders and many followers. In both, associations in great plenty have been formed for benefiting the tiller of the soil. In both, the government has been of some assistance in furthering agricultural progress. And in America, we observe that changes in farming have gone through substantially the same stages as in Europe, though of course, with much greater compression—necessarily in a shorter period of time.

Natural husbandry, a loose extensive system of cultivation in which nature is the recuperating element, has played a rôle in American agriculture that one would not expect, having in mind the advances in contemporary Europe. But settlers in America, at least for a period in colonial times, had almost to start over again. It is a commonplace of American history that English and other settlers reverted to the practices of their distant ancestors, when they adopted the agriculture of the Indians. It is an oft-told story how the whites, trying to get a foothold on the Atlantic coast, learned and eagerly learned, Indian methods of cultivating the soil; and how both in the north and in the south, they were even compelled at times to rely upon the crops and stored products of the Indians. *Natural husbandry*

It mattered not whether the variety of crops was large, or whether there was a tendency to specialization in some exportable staple, the upshot was that, after a few years, the land had to be abandoned to recuperate, before another crop could be taken. On the richer lands this was postponed somewhat, but sooner or later difficulty with the soil arose. At first, just so much of the land as was required, was cleared of forest and bush. And when this was impaired, more land was made ready.[1] In this way much of the coast area was prepared for agriculture, piecemeal and under pressure. Later, only one field, or a group of fields, was used, the rest being left to idleness for a long period of years in the hope that nature would recuperate what man had injured.[2] Or as an alternative plan, one-half or one-third of the land was left idle *each* year, uncultivated, as a kind of rubbish pasture.[3] *Cropping and resting*

The agriculture of early Massachusetts and Virginia bears marked resemblance to that of primitive peoples, for example, to that of the Germans in the time of Christ. This is only a *Vicious cropping persists*

285

small part of the story, however, for such a system of vicious cropping has persisted throughout the history of American agriculture, here and there as circumstances have dictated. In early New England it might be wheat and oats; in early Virginia tobacco and maize; in Georgia cotton and maize; In each case, a few years of cropping were followed by a period of temporary abandonment. At the present day, in North Dakota, it is wheat followed by wheat, till the yield is ruinously low. The land in that state might be recuperated by careful fallowing to eliminate weeds and parasites, or, better, by a change in the method of cropping.[4]

Southern examples of natural husbandry

1845

1883

We have a description of a farm in Georgia that was managed according to the system of natural husbandry. Two acres were devoted to flowers, shrubbery, and vegetables, be it noted in passing; and what is more important for our purpose, 75 acres of an apparently large estate were given over to field crops, corn and cotton. These were all that the farmer could plant and care for, all that he could keep well manured. Now this farmer was apparently up to date in all but his cropping methods, for he had machinery of the newest and most approved make.[5] In another instance, in South Carolina, a coast planter had 30 acres in cotton, and apparently 210 acres in other crops. One would not suspect from this that his farm was a large one, 1200 acres in fact. It is astonishing to see a cultivator use each year only one-fifth of his total estate, the other four-fifths remaining idle.[6]

Abundance of land as the basis of natural husbandry

The explanation of such a system in some districts is the lack of fertility of the soil, in others the general undeveloped condition of the market; but most commonly, perhaps, it is the abundance or cheapness of the land.[7] Where land is cheap it is used lavishly; where dear, it is cultivated with care. In new countries the system of natural husbandry prevails, because it is the most economical in the use of labor and capital, which are scarce, and the most prodigal of land, which is plentiful.

Agricultural villages

Early agriculture in America, then, resembled early agriculture in Europe. Like causes bring about like results. We can illustrate this not simply by the technique of agriculture but also by the arrangement of the farms. Generally, at first, there was a tendency to build houses near together along the coast, in fact, in the form of nucleated villages.[8] Although this was notably the case in New England where the village, or "town," became an established institution, it was found elsewhere, as defence, or the need of social intercourse, or the desire for close association of peoples worshipping in a peculiar way or speaking a foreign tongue, pointed to the desirability of compact formation. The effort of the nucleated village to make headway on American soil was not a success. Either the already established village grew into an economic town, where trading, shipbuilding, fishing and the like, took place or it was unable to compete with the isolated farmstead. In the passing of the infant village, America suffered a great social loss, for close proximity (in Europe and elsewhere) has meant daily social life, conversation, story-telling, singing, and dancing. Such things lead to peasant amenities and to peasant art, of which America has had all too little. Co-operation in social affairs prepare the way for co-operation in the business of agriculture, which in America has grown so slowly and with so many set-backs.

We have all stood on the hilltop in the evening watching **Scattered** the blue hearth smoke curl upward from the valley and then **homesteads** the lights break forth from the cottage windows. And so now we may look down from the vantage point of the twentieth century and see here and there, almost from coast to coast, the springing up of homesteads over the land. Some of them have been large plantations in the south, manors in New York and Maryland, but most are the small and humble homes of poor men. So imbued was the emigrant from Europe in settlement days, with the saving grace of economy, that he did not hestitate to sacrifice the social advantages of the village group to the managerial advantages of the isolated farm. On the individual holding, he could do what he liked, progress or stagnate; he could build his house near the center of his farm; he could make such changes as he wished without consulting his neighbors. But above all was the fact that the farms in America were too large to be compressed into a village organization.

Naked-fallow system

The change in cultivation which commonly supplanted natural husbandry in Europe, was brought about by the introduction of the naked-fallow system. Instead of just allowing the land, not under crop, to lie resting, without knowing either plow or seed, a regular routine of careful cultivation was undertaken. The land was plowed once or oftener; it was then harrowed, and sometimes rolled and harrowed again. The idea was partly to allow nature to restore the soil during a period of no crop, and partly, indeed more especially, to cleanse the land of weeds, fungus, and other parasites, which were cultivated to their death. In areas of scant rainfall, an additional reason exists: fallowing conserves the moisture in the soil. The accumulated rain of two seasons may be husbanded for a crop, which could not have been grown in one season's precipitation.[9] This is found in the dry districts of America, as an aid to the growing of wheat, from the western parts of the Dakotas and Kansas to the Pacific coast (except on the desert), and is most common in California, Washington, Oregon, Idaho, and Montana.[10] It is even more common north of the Canadian boundary.

Naked-fallow system in America

The story of the naked-fallow system in America is obscure in detail but discernible in outline. Probably here and there in the seventeenth and eighteenth centuries it was adopted in the east, and spread westward. Before the opening of the nineteenth century we find in Maryland the following system: maize, naked fallow, wheat, and resting (spontaneous growth of weeds). In this instance can be seen the transition from the old natural husbandry (with its resting system) to the naked-fallow system.[11] By 1850 the naked fallow had been used in Michigan [12] and even farther west.[13] But we hear of it both in east and west when being given up, discredited in itself and in comparison with some better method. In short, the fallow system never became general. The reasons for this are four in number, all of them very good ones where they apply locally. The land was cheap and each cultivator having plenty of it could produce sufficient crops for a living by the prevailing extensive system of cultivation, natural husbandry. Labor has been scarce and therefore the less the plowing and harrowing the greater the saving.[14] Indian corn, so widely grown in America, has been a cleansing crop. Shortly after appearing, this corn has to be carefully cultivated to eliminate the weeds. And when it grows, high and sturdy, it largely shuts off from the light such weeds as survive cultivation. And fourthly, when land finally became dear, here and there, some later method of cultivation than the naked-fallow system has been introduced into America.

The first of the systems following the naked fallow was **Legume** legume rotation. This involves, as we have seen,[15] the use of **rotation** some leguminous plant, such as beans, peas, or clover, in the cropping system. The function of this crop is not only to provide food for man or fodder for animals, but to help put the soil into good condition. When improvements in cropping were generally considered in America, the use of legumes came in for attention. Up to the second half of the eighteenth century, however, little progress was made along this line.

The advantage of planting one of the legumes, clover, in **Legume** preparation for wheat was pointed out by Jared Eliot **rotation** (1748–61), who was perhaps the first American to write essays on agriculture, finally published in book form.[16] A little **America** later clover was used in New England as a preparation for **1775** grain,[17] and in North Carolina beans and peas were alternated with wheat.[18] Later we find a Maryland farmer sowing peas **1849** with oats, followed apparently by clover and then by wheat.[19] Because of lack of specific statement we cannot tell whether these crops were all distinct from permanent pastures and meadows. Certainly there were permanent meadows and pastures in the period in question.[20]

If the clover fields just mentioned were used for hay or **Field-** pasture, and if the permanent meadows and pastures were **grass** abandoned, we would have a full fledged field-grass system. **husbandry** As has already been indicated,[21] field-grass husbandry is a system of alternation of a grass crop and a cereal, in other words, a green and a dry crop. The grass may be consumed

289

green or as hay. It may be a legume or not. After clover had become popular in Europe, that crop was the most obvious one to adopt. This system apparently existed in New England.

1775 Several years of grain were alternated with a clover meadow for some years. The practice is described as similar to that of the worst British farmers.[22] The conversion of meadow

1790 land to the uses of tillage was recommended, if the soil was suitable.[23] A central Atlantic farmer planned to divide his

1819 150 acre farm into ten fields, using four for pasture, four for clover hay and clover seed, one for tobacco, and one for

1819 wheat.[24] An Irish seed-store keeper proposed for Maryland a system of three crops of grain, then hay followed by pasture.[25] The existence of field-grass husbandry is indicated by the denunciation of the system by a Virginia farmer.

1850 Cropping and pasturing to him were distinct uses of the land.[26] On one farm in the granary county of Lancaster, Pennsylvania, clover and wheat were regularly rotated. The farm had been in use for a century.[27]

A transition type A system in between field-grass husbandry and the scientific rotation is sometimes found in America. One of the rotations planned by Washington included three fields of clover

1793-94 or grass, one of maize and potatoes, one of wheat, one of buckwheat for manure, and a seventh of wheat again.[28] It was clearly the intention to feed a number of animals which would constitute one cash "crop," the other being wheat. The pasture is a survival of field-grass husbandry. In Pennsylvania the

1797 farmers gave up their standing meadows (permanent hay lands), long highly prized, for clover fields in rotation with other crops.[29] The well-known agricultural writer, John

1813 Taylor of Virginia, denounced the three-shift system of maize, wheat, and pasture.[30] A rotation of wheat, rye, maize, buck-

1820 wheat, and two years of oats was recommended, the oats to be used as pasture. This system was intended to improve worn out soil.[31] A Virginian farmer experimented with two

1821 systems, one wheat and clover used alternately, the clover being pastured; the other maize, oats, and clover, the clover likewise being pastured.[32] The first is field-grass husbandry. The second is a step nearer to the scientific rotation. One cultivator in New York State used the rotation of maize and potatoes, barley (or peas), wheat, and grass.[33] Maize, wheat, and pasture, or maize, wheat, and three years of clover, were also recommended.[34] In Illinois one of several rotations suggested by a farmer was made up of wheat, maize, wheat (or oats), and then five years of grass.[35] These examples seem to illustrate a transition from field-grass husbandry to the next system, the scientific rotation of crops.

1834

1839
1865

By the middle of the nineteenth century legume rotation and field-grass husbandry had won places for themselves, though not unchallenged. In the north and northwest [36] the chief legume was clover, others such as lucerne, sanfoin, and vetches being comparatively little cultivated in the United States.[37] In the south it was the cowpea valued as a fodder and crop restorative since the early part of the century, but even now not so widely used as might be.[38]

North and south contrasted

Legume rotation and field-grass husbandry were never vitally important in Europe generally. In America they made much less headway. For some of the legumes, such as beans and peas, there was no demand wide enough to justify the devotion of many fields to their cultivation. In some parts of the country, notably New England, there was no chance of rotating fodder crops with cereals because the numerous permanent pastures were useful for growing grass and hay and those only.[39] They could not be made to produce large crops of wheat. The wide-spread practice of growing Indian corn precluded much of the demand that might otherwise have prevailed for clover hay for cattle. But above all was the fact that there was in sight a better system than either legume rotation or field-grass husbandry. When America was ready to improve her agriculture on a broad scale, it was possible to introduce the scientific rotation of crops, already worked out in Europe and known by a few leaders in American agriculture, such as Washington. This was almost as early indeed as the time their compatriots had begun to use legume rotation or field-grass husbandry. In other words, when and where there

Why legume rotation and field-grass husbandry had little success

291

was a demand for a new system, to restore or maintain the productivity of the soil, the most improved system, as was to be expected, was introduced.

Complaints of declining yield

1801

1838

1850

1853

1868

86. DECLINING PRODUCTIVITY. From the latter part of the eighteenth century down to our time there have been complaints about the decline in agricultural productivity. An Englishman visiting America was quoted as saying that agriculture in the United States afforded a bare subsistence and that fertility was gradually declining, notably in Virginia.[40] Complaints of bad conditions in the middle and south Atlantic states were common in the agricultural journals; [41] complaints of soil exhaustion and general rural decay. Not only did these occur in the east but in the west, as settlement was pushed farther and farther toward the Pacific. Fifty years of bad farming were said to be wearing out the new lands of Kentucky.[42] In an inland county of New York, the yield was said to have dropped from a high range (20 to 40 bushels) per acre in 1775 to about 7½ bushels in 1845.[43] Michigan was on the downward course a few years after it had been made a state. The awful example of Virginia, New York, and Ohio was held up to Michigan as her own fate, if something was not done to maintain fertility.[44] In Indiana it was said that the North Carolina settlers were skinning the land with continuous crops of maize.[45] And very early in Minnesota a considerable decline in the yield of wheat and corn was observed.[46]

Other evidence for diminishing productivity

Because of the danger of error in observation and exaggeration in statement on the part of those giving information, we must look farther into the situation to see what evidence there is for declining productivity, apart from contemporary statements.[47] The use of fertilizers is significant. At first there was no thought of putting anything on to the soil. Barnyard manure was dumped into rivers and cotton seed thrown away. Ashes were heaped up rather than spread out over the land. And leaves were left to blow into corners where they were of no service. But here and there the time came when all of these were eagerly seized upon as a means of restoring the soil. Soil amendments, such as gypsum, marl, lime, and commercial fertilizers such as Peruvian guano,[48] were purchased in large quantities at great expense, almost everywhere from Virginia to New England. Some farmers, on the other hand, thought they had only to plow more deeply and tap the subsoil to get larger crops. For a time such might be the case, but this practice in itself only the more surely hastened the process of decline. Efforts were made to stave off the trouble by introducing new varieties of grain. Accordingly, we find a great number of grains,[49] chiefly wheat, brought from other states in America and from various parts of the world to remedy the situation. Societies, too, were formed to counteract rural decline; fairs were held and prizes for good products offered. And if any more evidence is needed, there is the fact that sooner or later in each community improved methods of agriculture were adopted, the fallow system, legume rotation, field-grass husbandry, and the scientific rotation of crops. **Early 19th century**

It is somewhat easier to prove the decline of agricultural output than to understand exactly what was involved. It is obvious that when commercial fertilizers were so much in vogue, when cultivators were buying potassium, nitrogen, and other elements, they believed that the trouble was the loss of the necessary chemical constituents of the soil. But when, after about a generation of trial they found their lands as bad off as ever, they learned that they were on the wrong track. Gradually agricultural science has turned from emphasis on the chemical to the biological condition of the soil. Before there can be good crops there must be a favorable condition of plant growth, apart from the food itself. The trouble probably quite commonly arises out of the growth of fungi and other parasites which have so multiplied that the old crops show diminishing yields. Either other crops must be used or new varieties of the old ones brought from afar or developed locally. **Meaning of decline** **Chemical deficiency** **Bacteriological deficiency**

Besides chemical losses and bacteriological disorder, the land has suffered from the more obvious physical loss of the soil itself. In Virginia (and later in Kentucky) where the **Physical losses**

293

hill lands were originally fairly rich for a few inches deep, the plowing was always superficial, and accordingly each year a little more of the soil of the tobacco fields was made unfit for the staple crop. The land was often profitably turned to wheat cultivation, showing that chemical exhaustion had not gone far. But the fine pulverization of the soil for tobacco culture and the practice of plowing vertically up and down hill, instead of horizontally, had led to the loss of much of the surface soil itself. Rains carried it to the streams, where it was deposited on the banks or sent on to the rivers and even to the ocean. Erosion soon completed its work. Without spontaneous growth or the crops of man to protect the soil, huge inroads were made into the uplands and hillsides, till fair fields became pitted with gullies.

Results of declining yield

Following declining yields in agriculture in America have come changes of far-reaching importance. The farmers have suffered the pangs of misfortune. Ends could not be met. The acre brought forth enough seed for a second sowing, but left too little for the cultivator. The sufferer had but one of two courses open to him in the long run: he must either migrate or change his method of cultivation. Accordingly, while some moved off to fresh western fields, others remained at home to try a new system of agriculture. To many, migration to another district was easier than the adoption of greater efficiency in cultivation.

Scientific rotation described

87. SCIENTIFIC ROTATION OF CROPS: THE AGRICULTURAL REVOLUTION IN AMERICA. The scientific rotation of crops is the effective planting of grains and green crops so that as perfect an adjustment as possible will be brought about in both cultivation and marketing.[50] The crops are so arranged that one prepares for the next following, either in providing plant nourishment or in the cleansing of the soil. Such crops are chosen as promise the greatest insurance against loss from bad weather or low prices. These crops are for the use of man and beast: chiefly wheat, barley, and rye for man, and Indian corn, oats, hay, sorghum, and so on, for animals. A nice adjustment between these two classes of crops may be called a balanced agricultural system.

The new method of farming might take the place of any of the older systems. The introduction of this system, when supplanting legume rotation or field-grass husbandry, involved the following changes. Pasturing was largely or wholly done away with. More animals were kept than before, and, commonly, better ones. Instead of being allowed to graze, they were fed in the stall or yard. In the place of green grass devoured in the fields, they were given hay or ensilage.[51] The animal manure, deposited in the stable yards, was carefully spread on selected fields for the nourishment of the crops to which it would be of greatest service. Although the scientific rotation is not so exhaustive as other systems, it nevertheless does lead to reduced yields and manure must be used in conjunction with it. Apart from fertility, there is cleanliness and freedom from weeds and parasites. This is brought about by a judicious order of planting. *From field-grass husbandry to scientific rotation*

Although the number of rotations is legion,[52] depending on climate, market conditions, and personal preference, the following may be taken as one of the standard combinations— Indian corn, wheat, clover hay, and oats; or Indian corn, oats, wheat, and clover hay. *Examples*

Although all of these crops existed in early colonial times,[53] it was long before they were brought into an effective rotation. Somewhat before the American Revolution, Jared Eliot spoke of the Norfolk method, probably referring to the introduction of scientific rotation in England. He also had in mind the recent changes in Irish agriculture. But it is probable that neither his suggestions nor his recommendations had much influence on the people of New England, for whose benefit he wrote.[54] This was because, at the time in question, the problem was not land, but labor, conservation. A little later Samuel Deane pointed out that, while rotations were neglected in New England, great advance had been made in the mother country. He refers to the work of Arthur Young and recommends certain definite rotations for light and stiff soils.[55] George Logan of Pennsylvania, after making many experiments with rotations, pointed out the following as advantages of the new system: the greatest number of money crops, *When introduced into America*

1790

1797

295

the largest amount of fodder for keeping cattle through the winter, the even distribution of the farm work, and keeping the soil in good condition.[56]

Washington as agricultural improver

Although Thomas Jefferson,[57] John Randolph, Thomas Pickering, John Adams, and Henry Clay played a part in furthering the cause of agriculture, generally in the direction of a more balanced system, nevertheless it was George Washington who stood first—with the plow as with the sword. Washington was a business farmer who with great industry kept track of the 3260 acres that he cultivated. He knew the fields and their uses, watched the growing crops when possible, saw to the repair of buildings and fences, and sought the best market for his products. He corresponded with Arthur Young and Sir John Sinclair, and from England sought ideas, seeds (turnips and legumes), plows, laborers, a manager, and in his old age, well-to-do tenants to take over his whole plantation. Anxious to put his land into good condition and to get the maximum returns from the soil, he planned to introduce the scientific rotation, instead of the old system of Indian corn, wheat, and a period of idling (weeds and rubbish). But Washington found it easier to win a war than to introduce a new system of agriculture. There is no escape from the verdict that he failed. The reasons are overwhelming. His land was in such bad condition that it needed considerable application of leguminous crops, especially for plowing in as green manure. The scientific rotation does not, strictly speaking, admit of green manuring, for that is too great a waste for an efficient system, however necessary it may be to recuperate the soil. The use of two out of seven fields for pasture in one of his rotations is likewise not in keeping with the ideals of the new system that he sought to introduce. He was trying to cultivate too large an estate. His plantation was not too big for the old system, but it was for the new. If the estate had been 300 instead of over 3000 acres, he might have had more success. His manager was unskilled, his laborers ignorant and inefficient. He was trying to do the impossible, introducing new and often untried crops into practical farming before they had passed the experimental stage in his district. He succeeded neither with the new crops nor with stall feeding. His animals were relatively few in number and not of good breed or condition. A larger measure of attainment might have been his, if he had served himself more and his country less. His long absence from home, attending the convention that drew up the constitution and then as president, greatly hampered his effort at improvement.[58] It cannot, of course, be said that he failed utterly, for the effort was noteworthy. Friends going to visit him and strangers prowling around out of curiosity, doubtless brought back information about what he was trying to accomplish.

It is generally more difficult to identify progress in scientific rotation with particular localities than with specific individuals. Although we cannot be sure whch is the Norfolk of America, we can be certain that the new methods were developed in the middle states from Pennsylvania to Virginia. Like many new movements, this one was not fully understood. Some seemed to think that all the farmer had to do to maintain fertility was to adopt a good rotation. It was necessary for the agricultural writer, John Taylor to point out the danger in neglecting to manure the land.[59]

Where the scientific rotation first took root

1813

How clearly the introduction of the scientific rotation was an imitation of the English movement is seen, not only in the work of individuals, their correspondence with English leaders, and their reading of English books, but in the attempt to adopt the English type of rotation which included turnips as one of the crops.[60] So far had this gone, even in New England, that complaint was made that farmers invited their guests to view their turnips in the field (and animals in the stall and sty), before visiting their families in the parlor.[61] In spite of the fact that the unsuitability of roots as field crops in America, especially in New England, was fairly early pointed out,[62] men went ahead with them. One writer actually lamented the fact that there were not as many as six states in all America that grew turnips expressly for fodder, in spite of England's demonstrated success.[63] Gradually it was perceived that Indian corn was the American substitute for tur-

Imitation of England

1823

1834
1850

nips and other root crops. While the roots could be fed to cattle and sheep in the fields in England, they had to be stored up against frosts in America. If a cleansing crop was required and one useful for feeding cattle, then Indian corn was the ideal. Some had seen this from the first, but the power of slavish imitation was very great. During the early years of the nineteenth century English practices were further followed in introducing better breeds of sheep and cattle. Spanish sheep and English cattle (and some English sheep also) were brought in for breeding purposes. It was not long before these reached Kentucky and Ohio and then farther west.

Gradual spread

It would be tedious to go through the whole story of the spread of the scientific rotation of crops. Gradually as conditions have changed, crops have changed. This has been in the form of a slow moving wave, first slowly westward and at the present time southward. In the newer lands we see first wheat emphasised; then more attention given to oats, barley, and Indian corn; and finally hay and forage crops come to occupy a considerable percentage of the whole area of improved farm lands.[64] In 1874 the National Grange resolved, among its many reforms, to diversify crops. Roughly speaking, we may say that in the introduction of a balanced agriculture, a scientific rotation of crops, the middle Atlantic states were farther along in 1880 than the north central states were in 1920, and the latter states were more advanced in 1880 than the south in 1920.[65]

In the northwest

1860

1923

In the wheat growing states of the northwest, as in the cotton states of the south, farmers have been loath to give up their staple crop. In Minnesota, attention was early given to rotations[66] and stock raising was seen to have a future.[67] Progress in that state has been from the south and east to the north and west. But even to-day it has been necessary to wage a campaign to persuade some of the farmers of Minnesota (as well as of North Dakota and Montana) to give up their reliance upon wheat. The great slogan in this campaign is "diversify." The local implication is, that to cereal production should be added stock raising. Let there be more stock and better breeds. Eliminate the scrub herds. Develop cattle for either beef or dairying. The governor of the state, the journals, the agricultural college, the bankers, have joined in the cry. Conventions have been held, tours made, and lectures delivered. Minnesota, and the northwest generally, is threatened with declining prosperity under a régime of spring wheat. The quality of the wheat is deteriorating, the yield is uncertain, and prices are low. A common argument is that the farmer should have a money income every day—from his milk sales—instead of just once a year at harvest time. 1920–24

When the agricultural revolution is complete in the northwest, it will still have work to do in the south, where it already has made a beginning. Circumstances are changing and men are becoming aroused, both in southern towns and southern rural districts, at the relative stagnation of their part of the country. The twin driving forces of sick crops and uncertain market, will doubtless do for the south what they have done for the east and are still doing for the west. *In the south*

America has an agricultural revolution, as England has had one, but the two are different. America's has been spread over a long period because of the necessity of covering a wide area. America's has had a larger group of agricultural leaders, though with less literary distinction. America has relied upon Indian corn rather than roots. And in America the scientific rotation is superseding, not simply the fallow system, legume rotation, and field-grass husbandry, as in England, but also the primitive natural husbandry, as in North Dakota, and to a large extent in the south at the present time. *American and English agricultural revolutions compared*

88. PRESENT AGRICULTURAL STRUGGLES: SPECIALIZED INTENSIVE SYSTEM. Agriculture, like other kinds of production, presents a series of struggles, some of which, of course, have already been considered. It is itself a contest between man and nature. Man runs a race with weeds, insects, fungi, rains, and frost. He fights the wolves off from the flock and combats disease in the stall and the sty. One type of farmer really unwittingly competes with another. Often a sturdy farmer owns and tills a piece of very fertile land, but he is a better cultivator than a business man. He can get a good *Competition in agriculture*

yield and keep his land fit, but he does not raise the crops in demand. Sooner or later such a type must give up his good land to the farmer who is both cultivator and business man. As we have seen, two systems of land control also struggle one with another, ownership and tenancy. In England, tenancy has won; in France, ownership; in Germany the struggle is undecided, each system still maintaining itself firmly. In America the traditional farm has been owned by the occupier. And yet, there has developed a great deal of tenancy, some of it desirable and some of it not.[68] There has been some real difference of opinion among American citizens as to whether the government, federal and state, should be active in aiding the farmer. There has been a struggle to bring about such participation in face of great odds, but as yet there is no decision. In hard times, such as follow a war, the struggle for government assistance has so much strength that it wins at least some measure of success. American agriculture has long competed with European. Even before

1787

1870's

the French Revolution, American products in European markets were feared.[69] And about a hundred years later, European farmers had to gird their loins in order to hold their own. They made economic adjustment and political alliances. Where they could not keep out American wheat, they turned to other crops. And similarly the eastern part of the United States has had to struggle to maintain itself against the west. Either the easterner would move west to take advantage of the virgin soil, or he would change his method of agriculture so as to hold his own. The cultivators on Long Island, New

1849

York, gave up wheat production when the Erie Canal began to pour in the cheaply grown wheat of Ohio and other western states.[70] They turned to crops much needed at home, crops which by their nature could not be moved long distances with existing means of transportation.

Cotton vs. wheat

The classic illustration of a contest in American agriculture is expressed in the significant formula, cotton vs. wheat.[71] It is used to indicate the economic side of the Civil War, and it is more than a half truth. On the one side were cotton, the southern slave system, and the cotton manufacturing interests

300

of England. On the other side were wheat, the free labor system of the north, and the humanitarian cotton spinners of England, who chose to oppose slavery even at the cost of their daily bread. Many are the explanations of why the north won. To some God decided. To others it was the sea-power of the north. But according to the theory under consideration, the north won because of its wheat. During the early years of the war England sorely needed American wheat, her own, and European harvests generally, having partly failed. England needed American wheat even more than American cotton. The cotton kept the factories going, but the wheat kept body and soul together. Accordingly, the English government had to throw over its preference in favor of the south. It gave up the idea of recognizing the Confederacy, because the wheat of the north was more vital than the cotton of the south. The large crop of the north was a material bribe to England to throw its influence into the scale on behalf of human liberty.

The agricultural contest may be expressed in many different ways with varying shades of emphasis. It is generally the small farm against the large farm,[72] the homestead against the plantation, and the new and improved system against the old. It is the new system that wins. And this new system generally grows up in old lands competing with the old system. The victor is almost invariably a more intensive form of agriculture. Natural husbandry gives way to fallow, fallow to legume rotation, and legume rotation to field-grass husbandry, and that in turn to the scientific rotation of crops. And finally the scientific rotation is supplanted by the specialized intensive agriculture that promises much for the future. *Smaller farms and intensive agriculture*

Generally speaking this system develops first in the older sections, but there are many diverting local conditions; and wherever towns arise, notably large towns, and most of all where a metropolis comes into existence, whether in old or new sections, there is a demand for the new type of agriculture. Other conditions determine the local growth of intensive agriculture. A very rich soil in western New York State will be used to grow garden produce for daily shipment hundreds *Where intensive agriculture develops* of miles away to New York City. And the mild climate of Maryland and Delaware invite gardening for the raising of vegetables, especially for early marketing. The possibility of irrigating land, which, barring lack of moisture, is suitable for intensive agriculture, has made some impression on Americans generally but not very much. The arid lands of the Rocky Mountain and Pacific Coast districts offer great possibilities for the future. They are far from the great central markets but the chance to combine moisture, light, and heat in the growing season, almost as they are desired, has led to vast irrigation projects and to transportation arrangements for the marketing of goods that are a tribute at once to the imagination and to the constructive powers of man. The land so irrigated is cultivated as local circumstances dictate, but the two more intensive systems prevail, the scientific rotation of crops and specialized intensive agriculture. The result is that the yield on the average is higher on irrigated than non-irrigated lands. This is to be expected; otherwise there would be no advantage in incurring the great expense of irrigation.

1920 And yet nearly seven million acres more land might be irrigated by existing water systems than actually are so treated.

1920 And over two million acres of irrigated land are available for settlement.[73]

Horticulture   A significant development of specialized intensive agriculture is found in horticulture, for the production of vegetables, fruits, nuts, or flowers, and shading off into landscape gardening. At first, gardening was just a part of household management, or self-sufficing agriculture. Almost every farm came to have its kitchen garden and many had an orchard. New

1775 England and New Jersey were early noted for their fruit trees;[74] Maryland and Virginia were praised for their vegetable gardens.[75] As towns, cities, and especially metropolitan centers developed, specialization arose as between horticulture and general agriculture, and even within the field of horticul-

1817-48 ture. We may place such growth roughly in the early part of the nineteenth century. During that period treatises were being written in America on special parts of horticulture, fruit growing in 1817 and landscape gardening in 1841. Eastern

302

states set up horticultural societies, New York in 1818, Pennsylvania in 1827, and Massachusetts in 1829. Horticultural journals were started in Philadelphia in 1832, in Baltimore in 1833 and 1834, three in Boston in 1835, and one in Albany in 1846. By 1848 the new development was so strong that there were two societies disputing hegemony and enlisting the aid of the devotees of horticulture.[76] The third development came after the Civil War when horticulture came to be localized, not only according to accessibility to great markets but according to climate, its products being handled, however, through the metropolitan marketing agencies. Florida and California are outstanding examples of this growth.

The future of irrigation, and of intensive agriculture generally, is frequently a subject of speculation. The progress of a more intensive system depends upon increased demand, either in the home or the foreign market. If there is an increase in population in the present century anything like that of the past hundred years, more intensive agriculture must develop. All kinds of questions arise on the supply side, whether there will be an increasing supply of cheap commercial fertilizers containing nitrogen, phosphorous, and potassium; whether the amount of humus necessary will keep pace with the general demand; and whether there will be plenty of men with the requisite capital and capacity who are willing to engage in this kind of enterprise. It would seem that another kind of contest will arise in unprecedented strength, that between the town and the country, especially for capital. This is not simply a speculative anticipation, for it is already with us. *Future of intensive agriculture*

89. AGRICULTURAL ACCOMPLISHMENTS. It is not enough to know that agricultural technique has passed through various stages, developing types of cultivation in each. What we want to learn before passing judgment, is how such changes have affected agriculture generally and also other kinds of production. Certainly there has been a continuous increase in farm output and in the number of farms.[77] This has been paralleled by the increase in rural population, from less than four million at the first census to over fifty-one million at the latest enumeration. Not all of the persons assigned to rural districts, however- *Progressive results* *1790* *1920*

303

1920

ever, have been engaged in agriculture.[78]At the present over thirty-one million actually reside on farms.[79] Not only has agriculture given these people a livelihood, but it has provided the rest of the population with most of its foodstuffs and has had a surplus for export. The value of agricultural exports

1852–1911

has increased enormously. In sixty years the growth has been four-fold. Even if we allow for increase in prices, there is still a large margin for real development.

Agriculture as a basic industry

What cannot be even approximately measured, are the industries for which agriculture provides the raw materials. Some of these are flour milling, meat packing, fruit canning, butter making, tobacco manufacture, and the cotton, woolen, and leather industries. Besides manufacture, there is the storage of agricultural products, which is a business in itself. There are grain elevators, cotton and tobacco warehouses, and linseed tanks. Added to these are systems of transportation, many of them originally catering almost wholly to agriculture and some of them still dependent largely on it. Of course, all this is only one part of the accomplishment of agriculture, all characteristically on the side of agricultural production. Agricultural consumption (the farmers' purchase of foodstuffs, clothes, machinery, and so on) has given rise to many industries, storage businesses, transport agencies, and banking and credit organizations.

Relative position of agriculture

Truly broad is the foundation that agriculture has laid, and wise are those who identify its progress rather closely with national well-being and advance. Although agriculture has made absolute gains, in some respects it has lost relatively. There has been a continuous increase in rural population, but that increase has not kept pace with the growth of urban population. In other words, the town keeps gaining on the country. Some see in this, national misfortune. Two points need to be considered. The development may not continue, though it likely will for at least a while. And secondly, even if it does, it means that the surplus of each rural producer must be larger than before, and this indicates material progress.

1790

At the time of the first census, seven rural families had only about one townsman to supply with foodstuffs and raw materials, while to-day seven supply about eighty-four.[80] Perhaps 1920 the moralist would grant the growing efficiency of the farmer, lamenting at the same time the loss of preponderance of the traditional rural virtues and physical strength. The struggle between the town and the country is now going on. Each side has its sources of strength and its protagonists. It is our privilege to watch the issue of the contest.

90. Suggestions for Further Study

1. Useful lists of books and articles are to be found in the two pamphlets, *Introductory Manual for the Study and Reading of Agrarian History*, pt. III (1917), by W. Trimble; and *Topical Studies and References on the Economic History of American Agriculture* (1919), by L. B. Schmidt.

2. Read the articles on agriculture in America, to be found in the various encyclopedias, the *Britannica, New International,* and *Americana.*

3. For a brief historical outline of American agriculture, see A. H. Sanford's *Story of Agriculture in the United States,* 1916. See also H. U. Faulkner, *American Economic History* (1924), chs. III, IX, X, XIX.

4. Brief outlines have been written by Charles L. Flint, Progress of Agriculture (pp. 19–102), and C. F. McCay, Cotton Culture (pp. 103–126) in *Eighty Years Progress* (1864); and by T. N. Carver in L. H. Bailey's *Cyclopedia of American Agriculture,* vol. IV (1909), pp. 39–70.

5. Valuable articles are to be found in the *Yearbook of the United States Department of Agriculture* (1894 f.).

6. Just what did the Indians teach the settlers? See L. Carrier's *Beginnings of Agriculture in America* (1923).

7. Comment: the problem of learning technique first occupied the settlers; then it was chiefly exploiting the farm and improving the community; finally it has become a matter of technique again. Wherein does the present technique radically differ from the first? Consider the marketing of crops.

8. Which English crops were not suited to American conditions?

9. Why has poor technique lasted so long in America?

10. For the agriculture of southern New England, see P. W. Bidwell, *Rural Economy in New England at the Beginning of the Nineteenth Century,* Transactions of the Connecticut Academy of Arts and Sciences, vol. XX (1916), pp. 319–353.

11. What were the early agricultural accomplishments of Rhode Island? See L. Carrier's *Beginnings of Agriculture in America* (1923), ch. XV. Where does Rhode Island stand to-day?

12. Who were the best farmers in the new world, the English, French, Dutch, or Spaniards?

13. Why was Benjamin Franklin so interested in Agriculture?

14. Why have so many Americans regarded agriculture as production *par excellence?*

15. What is the conception of the agricultural revolution set forth above? Compare the view that it was the rise of western agriculture, 1860–1900, and the decline (relative or absolute) of eastern agriculture.

16. Explain this statement: American agriculture has been growing old and young at the same time.

17. What influences other than soil exhaustion or soil sickness brought about the scientific rotation? Consider the failure of the chief crop, wheat, in Iowa in the 1870's and in Dakota in the following decades.

18. A Georgia farmer of to-day plants 10 acres of cotton, 15 acres of Indian corn, 15 acres of small grains, and 3 acres of watermelons. He uses relatively little fertilizer, but devotes an immense amount of labor, especially in going over his cotton crop five times or oftener, waging war on the boll-weevil. To which stage of agriculture does this system belong?

19. Can you work out a statistical test of a balanced agriculture, so as to be able by an examination of census data alone, to tell whether a state has entered the stage of scientific agriculture?

20. In studying the subject of intensive agriculture why is it that in practice you have to take as your unit of land, not an acre but so many dollars' worth of land?

21. Do you identify agricultural prosperity in America with considerable exportation of agricultural products? Consider conditions before and after the Civil War.

22. Study the economic aspects of the Civil War to learn whether the traditional view of the struggle as cotton vs. wheat is correct.

23. What economic and social systems have arisen out of the scarcity of labor in America?

24. What are the mainsprings of agricultural advance, material or idealistic? How far was agricultural progress the result of economic conditions, such as rich land and demand for products, and how far the desire of farmers for a higher standard of living?

For further references, see the notes below.

91. Notes to Chapter XII

1. See Peter Kalm, *Travels into North America,* vol. I (1770), pp. 184–185.

2. [Anonymous] *American Husbandry* (1775), vol. I, pp. 31, 53, 126, 171–173.

3. [J. B. Bordley], *A Summary View of the Courses of Crops, in the Husbandry of England and Maryland* (1784), pp. 11, 14.

4. The average yield (in bushels) for North Dakota was as follows (*Yearbook of the United States Department of Agriculture, 1923* [1924], p. 605):

1910	5.0
1916	5.5
1917	8.0
1919	6.9
1920	9.0
1923	7.1
1908–23	10.5

5. *The Journal of Agriculture* (ed. by J. S. Skinner), vol. II (1846), pp. 182–183. Cf. also John Norton, *Notes for American Farmers* (1851), p. 17.

6. W. A. Schaper, Sectionalism and Representation in South Carolina, *Annual Report of the American Historical Association, 1900,* vol. I (1901), p. 288.

7. Cf. the statement of the anonymous author of *American Husbandry* (1775), vol. I, p. 145.

8. See above, ch. I, sect. 3, p. 10.

9. See below, ch. XIV, sect. 100, p. 342.

10. J. H. Arnold and R. R. Spafford, Farm Practices in Growing Wheat, *Yearbook of the United States Department of Agriculture, 1919* (1920), p. 129.

11. [J. B. Bordley], *Sketches on Rotations of Crops* (1797), p. 11.

12. *The Michigan Farmer,* vol. VIII (1850), p. 195; *ibid.,* vol. IX (1851), pp. 37, 73, 102.

13. *The Cultivator,* N. S., vol. VIII (1851), pp. 355–357.

14. See *The Farmers' Register,* vol. I (1834), p. 203.

15. See above, ch. II, sect. 10, pp. 31 f.

16. Jared Eliot, *Essays upon Field-Husbandry in New England* (1760), p. 36.

17. [Anonymous] *American Husbandry* (1775), vol. I, p. 55.

18. *Ibid.*, pp. 339–340.

19. *The Plough, the Loom and the Anvil* (Jan., 1850), p. 438.

20. See [the anonymous] *American Husbandry* (1775), vol. I p. 166; and T. G. Fessenden, *The Complete Farmer and Rural Economist* (1834), p. 299.

21. See above, ch. II, sect. 11, p. 36.

22. [Anonymous] *American Husbandry* (1775), vol. I, p. 76.

23. Samuel Deane, *The New-England Farmer* (1790), p. 170.

24. *The American Farmer*, vol. I (1819), p. 312.

25. *Ibid.*, p. 29.

26. *The Plough, the Loom and the Anvil* (Jan., 1850), pp. 444–446.

27. *The Genesee Farmer*, vol. XIV (1853), p. 45.

28. *The Agricultural Papers of George Washington* (ed. by W. E. Brook, 1919), p. 129.

29. [J. B. Bordley], *Sketches on Rotations of Crops* (1797), p. 13.

30. *Arator* (1813), p. 117.

31. *The American Farmer*, vol. II (1821), pp. 132–133.

32. *Ibid.*, p. 348.

33. *The Cultivator* (March, 1834), p. 15.

34. *The Farmers' Register*, vol. VII (1839), pp. 611–612.

35. *Prairie Farmer*, vol. XV (1865), p. 34.

36. *The Michigan Farmer*, vol. IX (1851), pp. 36, 119, 150; *Prairie Farmer*, vol. XII (1852), p. 32.

37. Henry Coleman, *The Agriculture and Rural Economy of France*, etc. (1848), p. 300.

38. T. A. Williams, Succulent Forage for the Farm and Dairy, *Yearbook of the United States Department of Agriculture, 1899* (1900), p. 622.

39. See T. G. Fessenden, *The Complete Farmer and Rural Economist* (1834), pp. 50–51.

40. John Taylor, *Arator* (1813), p. 17; cf. also p. 82.

41. See, for example, *The American Farmer*, vol. I (1819–20), pp. 57–58, 65–66, 73–74, 218, 330, 376, 414; *The Farmers' Register*, vol. I (1834), pp. 150, 423, 466, 537. These and other agricultural papers should be read critically. The editors were inclined to paint a dark picture so as to emphasise the need for their wares.

42. *The Cultivator*, vol. V (1838), pp. 39–40.

43. *The Genesee Farmer*, vol. XIV (1853), p. 299.

44. *The Plough, the Loom and the Anvil*, vol. III (Oct., 1850), p. 263; cf. *The Michigan Farmer*, vol. VIII (1850), p. 112.

45. *The Genesee Farmer*, vol. XIV (1853), pp. 119, 177.

46. *The Minnesota Monthly,* vol. I (1868), no. 1, p. 26. See also, no. 9, pp. 291–293 (1869).

47. Statistical inquiries would be of dubious assistance because of the fact that data are for census years only, and because the averages are not for fields or farms but wider areas involving both new and old lands, both new and old methods of cultivation.

48. It was claimed in 1850 that twenty-five years before guano had first been imported into Maryland. *The Plough, the Loom and the Anvil,* vol. III (1850), p. 127. Baltimore was said to have been the first port to bring it in. G. W. Howard, *The Monumental City* (1873), p. 235. Guano imports rose to 163,662 tons in 1854 and declined to 54,057 in 1858. *Hunt's Merchants' Magazine,* vol. XLI (1859), p. 645.

49. See, for example, C. W. Burkett, *History of Ohio Agriculture* (1900), pp. 70–72.

50. See above, ch. VIII, sect. 53, pp. 181–183.

51. The crops put into the silo are various, such as corn, clover, alfalfa, cowpeas, vetches, millet, sorghum. The silo is said to have been used in France and Germany before it was brought to America. The first recorded use here was about 1875. T. A. Williams, Succulent Forage for the Farm and Dairy, *Yearbook of the United States Department of Agriculture, 1899* (1900), pp. 616–617.

52. See L. H. Bailey, *Cyclopedia of American Agriculture,* vol. II (1907), pp. 99–106.

53. See L. Carrier, *The Beginnings of Agriculture in America* (1923), especially ch. XIX.

54. Jared Eliot, *Essays upon Field-Husbandry in New England* (1760), preface and p. 84.

55. Samuel Deane, *The New-England Farmer* (1790), pp. 236, 293.

56. George Logan, *Fourteen Agricultural Experiments to ascertain the Best Rotation of Crops* (1797), pp. 16, 17, 21, 23, 27.

57. Jefferson lists 54 treatises on agriculture, vine culture, and gardening. *The American Farmer,* vol. II (1821), p. 94.

58. For details of Washington's efforts as cultivator during the period 1785–1799, see *The Agricultural Papers of George Washington* (ed. by W. E. Brook, 1919), pp. 19, 22, *et passim.*

59. John Taylor, *Arator* (1813), pp. 221–222, 225.

60. See, for example, *The American Farmer,* vol. I (1819–20), pp. 132, 356–7, 365, 386; *The Plough, the Loom and the Anvil,* vol. III (1850), p. 101.

61. Oliver Fiske, *Address delivered before the Worcester Agricultural Society* (1823), p. 13. On this subject see also Daniel

Webster's address on The Agriculture of England, 1840, in his *Works* (16th ed., 1872), vol. I, pp. 449–450.

62. T. G. Fessenden, *The Complete Farmer and Rural Economist* (1834), p. IV.

63. *The Plough, the Loom and the Anvil*, vol. III (1850), pp. 623–625.

64. In 1919, a little over 96 million acres were devoted to hay and forage crops out of a total of 503 million acres of improved land in farms, that is 19%. *Fourteenth Census of the United States, Agriculture* (1922), pp. 6, 62.

65. This statement is based on census figures for the period 1880–1920, especially for the acreage devoted to hay and forage crops. Because of imperfections of census data for this particular purpose, no effort is made to analyse in detail the tabulations provided. Because of the fact that the totals include all kinds of farms, cereal farms and cattle farms, as well as farms following a balanced system, results are very inadequate.

66. See *Country Gentleman*, vol. XVI (22 Nov., 1860) ; *Farmers' Union*, vol. II (April, 1867) ; *Minnesota Monthly*, vol. I (Sept., 1869) ; *Winona Herald* (9 July, 1869) ; *Winona Weekly Republican* (1 Jan., 1868) ; *Rochester* [Minn.] *Post* (28 Dec., 1867) ; *Northwestern Farmer*, vol. VI (March, 1861).

67. See the *Joint Annual Report of the Chamber of Commerce and Board of Trade*, 1882 (Minneapolis, 1883), p. 64.

68. See H. C. Taylor, *Agricultural Economics* (1919), chs. XX–XXIII.

69. M. Kovalewski, *La France Economique et Sociale à la Veille de la Révolution*, vol. I (*Les Campagnes*, 1909), pp. 200–201.

70. *The Cultivator*, N. S., vol. VI (1849), p. 298.

71. E. D. Fite, *Social and Industrial Conditions in the North during the Civil War* (1910), pp. 17–21 ; and L. B. Schmidt, The Influence of Wheat and Cotton on Anglo-American Relations during the Civil War, *Iowa Journal of History and Politics*, vol. XVI (1918), pp. 400–439.

72. The struggle between farms of different sizes is seen in the following table.

PERCENTAGE DISTRIBUTION OF FARMS BY SIZE

Year	Under 20 acres	20–49 acres	50–99 acres	100–174 acres	175–499 acres	500–999 acres	Over 999 acres
1890	9.0	19.8	24.6	(44.0)		1.8	0.7
1900	11.7	21.9	23.8	24.8	15.1	1.8	0.8
1910	13.2	22.2	22.6	23.8	15.4	2.0	0.8
1920	12.4	23.3	22.9	22.5	15.6	2.3	1.0

STAGES IN AMERICAN AGRICULTURE

Report of the Statistics of Agriculture in the United States, Eleventh Census (1896), p. 118; *Thirteenth Census of the United States,* vol. V, *Agriculture* (1913), p. 257; *Fourteenth Census of the United States, Agriculture, Summary* (1922), p. 7.

73. See the *Fourteenth Census of the United States, Agriculture* (1922), pp. 18, 75.

74. [Anonymous] *American Husbandry* (1775), vol. I, pp. 56, 139.

75. *Ibid.,* p. 220.

76. Master's thesis, University of Minnesota, 1924, *The History of American Horticulture, 1800–1850* by H. P. Traub.

77. Table showing agricultural advance:

Year	No. of Farms	No. of Cattle	Bushels of Wheat
1850	1,449,000	17,779,000	100,486,000
1860	2,044,000	25,616,000	173,105,000
1870	2,660,000	25,484,000	235,885,000
1880	4,009,000	33,258,000	498,550,000
1890	4,565,000	52,802,000	399,262,000
1900	5,737,000	43,902,000	522,230,000
1910	6,362,000	61,803,000	635,121,000
1920	6,448,000	66,653,000	945,403,000

78. Data are available for rural and urban population, 1790–1880, inclusive, rural being confined to communities of less than 8000. Similar data exist for the period 1890–1920, inclusive, the rural district being the community having less than 2500.

79. *Fourteenth Census of the United States, Agriculture* (1923), pp. 891, 894.

80. This is a rough estimate. Foreign trade is arbitrarily omitted.

CHAPTER XIII

ANIMAL HUSBANDRY IN AMERICA

**Impor-
tance of the
subject**

92. THE EARLY HISTORY OF LIVESTOCK IN AMERICA (UP TO ABOUT 1790). We are justified in giving special attention to the subject of livestock for a variety of reasons. Animal husbandry may be and has been closely integrated with plant culture. It is the white man's peculiar contribution to agriculture in the new world. It illustrates the success that has come to Americans in the field of large-scale or mass production. It provides several types of cases illustrating agricultural specialization. And in recent times we observe great emphasis put upon livestock by leaders in agriculture, finance, and public affairs generally.

Horses

The ancients had chariot races and paid some attention to the excellence of their breeds. The Arabs have been noted for their horses, as beautiful as spirited. In the Middle Ages, in western Europe, there was some horse racing and many knightly tournaments in which temper of horse counted about as much as strength of the rider's arm. The Protestant revolution put a damper upon these as well as other sports, but revival came about in the seventeenth and eighteenth centuries in England, at the very time when Englishmen were migrating to America. Some of the racing fields gained national, even international, repute, partly for the contests that took place and partly for the social events connected with them. These were held at Newmarket since the seventeenth century, at Ascot since 1727, and at Epson (Derby races) since 1780. Although fine horses were to be found in all the American colonies, and although horse racing took place from New York State southward, it was in Virginia and Kentucky that most progress was made in the breeding of fast horses. Such notables as

312

Washington, Jefferson, John Randolph, and Henry Clay were patrons of the turf.   It was to England that horse breeders, fanciers, and owners of good stock looked for the best animals.

Cattle generally came from the same countries as the set- **Cattle** tlers.   French Canadians brought with them a race that became hardy and distinct, the well-known "Canadian Jerseys."   Virginians and then New Englanders brought in their undistinguished cows and bulls in the early seventeenth century.   The Dutch probably imported Frisian cattle, but of what quality **1623** we cannot now discover.   Delaware may have been stocked **1627 f.** with Swedish cattle.   Into the far south, and the southwest, Spanish cattle were early introduced,[1] some to escape to the **About 1540** plains and there, like the "buffaloes," to breed indiscriminately and develop qualities that made them better for beef than for milk.   From the same source came many of the horses that roamed the prairies and yielded their backs to the Redskins. The effective use of these hardy animals was clear evidence of the capacity of the North American Indians to advance, though slowly, from the condition of mere nomads to the higher state of mounted nomads.

Livestock in America up to 1790, and for some time there- **General** after, was largely nondescript, especially on the frontiers.   A **conditions** few fine specimens of horses and cattle existed, but generally speaking, the animals were more valuable for their hides and their fat than for anything else.   The cows gave a little milk and when aged could be eaten.   The pigs went about rooting and feeding in woodland and waste.   Often the owner could capture them only with a gun, so fleet were the long-legged razor-backed creatures.   Numerous as were these various kinds of animals, nevertheless, they did not constitute as important a source of food as did the cereals, except in some frontier districts.   Observers agree that the livestock was treated with inhuman neglect, partly an inheritance from Europe and partly a necessity of the times and circumstances.   Even as late as the 1870's it was necessary for the Grange to encourage careful treatment of livestock.   But little special fodder was grown for animals, and shelter was either inadequate or non-existent.[1a] Stagnation or degeneration was inevitable.

Livestock frontier   Even in the early part of the seventeenth century there was a special frontier for the use of livestock. Islands along the Atlantic, or peninsulas fenced off, were set aside for swine and sheep, both in Rhode Island [2] and in the south. Surrounded wholly or largely by water, the animals were unable to escape and could be easily rounded up and captured. Then on the western fringes of the colonies there were stretches where animals, escaped [3] or herded, were pastured somewhat apart from the general business of farming. Such extensive animal culture spread westward, till to-day the fringe is on the waning range and the threatened ranch. But this frontier, on the arid stretch from Texas to Montana, is stocked with fine animals, pure-bred or graded, flocks of merinos and herds of Herefords. The old frontier animal, however, survives in the south to-day where bacon hogs roam around rooting for themselves, costing their owner little, and supplying a prime article of diet for consumption on the farm. They are virtually the razor-backs of past centuries. [4]

Use of livestock   Most of the livestock was consumed on the farms where raised. This applies to the wool and hides as well as to the flesh and dairy products. Hides, tallow, and fat could, indeed, be exported. Both beef and pork in barrels were sent abroad **1770** but not in large amounts. Just before the Revolution a little less than 29,000 barrels of both beef and pork were exported **1791** in one year; somewhat later about 90,000 barrels were disposed of in this way. [5] Of course, we must remember the great aid that horses and oxen gave in the cultivation of the fields, in hauling goods of all kinds, and in transporting passengers, characteristically the families of settlers moving westward.

Breeding in Europe   93. LATER HISTORY OF LIVESTOCK (SINCE 1790): IMPROVEMENT OF THE BREEDS. In giving special attention to horses and neglecting other animals, Americans were merely following European practices. Englishmen, however, began to correct their careless ways in the eighteenth century; while Americans did almost nothing to reform their practices till the following century. Until the time of Robert Bakewell, [6] even in England, the careful breeding of cattle and sheep had been virtually unknown. It is said that men had formerly regarded incestuous breeding of animals with abhorrence. Little attention had been given to types, although these had grown up on islands (such as Jersey and Guernsey) and in isolated districts of the mainland (such as Switzerland and Frisia). The old-time cattle in England had been white, long horned, long haired, and with medium or small bodies. Some of these remain as curiosities, their places having been taken by locally developed or man-made breeds. Once a good breed was determined, that is, positive inheritable characteristics observed, the aim was to breed true to type. This kind was notable for flesh, that for milk. This was a good wool producer, that better for mutton. Accordingly, anyone wanting a specific kind of animal could be reasonably sure of being satisfied. In breeding, the usual practice has been to choose individuals with the desired qualities as sire and dam. But now there is a tendency to breed from pedigree, because in this way one knows not only the parentage but the family history. What counts is not simply the parents but the whole line of ancestors which will reproduce themselves in the offspring.

The men who have been responsible for the creation, improvement, or popularizing of the breeds are very numerous both in England and America. In England Robert Bakewell, already mentioned, the Collings brothers, Thomas Bates, and Amos Cruickshank were prominent. In America the breeders are somewhat different. It is not so much the task of American breeders to create or markedly to improve as it is to import European stock and to popularize by advertising or by forming associations for the maintenance of pedigrees or records of production. They constitute just one set of specialists, on whom the others depend directly or indirectly for their best stock, whether it be livestock men generally, the grazers, the feeders, the drovers or the local butchers, packers, commission men, or dealers in agricultural credit. There are at least two classes of breeders, as distinct from mere cattle raisers. There is the gentleman breeder who has gained wealth in some other walk of life, such as Colonel E. H. Taylor, a Kentucky distiller, or J. J. Hill, the railroad magnate of the northwest.

Characteristics of the breeders

Such people assemble magnificent specimens and house them princely. They do some fine breeding and capture many prizes. And yet they are not the typical breeders who make their living, or part of it, from animal husbandry. The professional breeders are themselves not only lovers of animals, but they have personal knowledge of handling the stock. They have patience and persistence. They have capital and business ability. They believe in the line of stock they handle, and advertise their brands with enthusiasm and conviction. They seek to persuade others that their breeds are best; and at all times they endeavor to keep up prices. Commonly they sell their stock to others at a distance, their immediate neighbors being often ignorant of good stock or indifferent to pure breeds. There is much merit in their work, seldom downright dishonesty, but, according to farmers, there is a good deal of buncombe in their claims. Sometimes these breeders handle only one kind of animal, but often they advertise various kinds, such as shorthorn cattle, Poland-China hogs, and Cotswold sheep.[7]

Some American breeders 1752–1818 1801 We may note some of the facts about the lives of a few of these breeders. David Humphreys was one of the first. Soldier, statesman, and author, he is of interest to us chiefly for the importation of merino sheep for the production of fine wool. In his home state of Connecticut, he established a woolen mill, thereby becoming a pioneer in manufacture as well as in the raising of fine sheep.[8] Stephen Atwood was also **1785–1867** a citizen of Connecticut and a breeder of merinos. Indeed he purchased stock from Humphreys, but was in a few years **1813** able to build up his own flock without drawing further upon the importations of other men. Although he had neither a large farm nor a large flock, he was able by care and selection to bring his sheep to such a high degree of perfection that, after his death, owners of his breed in Vermont formed a **1819–67** sheep club bearing his name.[9] R. A. Alexander was born in Kentucky of Scotch parents. He was educated in Scotland where he inherited an estate. Returning to America, he **1853** bought a farm and imported shorthorn cattle. Some famous individual shorthorns graced his herd. True to the interests

of his native state, he bred horses, both for running and trotting.[10]   W. B. Montgomery, educated at Princeton, entered   1829–1904
agriculture after some experience in business.   In the state
of Mississippi he played an important part in the introduction,
not only of new grasses for hay and pasture but of Jersey
cattle which have become so popular in the south.   Among his
many contributions was the establishment of the *Southern Live
Stock Journal.*[11]   In the northwest Colonel W. S. King, jour-   1828–1900
nalist and congressman, was a prominent local figure with something of a national reputation.   He had a farm of 1200 acres
now in the city of Minneapolis.   His shorthorn and Ayrshire
cattle, from imported stock, were sold at auctions attended by
breeders from many states.[12]   Because of elaborate expenditure, and possibly also because of little local demand for his
animals, he was forced to give up his business.   Solomon Hoxie   1829–1917
of New York State was one of the first importers of pure-bred
Holstein cattle.   An authority on cattle breeding and the com-
piler of many volumes of herdbooks and registers of Holstein
cattle, he claimed to be the originator of the first "system for
registering dairy cattle on the basis of product."[13]   Such
were a few of the leading breeders in America.   None of them
compare in reputation with their English predecessors.   In general, one can say about American breeders that they have
been very numerous and exceedingly active.   They have succeeded in handling many animals, occasionally the finest being
sent to England for further breeding; they have sold individuals
at enormous prices; and they have succeeded in establishing
records, especially in milk production, that challenge duplica-
tion abroad.

The first period of importations of pure livestock immedi-   **Beginning**
ately followed the Revolutionary War, and lasted until the   **of pure**
struggle in Europe and on the sea had made shipments difficult.   **breeds in**
It would be an easy and a tempting generalization to make,   **America,**
1783–1803
that the newly enfranchised nation sought to emancipate itself
from inferior farm animals.   Since the middle of the eighteenth
century England had been making progress in breeding; and if
war had not broken out in 1776, doubtless English and other
animals would have been brought over even before 1783.

1783, 1785   Shorthorn cattle from England seem to have been the first to have been imported. They went to Baltimore, to Virginia,

1792, 1796   and then to Kentucky. New York State was apparently the next to import. Another stream of animals were merino sheep,

1793   chiefly from Spain. A Boston man imported three of them and presented them to a Cambridge friend who, not knowing their value, ate them as mutton.[14] During the next decade isolated lots of these sheep were brought over for breeding. In Connecticut and New York they made considerable headway; then in Vermont they became an important part of the husbandry of the people. Massachusetts and the other New England states were not far behind. Soon the movement of these sheep started westward with the general migration.

Second period, 1817–37   The second period of importations, also covering about a score of years, followed the war of 1812–15. Massachusetts and especially New York State, Kentucky, and Ohio were prominent importers of sheep and shorthorn cattle. During

1823, 1832   this period the chief foreign breed of swine, the Berkshire, was being imported, and the American brands, Poland-China, Chester-White, and Duroc-Jersey, had either just been developed or were under way. The climax of the period was prob-

1834–36   ably reached in the activities of the Ohio Importing Company which not only sent for fine English stock but, in selling its cattle, aided in the spread of good animals southward and westward.

Third period, 1837–49   Following the crisis of 1837 there was a slackening in importations, which lasted some time. But the movement of cattle, sheep, and hogs continued from the Ohio valley to the

1839   south and the west. Shorthorn cattle moved from Ohio to Missouri. The fairs of the latter state still exhibited scrub cattle but also some grade and pure-bred stock.[15] During

1846   this period America saw its first herdbook—for shorthorns.[16] In such a book cows and bulls of pure breed are given a number and their pedigree set forth.

Fourth period, 1849–61   The next few years constituted a period of spread. Americans spread their interest over various kinds of cattle: Jerseys, Herefords, Ayrshires, Galloways, and Devons, practically all the important breeds except Holsteins, were imported.

ANIMAL HUSBANDRY IN AMERICA

Animals of all kinds spread westward, reaching even California. Ships brought to that state merino sheep and shorthorn cattle.

Although we are too near to the times to have any final judgment, it seems that the two decades following the Civil War constitute the golden age of animal husbandry in America. During this period [17] cattle increased from about twenty-five millions to about forty-five millions; horses from about eight millions to about twelve millions; sheep from over forty millions to over forty-eight millions; swine from nearly twenty-seven millions to about forty-six millions. Population grew rapidly, but animal husbandry kept pace with it. During the middle part of the period there was a tremendous boom of shorthorns,[18] such as has not been witnessed since. The range then had its innings, and Hereford cattle became famous for their beef. Exports [19] abroad showed a fair promise of a considerable future. Silos were adopted, and with them came better feeding and better stock. Refrigerator cars came in to help the meat industry. Cheese factories and to some extent creameries increased, and farm production of cheese and butter was threatened with ultimate extinction. Dairying became more highly specialized. Livestock journals came into existence, the *National Live-Stock Journal* in 1870, *Hoard's Dairyman* in 1870, and *Breeders' Gazette* in 1881, all still being published.[20] The father of livestock journalism in America is said to be J. H. Sanders who is thought (perhaps erroneously) to have established "the first livestock paper ever published." Certainly he was prominent even dominant in the affairs of the first and third of the three journals mentioned above. He had been a teacher, office holder, and later a banker in Iowa. Two of his books were once standard textbooks, *Horse Breeding* and *The Breeds of Live Stock*.[21] The period with which we are dealing saw published herdbooks for Holsteins (1872), Herefords (1880), Galloways (1883), Guernseys (1884), Jerseys (1886), and Dutch belted cattle (1886); also the *American Stud Book* (1868); a flock book for merinos (1882) and the *National Pig Breeders' Herd Book* (1885). Before the end of the period there was an associa-

Fifth period, 1866-86

1874-76

1877-86

1873-75

1868 f.

319

tion for the *Advance Registry of Holstein-Friesian Cattle.*
Such associations were to keep records of performances, notably of milk production and butterfat output of the chief
breeds of cattle.

Much remained to be done after this golden age had passed.
Livestock have spread to the north where wheat has been
king, and to the south where cotton has reigned supreme.
Great improvements have taken place in the transportation
of animals, in meat packing, and in dairying. Diseases have
had to be studied and overcome. Nutrition has remained as
a subject of investigation and experiment. The whole problem
of breeding has had to be taken up for scientific consideration.

In noting the various periods in the history of animal husbandry we have had occasion to observe considerable progress,
particularly in the cattle industry. The background of the
whole story of cattle in America is, of course, the original
scrub stock of the colonial period. Just how good or how bad
that stock was, we do not know, but it is reasonable to believe
that it was much like the Texas steer so famous two generations
ago. Its horns were long, its body lank, its face surly, its
color as diverse as the strains from which it sprang. A Wisconsin man asked the question whether there was one farmer
in a hundred in the western states, who could tell what breed
of cattle he was raising.[22] There is no question that to-day,
in both the United States and Canada, there are many farmers
who could not name their breeds. Indeed no specialist could
be sure of all the breeds represented in one scrub cow. Higher
in the scale of excellence are the grade or common cattle.
Usually these have pure-bred sires. Then there are the pure
breeds themselves, at least seventeen in number, which constitute probably less than 5% of the total cattle in America. At
the latest census it appeared that less than 3% of the dairy
cattle was pure bred registered stock.[23] The great advantage
in pure bred stock is that each breed has its own qualities and
commonly perpetuates them. The shorthorn cattle are a hardy
race, good for beef and for dairy pupuses. They have spread
to every part of America from ocean to ocean. The Jersey

1885

**Period
since 1886**

**Breeds of
cattle in
America**

1857

1924

1920

320

is a dairy cow producing rich milk. The Holstein, large in body, black and white, yields more milk by far, but that milk is paler in color, in other words contains less butterfat. Just as the Jerseys and the Holsteins have tended to replace the shorthorns for dairying, so have the Herefords replaced them for beef purposes. Not only do the Herefords yield the best beef, the beautifully marbled steaks so succulent and tender, but they have the best rustling or herding capacity.

Location of breeds

Different parts of the country have different preferences. Shorthorns are most numerous in the north central districts, where they stand the cold very well. Holsteins are largely confined to the northern section east of the Mississippi and on to the Atlantic, where dairying is important. Jerseys are most popular in the south, where the family cow is a prominent feature. Herefords are chiefly west of the Mississippi, where ranching prevails. Nondescript cattle are most numerous in the south.[24] In general, one can say that there are two cattle areas in America. The American beef belt runs east and west, from the Atlantic coast between central North Carolina and central New York State, and westward to the dry country. It includes Iowa and Illinois. Here fattening requires little time, the marbling of flesh is good, and the economy of feeding greater than either to the north or south.[25] In this area cattle are kept on farms and fed a variety of food. Animal husbandry is integrated with general agriculture. The other area, the cow country, runs north and south, from Texas north to the Canadian boundary. Animal husbandry here is much more "extensive" than elsewhere in America. At first the cattle roamed on the free range, then on the leased range, and now on specific ranches, often fenced, with well defined areas and definite shelters and watering places. Here in the land of hot summers and cold winters the cattle find various nourishing grasses, shelters from the wind and snow storms, and always dryness which keeps down certain diseases and eliminates others.

Other animals

Of horses and swine, something will be said below.[26] America has developed no sheep of its own, but its experiences have been interesting. Sheep moved westward with the settlers, and on the ranges vast flocks of merinos were established. The owners of these flocks had to fight the cattle men and only in recent times have been victorious. Enormous numbers feed on apparently barren lands in Utah and adjoining states. For a long time the merino held sway. Its wool was fine, though short, and it was a good traveller and remained close to the flock. Its flesh, however, was not so good as its wool; in fact, it was said to have a bad odor.[27] Partly because of the increased demand for mutton in the towns and partly because of the lack of long medium wools, the English sheep have come in as rivals of the merinos.[28] In America the goat is a joke. In Europe and Asia it is an asset. Long

About 1750 ago it was remarked that goats were kept in America only in towns to provide milk for sick people.[29] Perhaps the reasons why goats are scarce in America are that they had never been popular in England and that now a good goat costs about as much as a cow. To-day about one half of them are in Texas where they graze with cattle and sheep.[30] They seem to promise much not only for the mohair and the skins that they provide but for the milk which is more digestible for infants than cows' milk, and is said to be freer from disease. Many of them could be kept in small towns and in the suburbs of large cities. Because of their browsing habits, they are inexpensive feeders.

Alleged disadvantages of animal husbandry 94. IMPORTANCE OF LIVESTOCK FOR AMERICAN AGRICULTURE IN GENERAL. The objections to animal husbandry have been numerous. Clearly many farmers, having to rely upon their own family labor, see in animals one unending round of work. The cows must be milked early and in the evening. They must be groomed and the stables cleaned. The feed must be stored and prepared, if the best results are to be obtained. At the season of calving, lambing, and littering, the animals must be watched, often at night, to prevent loss. Disease must be fought, and epidemics faced. Hog cholera is a con-

Since 1870 stant menace, and the foot-and-mouth disease has periodically levied its toll in America up to the present day. It is hard for the farmer-owner to raise sufficient capital to buy good stock; it is commonly beyond the tenant farmer in America.

ANIMAL HUSBANDRY IN AMERICA

In spite of the difficulties, animals are necessary for general farming. In the past they have provided the necessary motor power. Horses, mules, and oxen still play a vital part, though the tractor, truck, and combination of service and pleasure motor car are making rapid strides as rivals. **Animals as motor power**

The loss of even the above-mentioned animals from the standpoint of fertilizers will be great. Animal manure has chemical, physical, and bacteriological qualities not found in commercial fertilizers. Some ameliorating crops are used only or chiefly by animals. This is true of clover and pulse. Indian corn has an enormous yield in grain and stock. It is invaluable for cattle and swine. And it keeps the soil in good condition, partly because of the cultivation it receives and partly because its vigorous growth helps to keep down the weeds. **Animals and condition of the soil**

Although animal husbandry sorely taxes the strength of the single-handed cultivator and his wife, it provides certain labor advantages under other conditions. The farmer's children can be utilized with profit to themselves and to society, up to a certain point. They can be interested in chickens, calves, lambs, and cows and can provide part of the labor required to tend them. A hired man can often be employed the year round when there are animals to be tended, because then there is work enough and there is income enough to pay his wages and something over for the farmer.[31] All this presupposes, however, that the farmer is a capable manager, something more than a laborer himself. Improved methods of feeding animals and handling manure lighten the labor burden. Much economy is possible if the farmer is ingenious and inventive. **Animals and labor**

There is a good deal of roughage available on the average farm that only animals can utilize. Some lands are good only for rough pasture. Cows may eat the grass and goats browse on the leaves of bushes. Forests provide valuable food for hogs. There is also spoiled grain unfit for man but excellent for cattle and hogs. There is refuse from the house which is valuable for swine. **Animals use roughage**

It is sometimes more profitable to market crops in the form of animals than to sell the crops directly. In the days be- **Animals and marketing** fore the railroads, cattle and hogs could be marketed on foot, while the corn and hay they ate could not be sold at all, at least not in the backwoods part of the country. Even after the railroads were in operation, the marketing of grain was neither smooth nor profitable at certain times, while hog raising was more certain and more lucrative.[32] Of course, it is an insurance against the uncertainty of the market, to have two cash "crops," one grain or cotton, the other cattle or hogs or sheep, because the chances are that, barring general business depressions, the prices of all will not go down together to the same extent. In the time of depression, however, animals and grains are both low. The farmer often has to sell pure-bred stock at butchers' prices in order to pay the debts he has accumulated. The wise far-seeing farmer should at such times provide himself with stock, buying even aged bulls and cows, so as to build up his herd.[33] By the same token he should be able to hold his own livestock till a better market comes along, all of which, however, is easier to assert than to accomplish.

Early meat packing

95. THE MEAT INDUSTRY. In early times, in Europe and America, the farmer was his own butcher and packer. To-day he less commonly slaughters and preserves hogs for his own use, for he often buys from the local butcher to whom he sells at least part of his livestock. Most of the animals, especially the better ones, are now sold, in the north at least, for slaughtering and packing in the specialized plants in large centers.[34]

Packers and packing centers 1660's

1818

1840

The first American packer, it is said, was William Pynchon of Springfield, Mass. First a drover of cattle, he came to pack hogs for export, especially to the West Indies.[35] Doubtless local specialized packers grew up here and there in various eastern American cities. The first regular packer in the west is said to have been Elisha Mills of Cincinnati, Ohio.[36] Soon Cincinnati was called "Porkopolis." But Chicago and St. Louis were fast becoming its rivals. Chicago took first place during the Civil War. Beef then came to occupy a position of prominence alongside of pork. Gradually new centers at Kansas City, Omaha, and St. Paul arose. Five large packing firms with headquarters at Chicago, however, came to dominate the packing industry in America.

To-day cattle grown in the middle west are sent to Chicago or elsewhere, there slaughtered and dressed, and then sent back to the district of production for final consumption. It seems a waste in transportation and so it is, but there are compensations. The large packing plant, such as Swift's and Armour's, can introduce economies that the local butcher, or even a moderate-sized plant locally situated, cannot attain. Prominent among these is the use of what was once called offal, now called byproducts. The bladders are sold as commercial containers. The hair of a steer's ear is sold for artists' brushes, the tail hair for upholstering, and the body hair for plastering. The glands and gall bag provide pharmaceutical goods, such as medicines and perfumes. The hoofs are valuable for making combs and buttons. The sinews are made into glue. Bones generally, not otherwise used, are valuable as fertilizers.[37] Thus there is a minimum of loss in each animal. Most people would probably be more concerned with the fact that concentration of slaughtering and packing has made government inspection practical. For many years federal meat inspectors have carefully passed on all the animals handled in these large establishments. Every year the government spends vast sums for this service, and every year it publishes statistics of animals condemned in whole or in part. It is not flattering to be told that this system of inspection was instituted, not to protect American consumers from diseased wares but to meet the objections of foreigners to American meat products; in other words, to capture a foreign market.[38]

The packers have been efficient and have reached out to control all parts of production and distribution that might bring them gain. On the one hand, they have owned stockyards where, the farmers alleged, they took undue advantage in buying livestock. On the other hand, they went beyond the handling of meat, meat products, butter, eggs, cheese, and poultry. They have even sold canned fruit and vegetables, tea, coffee, sugar, cereals, and other products, thereby incurring

Advantages of centralized packing

Acts of 1890, 1906

Position of the packers

1920

1906 f.

1919 f.

the wrath of the wholesale grocers. But they have agreed to draw back into their narrower field, and for the time at least opposition seems to have subsided. There is an American Meat Packers' Association, and also an Institute of American Meat Packers. These are charged with the duty of advancing the interests of the packers. The Institute is to study all questions of foreign and domestic trade, economies in production, loss in transportation, and the mastery of animal diseases which plague the packers as well as the farmers and ranchers. In the advertising campaigns that the packers carry on, both directly and indirectly, for the consumption of more meat, they are, of course, benefiting the farmer as well as themselves.

Use of meat and meat products

The consumption of mutton in America is only about 3 to 5% of the total meat consumed. There is a race only between beef and pork, sometimes beef reaching the point of 50% of the total, sometimes pork. Although America consumes an overwhelmingly large proportion of the total amount of meat leaving the slaughter house, about 95% just before the War and about 90% during the period 1917–21, nevertheless the

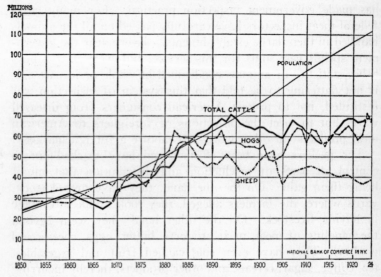

LIVE STOCK SUPPLY AND TREND OF POPULATION IN THE UNITED STATES, 1850 TO 1923.

326

amount exported is considerable. It made its phenomenal increases in the 1870's and again during the late War.[39] Although the export of live cattle began in the 1870's, the number never became very great, and in recent years imports have exceeded exports. This has been notably true of sheep. With hogs it has been different and may continue so for some time. But gradually, and many think inevitably, America is going to be compelled to rely upon foreign countries, such as Argentina, Australia, New Zealand, and Canada, for much of its meat supply, either dressed or on the hoof.

96. DAIRYING IN AMERICA. The dairying and meat industries supplement one another in a very essential way. Aged milch cows have to be sold for beef. Poor milkers must go to the shambles. All but a few of the males go to the beef market as calves or steers. In the making of oleomargarine, beef-fat and milk and cream are churned together, thus linking the two industries. The simple fact is that slaughtering animals for meat makes successful dairying possible. The full meaning of this is better appreciated when we remember conditions in India where Hindu religious sentiment is against the killing of cattle. Accordingly, old cows and males must be kept until they die. In times of fodder shortage all animals, both good and bad, suffer greatly. Careful breeding is very difficult. In general, the cattle of India are useful for draught purposes and to a much less extent for milk which is astonishingly and pitifully meagre in amount.[40] Some in America would regard the dairy industry as the master craft in animal husbandry. A larger yield per unit of food comes from the milking cow than from a cow fed for beef. Dairying uses the products of the animal, while the meat industry consumes the source of the product. Much of the cow's yield requires little preparation for consumption, that is, when the milk is consumed as such rather than in the form of butter, cheese, or condensed milk.

Dairying and meat industry

Two classes of producers dispute the dairy field. There is the small farmer who has a few cows, utilizes the slack or available labor on his estate, and depends to a greater or less extent upon roughage for fodder, roughage which would

Two kinds of milk producers

otherwise be largely waste. Such a producer only slowly appreciates the value of good breeds and almost reluctantly learns habits of cleanliness. The other type is the specialized dairyman who has virtually no source of income, except from milk. Ordinarily he has more cows than the general farmer, must hire laborers, especially for milking, and has either to produce by special effort, or to buy, the fodder that his cows require. The best of such producers fully appreciate the value of good milking breeds and develop exemplary habits of cleanliness. Although much more efficient producers of milk in many ways than the general farmer, this class is often hard put to it to compete with him because of the special expenses incurred.

Location of dairying

1839

1919

1920

Dairying is found to a greater or less extent practically everywhere in America. But it has had pre-eminent development in certain parts. In the early part of last century the dairying belt extended from New England to Maryland, while now it comprises this territory and much of the district westward to the Missouri river.[41] The premier part of it includes New York State, Pennsylvania, Ohio, Michigan, Illinois, Wisconsin, Iowa, and Minnesota. Thus, from the Atlantic westward the only break is Indiana. At the last census, Wisconsin showed itself clearly the leading dairy state, with New York as second. Wisconsin leads for condensed milk, with New York again as a close second. For cheese Wisconsin is so far ahead that there really is no second place. Minnesota leads for butter, with Wisconsin and Iowa following. Three factors stand out prominently in making a district good for dairying: plenty of moisture for pasture and hay, the deterioration of the land for grain production, and the growth of large towns and cities with good transportation connections.

Early period of improvement, 1860-90

1875

Up to the Civil War there had been but little progress in dairying. Centuries had gone by in Europe and America and yet the traditional methods and the old stagnation remained. But during and particularly after the Civil War, changes took place. Cheese factories began to multiply, and creameries and condensed-milk factories [42] got under way. Better transportation was provided, especially when refrigerator cars were made available. State dairy associations were established first in

Vermont (1869), then in New York (1871),[43] Illinois (1874), and Minnesota (1877). *Hoard's Dairyman,* a journal devoted to the industry, was started in Wisconsin, where it has remained. On the whole, most promise is observed in the manufacture of cheese in factories, and least in the making of butter which was still overwhelmingly a product of household industry.

1870

Since 1890 progress has been chiefly in milk preparation and in butter making. Machines have revolutionized the dairy business. The first to be noted is the separator, worked by hand. The old way of separating cream from milk was by allowing the former to rise gradually to the top in wide shallow pans. The new way was to put the fresh milk into the machine and turn the crank. Henceforth there was no delay in waiting and less labor involved. There was less loss of cream. The skimmed milk was in better condition for use. The butter made out of such cream was better, because there was less loss of time between milking and churning. The separator is really a foreign invention (1877), but came to be widely used in America. In recent years separators made in America have been in some demand abroad. The second improvement is not so much a machine as a method, though a simple hand machine is indeed involved. This is the Babcock test,[44] the use of which spread soon after the invention, till now foreign nations have adopted it as well as America. It is but one of about a dozen available tests but very simple and effective. The apparatus (hand machine, test tubes, etc.) costs but little and the time required to operate it is short.[45] The advantage is that the exact amount of butter fat in either milk or cream can now be determined. Formerly the common practice had been to sell according to the *quantity* of cream; henceforth it has been according to the *quality* or butter-fat content of the cream. The result is that an unprecedented emphasis has been put upon individual cows and breeds that yield quality rather than quantity of milk—that is, for butter purposes. The milking machine has been on the horizon of possibilities in America and Canada for a long time. Its use is spreading as the apparatus is perfected. For medium-sized

Later period, 1890-present

Machinery

About 1890 f.

1890 f.

329

and large dairies it is an effective device for saving labor and for increasing cleanliness. Although America uses nearly all the machines that it makes, it actually does export a few. Machinery and processes for condensing milk go back a long way. One American patented the process and another introduced it into Europe (Switzerland). The first American factory was established in Connecticut, but recently the chief manufacturing states have been Wisconsin, New York, and Pennsylvania. Other machines of great service in the dairying business and of recent application are gas motors for providing water, machines for carrying in fodder and carrying out manure, and, of course, motor trucks for delivering the milk and cream.

Although the best American butter compares very favorably with the best produced elsewhere, it has long been difficult to procure high quality in America outside the dairy belt. This has been owing to the fact that so much of it has been made in the homes of farmers rather than in factories. Careless, unclean practices have prevailed to such an extent that in the past the fastidious townsman has often had to bargain with clean farmers for a supply, and has had sometimes to drive long distances to meet his current needs. In recent years but little butter has been made on the farm, except in the Mississippi Valley and in the south Atlantic states. We may expect to see butter-making leave the farm in the near future,[46] as cheese-making did in the immediate past, though perhaps not so completely. The increase in the amount of milk produced and in the amount of the derived products, butter, cheese, and especially condensed milk made in factories,[47] has been enormous within the last generation. The increase has come through the milking of more cows, the improvement of the breeds, the perfection of feeding, and the elimination of inefficient cows.[48] Such elimination has been made possible by cow testing. Since about 1905 there have been cow-testing societies in America, following the practice developed in Denmark. Already we find that, while the average of the American dairy cow is about 4,000 pounds of milk a year, the average

330

for the 40,000 cows in cow-testing associations is almost 6,000 pounds.[49] With the increased production, has gone greater cleanliness. This has been made possible by pasteurizing, bottling, the elimination of diseased animals, and the introduction of sanitary practices in the stables. The acme has been reached, some think, in the certified milk so eagerly purchased by fond mothers with ample or even moderate incomes. The low bacterial count of this milk has been made possible by the following of strict rules of cleanliness in the dairy, rules originally worked out by a committee of physicians in a New Jersey county.[50] Other improvements may be expected, especially if the plan to establish a Dairy Institute is put through.

1893

The consumption of milk in America is not high relatively, since America ranks sixth among nations in *per capita* use. But consumption is increasing, certified milk for babies, ordinary milk for children and athletes, fancy milk drinks and ice cream for all, and condensed and powdered milk for the explorer and camper. American cheese of the ordinary sort is liked by workingmen abroad. Some American imitations of foreign brands are highly thought of at home. The fact that Americans rank as ninth among cheese consuming nations [51] is no accident. Butter is more popular than cheese in America. But as the price of butter rises, the consumption of the substitute, oleomargarine, increases. The consumption of condensed milk grows somewhat at the expense of fresh milk. The east seems to get the best butter and cheese, much of which is made in the west. The poor, particularly in the towns and cities, use little milk, know only the cheapest cheese, and color their own oleomargarine. The rich enjoy fresh milk and cream, the finer American or imported cheese, and creamery butter. These things belong more to distribution than to production, but they seem to be facts in the general dairy situation. The poor man has in truth lost his cow; it was an inferior beast, but it gave him butter and his children milk. Now America has wonderful cows, some worth a fortune, with plenty of milk for condensing, evaporating, and powdering.

The General dairy situation

Government aid
1897
1906
1873, 1906
1921

1913–21

The people's part

1915

Animal aristocracy

97. AMERICAN ATTAINMENTS IN ANIMAL HUSBANDRY.
The federal government first inspected all meat exported and
then all meat entering into interstate trade. It does much to
keep down and to eradicate animal diseases. It has laws providing for feeding, watering, and resting animals being transported on the railroads.[52] It co-operates with 3,243 livestock
owners in an educational movement to improve breeds. It has
seemed to protect by tariff American cheese since 1789, and
American butter, butter substitutes, and condensed milk since
1861, except for one short period. Imported raw milk, though
taxed at times, has hardly been concerned with a protective
tariff. The farmer can complain only of the fact that the protection has not been as high as it might have been.

Americans have produced three breeds of lard hogs, the
Chester-Whites, the Poland-Chinas, and the Duroc-Jerseys.
They have to their credit Plymouth Rock and Rhode Island
Red chickens. The American trotter has an international
reputation, deriving high qualities from the English thorough-
bred as the latter did from the Arab steed. The world record
of milk production is said to have been made by an American
Holstein cow. Generally speaking, American contributions are
not so striking as American utilization. This is as we should
expect. America has been so busy learning animal husbandry
that it has had too little time to go beyond its inheritances
from Europe. That it has done something, however, this
chapter at various points amply testifies.

Americans are prejudiced against kings and aristocrats.
But the animal aristocrats of Europe have been given an exceptional place. America has had its duchesses, and lady this
and lady that. And their milk records are carefully set down.
The herdbooks are genealogies. The advanced-record registers are chronicles of noble knights and fair ladies. There
are state and national patriotic societies that discuss importations of pure-bred stock. There are immigration restriction
laws against diseased animals. Everywhere there is a battle
of standards. There are disputes as to which are the aristocrats, Spanish or other merinos. The pure-bred shorthorns
must have crossed in a ship, and must have had at least seven

generations of recorded blood before embarking.[53]   On the whole, Americans have chosen the superior aristocracy: it has something real to show, fine lines, attractive color, milking qualities, eating qualities, gentility.   Perhaps the chief fault arises out of our lack of sufficient knowledge of eugenics to prevent degeneration or extinction.   Animal, like human, blue-bloods tend to disappear.   The one widely recognized American breed, the Poland-China hog, is degenerating and is likely to die out.   Thus do animal kingdoms fall.

98. Suggestions for Further Study

1. Read the section on Meats and Related Products in L. H. Bailey, *Cyclopedia of Agriculture,* vol. III (1908), pp. 246–272.

2. What are the interests and contributions of the Bureau of Animal Husbandry?   Write to the Bureau or consult E. Wiest, *Agricultural Organization in the United States* (1923).

3. Investigate the work done in animal husbandry in your state agricultural college.

4. Which American agricultural college has been outstanding in the east; which in the west?

5. Read the article on Dairy and Dairy Farming, in the *Encyclopædia Britannica* (11th ed.).

6. Read on the subject of dairying, L. H. Bailey, *Cyclopedia of Agriculture,* vol. III (1908), pp. 175–246.

7. For the dairy industry, see C. H. Eckles, *Dairy Cattle and Milk Production* (1911), and R. M. Washburn, *Productive Dairying* (1917).

8. If interested in the ranch and the range, study the work by B. Youngblood and A. B. Cox, entitled *An Economic Study of a Typical Ranching Area on the Edwards Plateau of Texas* (Texas Agriculture Experiment Station Bulletin no. 297, 1922).

9. Learn the names and peculiarities of the leading breeds of cattle in America.   Which would you prefer for a family cow in a small town?

10. For a mine of information, see the *Report of the Federal Trade Commission on the Meat-Packing Industry,* parts I-IV and summary (1919–20).

11. Is the dairy business of your district based largely on pasturing or on soiling (feeding fodder in enclosures and stables)?

12. What are the chief qualities and attainments of a good live-stock man?

13. Why do farmers hesitate before embarking on animal husbandry jointly with their field culture?

14. What breed of cattle is dominant in your state? Why is it so favored?

15. What would be the advantages in having only one pure-bred line of livestock in each district?

16. What are cow-testing associations? How many of them are there in operation in your state?

17. What was happening in animal husbandry in the following parts and at the following times, in New England, 1820–40; Ohio, 1830–60; Texas, 1850–90; Wisconsin, 1870–present; Iowa, 1880–present; Minnesota, 1900–present; and the south, 1915–present?

18. In what part of America is animal husbandry making most progress to-day?

19. What factors have determined the course of animal husbandry in America?

20. The special contribution of the Arabs is horses, of the Spaniards sheep, and of the English cattle. What comparable contribution has America made?

21. Why has America lost relatively and absolutely in the business of sheep raising?

22. Do you expect to see over-production in meat and dairy products in America? What will tend to offset it?

For further references, see the notes below.

99. Notes to Chapter XIII

1. See Charles L. Flint, Progress in Agriculture, *Eighty Years' Progress of the United States* (1864), pp. 37–38.

1ª. On this subject, see the anonymous *American Husbandry* (1775), vol. I, pp. 78–79, 80, 167, 351.

2. L. Carrier, *The Beginnings of Agriculture in America* (1923), pp. 146, 191.

3. See Peter Kalm, *Travels into North America* (about 1750, translation 1771), vol. I, pp. 60–62.

4. *United States Department of Agriculture Yearbook, 1922* (1923), p. 206.

5. T. Pitkin, *A Statistical View of the Commerce of the United States of America* (1816), pp. 103–104.

6. See above, ch. IX, sect. 61, pp. 214–215.

7. For interesting advertisements, see, for example, the *National Live-Stock Journal*, vol. III (1872), pp. 36–39.

8. *Cyclopedia of Agriculture* (ed. by L. H. Bailey), vol. IV (1909), p. 586.

9. *Ibid.*, p. 553.

10. *Ibid.*, p. 549.

11. Ibid., p. 597.
12. See the *Farmers' Union,* vol. I (Sept., 1867), p. 5; vol. IV (Jan., 1871), pp. 4–5, and vol. V (June, 1872), p. 6.
13. *Who's Who in America, 1916–1917.*
14. I am here following, with some hesitation, the oft-quoted authority, Charles L. Flint, Progress in Agriculture, *Eighty Years' Progress of the United States* (1864), pp. 47–59.
15. J. Ashton, *History of Shorthorns in Missouri prior to the Civil War* (1924), pp. 21, 30, 32.
16. L. F. Allen, *Shorthorn Herd Book* (1846).
17. Census figures for 1870 being the starting point; estimates for 1886 constituting the second figure.
18. A. H. Sanders, *Shorthorn Cattle* (1916), p. 434.
19. Table of exports of animals, and meats and meat products (in dollars) :

Period	Animals	Meats and Meat Products
1855	297,613	15,557,926
1860	1,855,091	14,224,412
1865	461,809	35,072,054
1866	584,031	
1867–76 (av.)	1,679,837	
1870	1,045,039	21,396,050
1877–86 (av.)	12,083,978	107,614,628
1896	41,840,969	127,077,979
1906	49,139,568	202,236,842
1914	5,803,659	143,261,846
1921	17,867,056	298,213,397

(Taken from *Treasury Reports* and *Statistical Abstracts*).
20. See the *United States Department of Agriculture Library Catalogue* (1901).
21. L. H. Bailey, *Cyclopedia of American Agriculture,* vol. IV (1909), pp. 610–611.
22. *Northwestern Farmer,* vol. III (1858), p. 15.
23. *United States Department of Agriculture Yearbook, 1922* (1923), p. 327.
24. *Ibid., 1920* (1921), p. 731.
25. R. A. Clemen, *The American Livestock and Meat Industry* (1923), p. 4, quoting J. W. Thompson.
26. See below, ch. XIII, sect. 97, p. 27.
27. *National Live-Stock Journal,* vol. III (1872), p. 65.
28. *Ibid.,* vol. IV (1873), p. 25.
29. Peter Kalm, *Travels into North America* (trans. by J. R. Foster), vol. III (1771), p. 189.
30. W. B. Bizzell, *Rural Texas* (1924), pp. 218–219.
31. Cf. R. M. Washburn, *Productive Dairying* (1917), pp. 16, 19.

HISTORY OF AGRICULTURE

32. Cf. the *Northwestern Farmer* (Nov., 1859), pp. 355–356.

33. Cf. *The Shorthorn World and Farm Magazine* (1924), no. 5, p. 1.

34. In recent years animals have been slaughtered under U. S. inspection in the following order of importance: sheep, cattle, swine, calves, goats. Many old dairy cows are sold to local butchers.

35. R. A. Clemen, *The American Livestock and Meat Industry* (1923), p. 23.

36. *Ib·d.*, p. 4.

37. See on this subject *Swift and Company Year Book . . . 1922* (1923), pp. 26–29.

38. Cf. R. A. Clemen, *The American Livestock and Meat Industry* (1923), p. 323.

39. The exports of meat and meat products (in millions of dollars):

1860	14	1900	175
1870	21	1910	128
1880	114	1920	642
1890	124		

40. G. Keatinge, *Agricultural Progress in Western India* (1921), pp. 111–115.

41. *United States Department of Agriculture Yearbook, 1922* (1923), p. 305.

42. Cheese factories began in the period 1851–54, in New York State.

43. E. Wiest, *Agricultural Organization in the United States* (1923), p. 351.

44. S. M. Babcock, born in 1843, holding the degree of Ph.D. from Göttingen, Germany, was professor of agricultural chemistry at the University of Wisconsin, 1887–1913. He has been much praised for giving his test freely to the world rather than patenting it.

45. For a description of the apparatus and method, see L. H. Bailey, *Cyclopedia of American Agriculture*, vol. III (1908), pp. 178–179.

46. According to census figures, 995 millions of pounds of butter were made on farms in 1909, only 708 millions in 1919.

47. Factory output in the United States (in millions of pounds), according to the census:

Year	Butter	Cheese	Condensed and evaporated milk
1899	420	282	187
1904	531	317	308
1909	625	311	495
1914	770	370	873
1919	921	474	2,094

Census data for factories making cheese, butter, and condensed milk are as follows:

Year	1879	1889	1899	1904	1909	1914	1919
No. of establishments	3,932	4,552	9,242	8,926	8,479	7,628	7,669
Wage earners	7,903	12,219	12,799	15,557	18,431	23,059	35,313
Primary horsepower	——	25,526	88,062	93,845	101,349	130,862	168,871

48. Consider especially the work of H. P. Armsby, agricultural chemist, director of the Institute of Animal Nutrition (Pennsylvania State College), 1900–21.

49. J. C. McDowell, *United States Department of Agriculture Yearbook, 1920* (1921), p. 404.

50. L. H. Bailey, *Cyclopedia of American Agriculture,* vol. III (1908), p. 175.

51. *United States Department of Agriculture Yearbook, 1922* (1923), p. 289.

52. E. Wiest, *Agricultural Organization in the United States* (1923), pp. 100–103.

53. *National Live-Stock Journal,* vol. VIII (1877), p.23.

CHAPTER XIV

RURAL TYPES HISTORICALLY CONSIDERED

Basis of classification

100. TYPES OF FARMS: NATURAL RESOURCES. The progress of animal husbandry, of agriculture in general, has been real, even great, but slow in one place rapid in another, partial here, complete there. To indicate the general drift, has been comparatively simple; to explain the causes, is more difficult. Among the determining factors, is the type of farm. In classifying farms we have at our service many criteria. There is the kind of soil—sand, chalk, clay, humus. There is topography—hill, valley, plain, mountain. Rainfall is a possibility —dry, moderate, moist. There is temperature—hot, moderate, cold. And to go no farther, there is the flora, notably forest, prairie grass, or sage brush. For historical purposes none of these is quite satisfactory, and to take them all into account would be uneconomical and impracticable. On the other hand, there are six general types that are comprehensive and historically suggestive: woodland, prairie, ranch, irrigated, dry, and left-over farm.

Woodland farm

The oldest type in America is the woodland farm. It is the estate carved out of the forest. Fields are prepared in the midst of trees, a few at first, more later. This is found throughout the eastern parts, generally speaking, and westward beyond the Appalachians even to the Mississippi River and farther in places. Here the Indians had made their clearings and planted their corn and gourds. The whites followed their example. The ground was rich in humus from the decaying roots, leaves, and trunks of fallen trees. And, when timber was burned, rich chemicals were added to the native elements. In places this rich soil was very deep, elsewhere quite shallow, notably near the Atlantic coast. The occupier of a woodland farm had many advantages and disadvantages peculiar to his situation. It was easy for him to build a log cabin, for the trees stood right at hand. Materials for barns and bridges and fences were there too. The abundance of wood, often the finest, explains why such excellent timbers were put into barns and into the ugly worm-fences still symbolic of the lavish expenditure of wood and land. The trees sometimes provided acorns for the hogs, nuts for the children, and materials for subsidiary industries, carried on by the parents, such as the making of axe-handles and pot and pearl ashes. The trees were valuable and useful, but in case of forest fires they brought disaster; and in normal times, they increased the feeling of isolation and shut off many a lonely group from the sight of neighbors. So that at times from sheer hunger for association, the family had to walk or drive often long distances to hear the voices and see the faces of their fellow-beings. The romantic appeal of an untouched forest gradually gives way, as we linger on, to the feeling of human insignificance and the fear of impending disaster. The joy of the hunt is balanced by the danger of sudden attack by man or beast. And in miasmic districts there are the dreaded ague and malaria.

In general, the woodland farm resembled the average holding of western Europe, from which Americans have derived so much of their agricultural experience and lore. Of varying degrees of fertility, it showed signs of exhaustion in places even as early as the seventeenth century. Accordingly, recuperative devices were adopted, the fallow and the legume system, and field-grass husbandry. And, when general conditions were ripe, the superior scientific rotation was introduced. Where fertility was considerable, and occasionally where not, the specialized intensive system was most profitable, provided marketing conditions were satisfactory. In short, the woodland farm as a type has lent itself to the normal growth of agriculture. All stages or types of farming have had a chance. **Woodland in America and Europe**

Beyond the woodland, lie the prairies or grass plains of the Mississippi valley, from Illinois to the western reaches of the Dakotas, Nebraska, and Kansas. Here the eye could range where it would. The sun rose and set with an assurance that **Prairie farm** the early woodland farmer never knew. The chief dangers lay beyond the horizon in cyclones and prairie fires. The soil was rich in humus and thickly matted. It required a special plow to break it; and as time went on, improved machinery made possible the cultivation of enormous stretches of this fertile soil. The early settlers had painfully to learn what kinds of crops to raise. They were at a loss to provide shelter for sheep and cattle. The penetrating blasts of winter encountered no wind-breaks on the prairies: in some parts fences were not to be thought of for many years. Hard enough it was, to secure timber for houses, stables, and barns. The **1875–80 f.** barbed-wire fence finally enabled the farmer to care for his stock and separate his fields as he wished. Twisted hay and dried dung, not wood, had to be used for fuel. Although it was easy to migrate across such stretches, it was difficult to market crops till the railroad came to bring rapid and almost complete relief. On the prairie farm natural husbandry was the obvious and first system. It struck deep root and lasted long, partly because the soil was very fertile. When a change in technique was advisable, the rich prairie land needed no fallow, legume rotation, or field-grass husbandry, at least not generally. Sometimes in the new world as in the old, land was so far gone, that only a legume rotation or field-grass husbandry could help it. As has been seen, George Washington on his woodland plantation sought a scientific rotation, but had to be content with something far short of it. The prairie soil was so rich in humus, however, and the period of cultivation so relatively short, that a scientific rotation could be introduced at once to care alike for the soil and the market.

Ranch
Farther on, west of the well-watered prairies, came the ranch. Genetically, it is older than the woodland and prairie farms, but historically in America it is younger. For a time, cattle had ranged over vast stretches of unclaimed land, searching for grass, northward in the spring and southward in the autumn. Then the range gave way to the staked and fenced ranch, vast in extent, and, like the range, famed as the abode of the picturesque cow boy of juvenile romance. Livestock were carefully watched and protected from wolves and

thieves. The owner was generally in the business for profits. He was often an easterner who never regarded the ranch as his permanent home. His investment was in his cattle or sheep to be shipped in large quantities to the shambles of Chicago, Omaha, or Kansas City. By prairie farmers and the American press, he was regarded as a capitalist, a member of a privileged class, the common enemy of the common man. In Oklahoma he intrigued with the Indian chiefs and bands for land privileges and sought the good will of government agents. He joined his fellows to form associations for self-protection, in which courts of arbitration were set up. He fought a hard fight to hold his own, but finally lost in the agricultural states—last of all in Oklahoma.[1] In other states, **About 1889** or sections of them, for instance in Texas,[2] Utah, Wyoming, and Montana, the ranch, of course, prevails and is deeply intrenched in climatic conditions.

Beyond the ranch, and reaching practically to the Pacific **Irrigated** coast, there developed the irrigated farm. Although some of **farm** the Indians of the south had long practised artificial watering, and the Spaniards had done something in the southern parts from the sixteenth or seventeenth century, it was not **1849** until the Mormons in Utah diverted the waters of a mountain stream, that the American people made any real beginning in irrigation.[3] It was later developed in Colorado and southern California, and from a feeble first step has gone on with giant **1920** stride until to-day about 19,000,000 acres are actually irrigated in the United States. This is only about 4% of the improved acreage, but engineers stand ready to increase the flow of water.[4] The future seems to depend upon the demand for agricultural products, but already the green spots of irrigated desert land constitute oases of hope for the years to come. The occupier is generally located in a valley. Where the water is abundant, there may be many farms; where it is scant, there will be but few. The chief problems are to raise crops that can be sent long distances—for the markets are commonly far afield, and to develop rotations that will keep the soil in good tilth and provide many products as an insurance against the low price of one. The nature of the farm makes possible any of the stages or types of agriculture, dealt with in the preceding chapters. But the fallow system will rarely, if ever, be seriously considered, unless by chance a large crop of obstreperous weeds has to be eliminated. The capital invested is too great to justify the laxer and more extensive systems. Always hanging over the head of the farmer in irrigation districts is the fixed charge for water, to be paid to the agency that supplies it, whether public or private.

Dry farm

1880's

Although in the four general types of farms above described, we have passed from coast to coast, we have not exhausted the historical development of farm types. For better or for worse, it was perceived that, in the district formerly partly occupied by ranches, grain crops could be grown. Experiments were followed by favorable yields and many settlers tried their fortunes on the new type of farm. The initial difficulty has been that old methods were continued in new surroundings and under different conditions. The land was fertile, but the rainfall was uncertain in amount and came at the wrong time. To meet the peculiar difficulties of the situation, it has been necessary to plan carefully. The farm must be very large, for much of it may have to remain fallow. Special machinery is necessary for preparing the soil to conserve moisture from one year to another. The surface must be finely cultivated and the sub-soil packed. Crops need to be chosen for their ability to withstand the dryness. Durum wheat and alfalfa have met the need in this respect. The old and common danger must be avoided, the danger of one crop. Animal culture needs to be adopted to balance plant culture on this type of farm as on others. Because of the dryness and the resulting necessity of fallowing the land, one can in a sense say that this type of farm can never get beyond the fallow system. Since legumes are alternated with cereals we can identify this system with the old partial- or fallow-legume system, described above.[5] It would seem that the next step possible and advisable is more emphasis on cattle raising, a more balanced agriculture in fact: but at best this would lead to a modified scientific rotation— as long as fallowing is practised. On the whole, it is not a very hopeful spectacle that meets our gaze in the dry farming district, whether in America or in Canada. A shabby, often a very wretched, house is located near the center of a large holding of several hundreds of acres of parched ground. The owner is hoping, still hoping after several years of disappointment, that this season he will get a good crop. His neighbor has already gone, leaving to his creditors stock and buildings as well as land. This situation is not found in all dry farming districts, but it threatens to prevail in all during certain periods. So that some have thought that many of the dry farms should be thrown back into ranches, for which, they maintain, nature intended the land should be used.

Our last type of farm is the left-over. It is found in all **Left-over** parts of America, in Maine and Missouri, in northern Min- **farm** nesota and eastern Kentucky. Such a farm is taken up last of all by the late-comers in each district, the rag-tag-and-bobtail farmers. Here it is rocky land of slight fertility: there it is almost barren sand. Here it is cut-over swampy land almost impossible to cultivate; there it is peat, fenny land that lacks some of the chemical constituents for plant growth. Here it is a rough stretch along a lake shore; there it is the mountain side, almost too steep to provide a potato patch. All in all, one wonders why any effort is made to use such land. From the point of view of economic efficiency, it would be far better for such occupiers to go to the richer lands to work for other people. But man is guided by many motives and forces. Some people like to fit into an out-of-the-way spot where taxes will be low, where they can get a living, bare though it be, and where hunting and fishing are good. They have a passion to own land, though it be of the poorest sort. Perhaps many even prefer such holdings, for which there is but little competition, on which to eke out a lazy existence. On these pocket farms the crudest methods are found, the poorest stock, and lowest standard of living, and the most numerous progeny. Enough of this world's goods for survival, is sufficient for this farmer. Instead of a cow he may have a goat. Instead of a barn he has a shed. Sometimes he earns a little working for others, building roads, gathering in the harvest, cutting down trees. We may compare him with

343

the squatter of the Middle Ages, without being able, however, to prove any lineal descent, even though in many cases we may strongly suspect it. Both were located on left-over land. Both eked out a living by working for others. Both used primitive technique, doubtless natural husbandry. Both had little of this world's goods and from the economic standpoint deserved less than they had. In short, both were types of farmers occupying types of farms commensurate with their capacities.

Poor whites of Georgia

In the sandy pine barrens of southern New Jersey many Italians have settled. Going at first to pick berries, they stayed to farm and have turned a desert into a garden of fruits and vegetables.[6] On the other hand, the pine barrens of southern Georgia, scorned by the rich planters, have been inhabited since the eighteenth century by an unprogressive group of poor whites of long American descent. Over a hundred years ago their principal means of livelihood was said to be hunting.[7] They are described as ignorant, brutal, proud, and penniless savages, who steal and starve on the fringes of the lowest of all civilized societies, that of southern slavery. These hardy denizens of the wilderness fought long and fiercely in the Civil War to maintain slavery,[8] to perpetuate a system which gave to them the only prestige they were ever likely to possess. Legally free, they were actually the slaves of ignorance, prejudice, sloth, and improvidence.

Rise and spread of the plantation 1607

1617-19

101. THE SOUTHERN SLAVE PLANTATION. The southern plantation developed in Virginia and spread southward as far as Florida and westward as far as Texas. The first plantation was the settlement at Jamestown, Virginia. Soon that colony was divested of its company ownership, and the lands divided. The private plantations began at this time, in the division of the land and in the importation of slaves. Of course the Spanish plantations in the West Indies and on the mainland were much older, but with these we are not concerned. The history of the plantation is the story of clearing land, importing slaves, exhausting the soil, moving westward, and finally fighting to maintain its existence in competition with the free farm. The plantation fills a long chapter

in American history, but withal one that is in a general way well known, best of all perhaps through the agitation and struggle that led to its abolition with the actual freeing of the slaves. **1865**

The plantation was essentially a large estate, managed with considerable uniformity by means of officials. Because of the size of the holding and the number of workers, planning was necessary. There was the field work to be considered, from plowing to harvesting. The slaves were obstreperous laborers needing supervision both at their work and in their own houses. The crops had to be divided, some remaining for food and some being sold for use elsewhere. Supplies in large quantities had to be purchased, generally from afar. Money had frequently to be borrowed and paid back. All this might be done on a small plantation of 200 acres or so by a resident owner, but on a large estate an overseer was generally employed. Many were the complaints about the inefficiency, dishonesty, and immorality of this official. His was a hard task. A man at the beginning, he often became a brutal bully. His goal, frequently attained, was a plantation of his own in the newer lands of the west. Such an official had to handle, not only large number of blacks but considerable sums of money. Indeed the plantation was a capitalistic institution. The land and equipment were often valued at hundreds of thousands of dollars, the gross yearly income at tens of thousands. Much of the capital was sunk in slaves who, before the Civil War, might be worth from $400 to $1200, according to age and capacity. With such a combination of slave labor, incapable management, and absentee ownership, the cultivation was necessarily routine and the effect on the soil slowly disastrous. **Economic characteristics**

The plantation system was rooted in local conditions. The land would yield crops which were in great demand in Europe. The climate was warm and debilitating. The lowlands, especially those devoted to rice, were beyond the endurance of the white man for a part of the year because of heat, humidity, and malaria. The African negro could stand these better than the white man, so he was ruthlessly snatched from his native villages and brought across the sea to do the white man's **Bases of the plantation**

345

bidding. It was the opportunity for gain that led Anglo-Saxons and Anglo-Celts to clear the land and seek far-off slaves. From the purely economic standpoint, it was a great accomplishment, to unite three continents. Africa gave its labor, America its land, and Europe the capacity to exploit.

Tobacco plantation

1767

The earliest plantations produced tobacco as the staple money crop. Virginia and North Carolina were the first colonies to find profit in the poisonous soothing weed. One of these tobacco plantations of Virginia contained 3000 acres, lying in two separate districts. On one of the estates there was a large brick house, two stories high, with eight rooms, each provided with a fireplace. There were the usual out-houses and barns, a mill, and an apple orchard. A marsh of fifty or sixty acres seems to have provided coarse hay. A large garden furnished the vegetables, and everywhere there was wild fowl. There were several fine meadows, doubtless permanently set off from the arable fields. Besides the staple crops of tobacco, there were maize, wheat, and oats, doubtless largely or wholly for consumption on the plantation. This estate was offered for sale and with it the livestock (cattle, hogs, and horses being mentioned). Several blooded mares are rather significantly specified.[9] The plantation owner usually had more interest in fine mounts and trotters than he had in pure bred cows or hogs. Another Virginia plantation produced tobacco, maize, wheat, and clover. The last-named crop is evidence that the old system of natural husbandry had to give way to legume rotation in order to conserve what remained of the fertility of the soil. On this estate there were 125 slaves for household service, work in the fields, and for manufacturing some of the articles needed on the plantation. Machines existed, but they were of the simpler kinds and insignificant when compared with the hand tools. There were work horses, mules, and oxen in plenty, a surplus of pleasure horses, and a great deficiency of other animals such as cows, sheep, and swine. The amount of labor on this large plantation, as on others, was immense and continuous throughout the year. If we begin with the stripping of the tobacco, we soon pass to cutting wood, hauling tobacco and flour to the

1854

boat landing, bringing back guano and other fertilizers, spreading manure, burning brush, preparing seed, plowing and sowing, setting the tobacco seedlings at the fall of every rain, mowing hay in the meadows (both permanent and alternating), cultivating the tobacco, harvesting the grain, plowing for winter wheat, cutting and housing the tobacco, harvesting the corn, sowing winter wheat, cutting the year's supply of ice. Of leisure there was little, only on Sundays, very wet days, Christmas week, and a few feast days.[10] The efficiency expert would probably say that the distribution of labor was excellent.

The second kind of plantation, producing rice, was found in the Carolinas and Georgia, though now it has developed greatly on the Gulf Coast in Louisiana and Texas. Unlike the other plantations which worked the slaves in gangs from morning to night, the rice plantation used the task system. Each slave was assigned a day's work, and might quit when he had finished. On a Georgia rice plantation of about 1800 acres or more, there were 1500 acres diked and drained for the production of rice and other crops. Rice occupied about two-thirds of this land, and maize, oats and sweet potatoes the rest. Over 200 acres were high lands, on which the farm buildings and mill were located, and where the provisions were grown. There was a steam thresher for the small grains, and a tide mill for pounding rice. The staple crop was taken to the wharf where it was loaded on to a steamer for transportation to a distant market. This plantation—really an island—was owned by one man and worked by 700 blacks. The plantation house was an unpretentious cottage, sheltering an unusual master, who lived at home and thought more of the welfare of his people than of material gains.[11]

A large cotton plantation in Georgia provided a yearly supply of the staple crop and relatively little else, except hogs. Later it yielded a surplus of wheat and rye as well as cotton. In one year the maximum yield of $21,300 was attained, one half going to meet expenses and improvements. The purchase of Peruvian and Mexican guano was a significant occurrence. The buying of a steam engine and of reapers meant

Rice plantation

1850

Cotton plantation
1850's
1847

1856

the supplementing of slave labor, a transfer of capital from black men to machines.[12]

Sugar plantation

Near the mouths of the Mississippi River, sugar plantations abounded before the Civil War as now. One along the banks of the Mississippi contained 15,000 acres, but had only about 1250 in crops, the rest being swampy forest producing chiefly firewood. About 800 acres were planted with sugar cane, 300 with maize, and 150 with the slaves' own crops. The labor was provided by 215 negroes and 64 mules. There was a hospital and a nursery. An up-to-date sugar mill had been erected on the estate. In all, the plantation was valued at over $700,000, the gross yearly return being almost $100,000. This came from the sale of sugar, the other products, maize and hay, being probably used on the plantation.[13]

1852

Social and cultural conditions

It is difficult to appraise the social and cultural conditions of the slave plantation as such, because of the diversity of the situation. It is a common error to ascribe to the plantation system the faults of negro society and the terrible results of an enervating climate. Some things, however, are tolerably clear. The negro women were grossly overworked on many estates, especially before and after the birth of their children. The impairment of the home life of the black people meant a weakening of the whole social fabric. Lying and cheating arose out of a system of inequality and force. The hopelessness of life on earth resembled that reserved by Dante for the spirits of evil men after death. For the master and his family life was a matter of will and command. There was no opportunity for the blossoming of a conception of the dignity of the individual and the nobility of work. Labor was degrading, not elevating. Accordingly no strong middle class could emerge, with its careful management of detail, its saving in small things, and its gradual rise to at least material comfort. It is true there were poor whites in rural parts and traders in the towns, but neither class displayed much promise. No manufacturing for sale could have any healthy development, because it must depend on a free intelligent labor system, which was, of course, impossible in a land where labor was the badge of degradation. In short, where plantations flourished, society

could not rise much above the first phase of town economy.[14]
The small commercial or market town was the highest promise
that the future could offer. This meant that the south could
develop no high position in the professions or attain cultural
independence. Socially its position was circumscribed by the
lack of opportunity to specialize—to use personal aptitudes
in craftsmanship, art, or science. Culturally the south faced
the black despair of a parasitic community.

The southern plantation was like the Roman *latifundium*, **Comparisons**
in so far as both were worked by slaves, both were cursed by
inefficient overseers, and both were clouded by revolt, actual
or potential. The southern plantation also resembled the medieval manor. Neither the black slave nor the medieval
serf might go off the estate without permission. Both had
houses and generally gardens. Both poached and otherwise
pilfered. Both had to submit to officials. The southern overseer was the medieval bailiff. The southern slave driver was
not unlike the medieval reeve. The slave and the serf both
bore heavy field tasks and both received allowances of food
and drink from the estate. The American plantation and the
medieval European manor were characterized by a cluster of
houses, barns, stables, cook houses, and the like. The big
house of the plantation had a large drawing-room, as had the
manor house, and both were flanked by the cottages of the
workers. We know how filthy the cottage-hovels of the negroes were; [15] we may surmise that the abodes of the European
villeins were about the same. But the villeins had rights as
well as considerable holdings of land. They were serfs, not
slaves. They were submerged people, not lost souls.

The plantation was a large estate made up of woodland, **Planter
and farmer**
prairie, or irrigated, land. The planter had more land than
the farmer, though he frequently came from the same class of
workers ambitious to possess land that would yield an income.
The planter was first and last commercial; the farmer developed commercial habits rather slowly, as we shall see. Both
hastened to impair the fertility of the land that gave them
bread, but the planter debauched the society in which he moved.
The farmer was less pretentious in matters of culture, but more

insistent on spreading the advantages of education, such as he conceived it. Each represented a social system, age long in its operation, and effective in accordance with its ideals. The farmer was democratic, the planter aristocratic. The Civil War decided in favor of the farmer and his system. The black man was freed, and the plantation generally changed from a unit of cultivation to a unit of rent-taking. The old prejudice against rich men was heightened to a point where it turned from destroying plantations to sweeping away ranches from districts suitable for general farming and curbing the excesses of corporations engaged in transporting, manufacturing, and storing goods.

Types of farmers

102. THE PIONEER FARMER. We have already noted the various types of both farms and plantations. We have contrasted the aristocratic planter with the democratic farmer. The latter class has had such a long and continuous history and has gone through such changes that we must stop at least to note the chief types and the way in which one type gives way to another. The farmer may be the victor in American history, but he is constantly losing within his own ranks to the new and ever changing generation of new types.

Significance of types

With types and categories we often become impatient. We want real cases, specific farms and real farmers. But on second thought, we observe that this desire is impracticable, because there are too many individual cases. On the other hand, we may demand an average of them all, but this is frightfully unreal, though it may prove valuable as a corrective. So we are thrown back upon types, as the clearest indication of the essentials and as the most economical and practical of approaches logically possible. In using types of this or that (and we may add also, stages), we may well remember that the type is just an approximation, or point of departure of the further study of individuals or particular situations wherever that is possible.

Pioneer

The earliest type, historically and genetically, was the pioneer. Different as he was in cultural background, he found himself resembling the Indian in material situation. Like the Indian, he tilled a little land and hunted and fished.

350

This is the common story from east to west, from the sea-coast inland to the farthest place of settlement, except in the case of the ranch already considered. Some of the pioneers, notably the early ones along the Atlantic coast, stuck to their original homes adopting gradually, as circumstances permitted, practices more nearly akin to those they had left at home. How they stayed in the one district, generation after generation, may be read on the tombstones in the cemetery at Plymouth and elsewhere. Such persons were pioneers by necessity, not by choice. They did not, as persons, belong to the type. The true pioneer was a character, a disposition, a case. He stood out from his fellows. Like some of the very primitive animals, found surviving here and there, he lived in out-of-the-way places. He would not change his habits to conform to a progressive society. And so he found it necessary to move, generally from east to west, but sometimes from north to south, as in the case of the Scotch-Irish who followed the mountain valleys of Pennsylvania, Virginia, and North Carolina into South Carolina and Georgia. Shiftless and thriftless, he had no capital but the bounty of nature. Pugnacious in spirit, he liked the running fight of the frontier. Perhaps it was the necessity of fleeing from advancing civilization, of always skirting the fringes of higher human effort, that gave him the lust for moving onward. He loved frequent change, finding monotonous the (relatively) unprogressive district in which he lived. Unable or unwilling to bring about new conditions of his own, he sought the variations that nature provided. He was a nomad struggling against permanent settlement, and like the nomad he was a trader. He sold his horses, his cattle, and his land. His trading, however, was sporadic and was not confined to regular surplus products, but included the very productive agencies themselves. Perhaps he dickered for the love of novelty of new possessions. Like the nomad he was also a hunter and fisher. On the frontier, work and play were one, and profit and adventure went hand in hand. The worst of the pioneers were little more than vagrants; the best were magnificent members of society.[16] All contributed, in high or low degree, to agricultural progress.

They blazed the trail; they built the first cabins, and made the earliest clearings; they picked out the fertile soil, and learned which Indians were friendly, which were hostile; they hunted or raised their own food, provided their own clothing of linen, wool, or skins, tanned their own leather, made their own shoes and harness, and many household articles, buying chiefly iron and salt and a few household utensils.[17] And when new-comers arrived ready to buy them out, they obligingly sold their holdings, content to move on and to perform the same functions for others who followed. For these they paved a way that they themselves could not travel. Ever profiting from their heroic efforts, their successors can admire them more for what they did than for what they were.

Survival of the frontier

Neither the frontier [18] nor the frontiersman has gone. The margin of settlement extending from the north to the south and gradually moving westward has disappeared, it is true, but the parts remain, here and there in out-of-the-way places. And the frontiersman, unless he has escaped to Canada or Alaska, now by circumstances cornered and prevented from moving on, holds the fort for his traditions, or as many of these as could survive, in the left-over farms which have already been considered. Or it may be, his passion for novelty has broken bound, driven him off the frontier spots, into towns and cities, there to flit from pillar to post, always losing here what he gained there, but rich in experience, luxurious in variety of occupations.[19]

Pioneers by circumstances

So far we have been considering chiefly the pioneers by choice, those who fitted the environment and, where possible, stuck to it. There were others, however, who, as we have noted, were pioneers by the circumstances of their surroundings. Personally they were above the crude society of their time. Always they were capable of rising to the economic and cultural heights of the districts they had left in Europe or in the eastern part of America. To them we pay tribute as to those who sacrificed something for society, who paid a temporary price for their submergence, but who gloriously rose above their surroundings and pulled their fellows up with them. As these men have grown grey, we find their admirers occasionally recording in journals or on tablets of brass the accomplishments of their lives. But generally, from the Atlantic to the great desert, their careers are forgotten in the aggregate of effort that has gone into the up-building of American civilization. Those who have turned from the fields to make their chief contributions in local journalism or politics, have received more attention. Those who have stuck to the business of farming have not usually been given the consideration that their accomplishments deserve, so accustomed are we to ignore, or accept, the solid work of material production. Of the many examples of worthy pioneers, we shall take but one. A farmer lad migrated from Norway to the American west, **1874** and in a covered wagon faced the hardships of travel across plain and river, from Iowa to eastern North Dakota. Wisely choosing a high piece of land covered with oaks, he settled down to the business of cultivating the virgin soil and caring for his cattle. He had significantly brought with him an ox team and two milch cows and a calf. As soon as practical, with these and such additions as he could make, he improved his system of cultivation, so that in after years he was known as a pioneer in the scientific rotation of crops. His success led him to acquire a vast estate which he now rents out to tenants. After many misfortunes and fifty years of effort, his work is fittingly recognized by the state in which he lives, and enthusiastically recorded in a journal of a neighboring commonwealth.[20]

103. THE CULTIVATOR. As the pioneer gave way, the **Cultivator** cultivator took his place. It is true that some of those who had been pioneers by compulsion, became cultivators by choice, such as the early Atlantic coast settlers and the North Dakota pioneer, but in most cases the pioneer held to his type, the cultivator to his, one following the other westward as army follows vanguard. The cultivator was more permanent than the pioneer. Although he moved when disheartened by local unhealthfulness and failure of crops, nevertheless he was relatively fixed. While the pioneer was something of a nomad, the cultivator was much like the settled villager sometimes becoming restless and moving off where change promised greater

advantages. With eyes fixed upon his own habitat, he became an improver. The log cabin with its mud floor, gave way to the frame or brick dwelling with home-made carpet. The trail became the road; the ford yielded to the bridge; self-help gave way to an organized judiciary. There was more capital and more planning for the future. The relative self-sufficiency of the pioneer gave way to the relative dependence of the cultivator.

This is the great farmer class of American history. We must not regard it, however, as homogenous throughout all parts, or devoid of changes as time went on. We may perhaps speak of at least two grades of cultivator, one giving way to the other. The first exhausted the soil. He worked hard, at certain seasons, but not at soil conservation. His technique rarely got beyond natural husbandry or the fallow system at best. With but little book learning, he did what was immediately practical. He made the most out of a system of much land and little labor. What he failed to attain in cultivation, he gained in general social advance. He might be called the speculator-cultivator, were it not for the fact that, to some extent, all occupiers of land in America have been speculators, relying upon rising land values for gain, rather than exclusively upon year to year profits from animal and plant cultivation.

Exhausting cultivator

Husbanding cultivator

The second grade of cultivator was much more of a husbandman. He sought by observation, experimentation, and reading, to treat the soil in better fashion. Ameliorating crops, such as the legumes, or at best a scientific rotation, provided him with the ways and means of solving his big problem of continuing to derive an income and at the same time obviating soil depletion. The best that may be said of him is that he saved the soil. The worst is that he lost the market. Education for farming meant to him agricultural technique. It included little or no farm management or agricultural economics. The business side of farming was beyond the horizon.

English classes and American types

About three generations ago (1848), an Englishman made an interesting analysis of conditions in America.[21] For eighteen years he had resided in the part of America described, and accordingly knew the situation at first hand. He recommended to Englishmen that agricultural laborers and small proprietors take up land in America. They were not very skilled in cultivation and had little capital. They would be about on a par with the lower grade of cultivator already on the land. But the English tenant farmer was advised to stay at home. Such a farmer was conversant with the latest improvements in agricultural technique and was a manager rather than a laborer. In England, general conditions and his own capacities put him in the highest class of farmers; in America he would probably be no more than a careful cultivator. He, with his advanced methods, could hardly compete with the cultivators who mined the soil, at least not at first. He could get along well enough in England, even under conditions of keen competition. But the time did come when such a high-grade cultivator migrated from England to America most profitably to himself, and when such a class also developed independently in America, as we have seen.[22]

It is a painful but obvious reflection that we all seem—and with us the cultivator—to learn slowly, by degrees, and one thing at a time. So, those who come after us can say, he made some advances but he had not a few short-comings. Like the average retailer and workshop owner, whom he resembles, the cultivator is both laborer and manager in one. How far this is by choice and how far by necessity in many cases it would be difficult to say. At any rate the function of doing the manual labor on the farm has been so engrossing of time and absorbing of energies that management has had but little attention. And yet on the side of improving crops and bettering livestock, it has not been wholly lacking. Indeed, it has been real, and the improvements growing out of it genuine and promising, but the careful choice of seed, the proper rotation of crops, and the selection of the finest stock, may not lead to the largest money returns, if the market has been neglected. If the cheapest buying of supplies and the dearest selling of products are not accomplished, something far short of material success is inevitable. Arising largely out of the dominance of a labor rather than a manager system, is the farmer's fondest hope of finally

Weaknesses of the cultivator

retiring from drudgery to a near-by town, leaving his estate to one of his sons. The kindly mother, knowing toil more than pleasure, instills into sons and daughters the advantages of town pursuits, such as commerce and the professions. And so the country-side suffers. Those who have a propensity for business and a capacity for management, tend to leave the farm for the factory and the office. Here is an example of social selection that helps build up the town and keeps down the country. If the fittest of the country lads and lassies could be saved for the farm, rural advance would probably be more rapid. It is just this draining-off process that tends to perpetuate the cultivator type of limited capacity.

Competition changes the types

104. THE BUSINESS FARMER. Marvellously subtle and effective is the element of free competition. America has had the good fortune to have had it in plenty. Indeed it is the land *par excellence* of competitive economic life. Traditions, caste, legal restrictions, political limitations, have been slight and disregarded. One type of producer competes with another and falls before him or pushes him to the wall. This has not been without loud murmur, temporary resistance, and spasmodic uprisings, but it has gone on, working its ruthless will, eliminating the economically unfit, and enjoying the plaudits of *laissez-faire* economists and liberal politicians. The exhausting cultivator pushed the willing pioneer; the husbanding cultivator took the land misused by his predecessor. And now, we can see evidence that this superior cultivator, in turn, is giving way to another who can make still better use of the soil. This is the business farmer. When the time is ripe, the new type supplants the old.

Business farmer

The business farmer is the cultivator plus the business man in one. Like the capitalist, he is an historical category. He has come late and embodies in himself the most effective qualities of preceding types, as well as those qualities that distinguish him from his forebears. In other words he is efficient as a cultivator and capable in buying and selling. He has one eye on the farm and the other on the market. He is a skillful balancer of supply and demand. He knows the seasons' fluctuations, and he is watching the cyclic changes occurring in long periods of many years. He has capital, or commands it. His rating is known in the local banks, and some day may be published for national use. He is a manager primarily, and only, where the estate is very small, is he a field worker. He is a trained man, perhaps a graduate of an agricultural college. He knows the technique of farming, but his distinguishing quality is his grounding in farm management. He has a copy of the deed of his farm, a blue print of the survey, an inventory of his stock and general equipment, and accounts exactly balanced from time to time. He has had his soil passed upon by experts and his cows tested. He cares but little whether he owns the land. His interest is in the income from successful farming. In other words, he is less of a peasant-cultivator and more of a capitalist-farmer.

The pioneer and his wife supplied many of their needs by home manufacture. The cultivator has given up a good deal of industrial activity, but in varying degree. Almost everywhere except in out-of-the-way places, such as the mountains of Kentucky and Arkansas, the cultivator has abandoned the making of furniture, household utensils, and tool handles, and his wife no longer makes cloth or men's clothing. The business farmer necessarily gives up whatever household manufacture remains. His wife ceases to make cheese or butter, and in many cases even bread. But where personal taste and convenience enter in, doubtless home manufacture will prevail in the country as in the town. The passing of such industrial pursuits does not necessarily bring more leisure for higher things. For the farmer it may mean more opportunity for repairing his machinery, and for his wife more time for poultry raising or whatever else she may have undertaken. *Farmer types and home manufactures*

It seems to be inherent in the nature of changes, that where there is a gain there is a loss, though the two may not, of course, exactly balance. When the pioneer gave way to the cultivator, the land gained an exploiter, one who would use it more nearly up to its capacity; but the country lost a care-free picturesque type of man, to whom life was larger than work. When the cultivator gives way to the business farmer, we gain in economic efficiency, but we lose the influence of a large group *A new type means both gains and losses* of persons not greedy in their daily affairs, though circumstances may force them to husband what they have. The business farmer will bring the dollar into the country as the equivalent of one hundred cents. When one farmer helps another, it will be in terms of exact equivalents, though there is no reason to expect that charity will cease to exist. The business farmer will realize that time is money. This is a blessing and a curse in one. It shuts off the waste that has prevailed. The farmer will not go to town to sell a dozen of eggs or to buy a spade. He will not be idle during the winter, nor, if he has laborers, will he fail to keep them busy with worth-while tasks. The reflective attitude, leading to the crude but significant philosophy of the cultivator, will give way to the eternal round of things. The world's affairs will be a whirlpool in which the farmer must circle mechanically round and round. The boasted independence of the farmer will be gone. Working on the land and with the market, he will be dependent on both nature and man. As his forebear, the cultivator, was a weather prophet, he will be also a market prophet. He will read the horizon for clouds and the morning despatch, by telegraph or radio, for market news. His ample credit at the bank will enable him to keep his grain in his own or a neighboring cooperative granary until the most favorable time for sale has arrived. Si Hayseed and Reuben will have gone. No more will the farmer be the easy victim of swindlers. When at home he will escape the pedlar of worthless bonds; when in town he will scorn the seller of gold bricks. The farmer will then be on the plane of the wholesaler, factory owner, broker, and railroad executive.

Prototypes of business farmer

The qualities that are making the cultivator a business man, do not drop fresh from the modern sky. There have been prototypes and much gradual growth; and just where the cultivator leaves off and the business farmer begins, cannot be exactly stated, though here and there we see clearly enough when the change takes place, as the old cultivator, failing to make ends meet, gives up his holding to the new type. The English tenant farmer, already considered,[23] was a business farmer, though he had not gone so far as the American farmer promises to go in the near future. The southern planter was somewhat analogous. He was a profit taker. He had capital and credit and catered to the market. But he was not the careful cultivator and market expert combined in one. The early livestock breeder, though often far from rich, was a business-like entrepreneur. And the bonanza farmer, from first to last, thought of his investment and the interest and dividends it would pay. But he did not think much about conserving the soil. The market outran the agricultural technique. The dairyman, too, is a business farmer in the making. He has a daily money income. Every day is harvest day with him. He belongs to co-operative societies and borrows money and lends it. He manages labor as well as cows and fields. His specialty tends to be the business of farming. The truck gardener, and other specialized intensive farmers, produce what will sell as well as what the land will bear. He sells a relatively large product and buys a relatively large amount of labor and fertilizer. He is an adjuster of demand and supply.

It is perhaps not too much to expect of the new type of farmer that he will be sounder in general economic outlook than the agricultural technicians, the cultivators, who preceded him. He will be able to see his relation to the tariff better. He will understand the function of middlemen and speculators. He will not cry out for a guaranteed price for this commodity or for that. He will not refuse to co-operate to reduce the area devoted to a crop that is clearly a drug on the market, whether it be wheat or pork, cotton or corn. More of a business man, he will be less the victim of demagogues promising what the market cannot provide. And yet, remembering the monopolistic demands of the factory owner, we should not be too optimistic about the immediate economic policy of the business farmer.

Economic policy of the business farmer

105. Suggestions for Further Study

1. Does your knowledge of farms in your locality enable you to add to the types of farms, or does it substantiate the analysis given in the text?

2. Study L. C. Gray, *Southern Agriculture, Plantation System and the Negro Problem, Annals of the American Academy of Political and Social Science*, vol. XL (1912), pp. 90–99.

3. Read P. A. Rollins' *The Cowboy, his Characteristics, his Equipment, and his Part in the Development of the West* (1922), chs. I, II, XIII.

4. Which type of farmer is at present numerically preponderant?

5. What is meant when we say that the frontier has now gone? What justification is there for saying that it still remains?

6. Why did the English (American) settlers slaughter the forests in favor of woodland farms, while the French accepted the forests and derived much of their income from forest wild life? Consider the colonial systems and home conditions of England and France.

7. Would we not grant that the pioneers, of early times and on present-day left-over farms, have a merit all their own? They may have, in their love for the picturesque and care-free life, the potentialities of musicians, literary men, and painters. Nature may live on in them and express herself in the work of their hands. In short, their humble homes may be the nurseries of non-business genius.

8. A realistic picture of pioneer life in Wisconsin is painted by the naturalist John Muir in his book called *The Story of My Boyhood and Youth* (1912). See especially, pp. 218–234.

9. After having written these chapters on agriculture, the author read Hamlin Garland's autobiographical story called *A Son of the Middle Border* (1913). The period covered is 1865–1893; the chief district dealt with is Wisconsin, Iowa, and South Dakota. Read this book to learn the spirit of the pioneer, the position of the pioneer's wife, and the general atmosphere of early rural existence. Garland was impressed with the hard work, nasty smells, and small reward of farm life.

10. Comment on the following: the pioneer is not gone; he has just changed his labors, going upward in the cultural scale. Some of the descendants of the pioneer settlers are now pioneer literary men. Examples of these are Hamlin Garland, mentioned above, and Herbert Quick. (*Vandemark's Folly*, 1922; *The Hawkeye*, 1923, depicting Iowa life). Compare also the work of Willa S. Cather (*O Pioneers!* 1913, on Nebraska), Laura G. Salverson (*The Viking Heart*, 1923, on the Canadian northwest), and Edith S. Kelley (*Weeds*, 1923, on rural Kentucky).

11. See specially Miss W. S. Cather's novel, *O Pioneers!* (1913). The scene is Nebraska, the period about 1880–1900. On the one hand there were the slow Swedes, Norwegians, and

Germans; on the other the more alert Bohemians and French. Disasters came in the form of hog cholera, loss of cattle in blizzards, and prolonged droughts. The settlers, many originally artisans in Europe, were badly equipped to face the difficulties. Many went back eastward; others bought up their land. Progress then was possible, with the elimination of the less fit. The use of alfalfa and the raising of more livestock brought prosperity. The State University had its influence. The uneducated were jealous of the farmers' boys who attended it. Uniformity, lack of individualism in habits of thinking, characterized the community. The best cultivator, the heroine of the story, looked away from the farm to town and city life for light and inspiration, even though she thought that she belonged to the land.

12. The novel called "Weeds," by Edith Summers Kelley (1923), is a story of a country girl of unusual ability, held to an uncongenial life of marriage and motherhood because of a badly adjusted environment. The scene is Scott County, Kentucky, and the period is the present. The people are prematurely old, the children largely unschooled. We find profanity, intoxication, shiftlessness, monotony of food, poor agricultural technique, much tenancy, horse trading, waste of time, bad roads, poor houses and livestock, and marketing as soon as the crops are ready. The people have no surplus, read no newspapers, and rarely go beyond the county.

13. Why did men go west, over the hills and far away? Was it greed, adventure, imitation of others, or something else?

14. Where will the business farmer experience his gains or losses, in his wages, profits, interest on investment, or in psychic satisfaction?

15. What are the assumptions underlying this chapter? Can you justify socially and culturally the existence of the pioneer type on the left-over farm at the present time?

16. Complaints have been made that the American farmer lacks business ability, capital, ownership of land, skill in cultivation, thrift, credit, application, co-operation, cheap transportation, good highways, hired labor, and storage capacity. Which of these deficiencies prevail in your district?

17. Someone has suggested that the south erect a monument to the boll weevil. What is the point?

18. Comment critically on the following aphorisms:

Man likes to mine the soil; he cultivates only through compulsion.

Dirt farmers make progress, but it is slow.

As knowledge of agriculture has increased experiments, progress has been accelerated.

Fortunately knowledge of how to get results has not depended on a knowledge of the causes.

The farmer in China is a "slave"; in England a gentleman; in the United States a free laborer.

The American farmer has been, first a nomad, second an exhausting cultivator, and third a careful cultivator. He may become a business man.

All occupiers of farm land in America have been more or less speculators. At last we are developing a business type.

The farmer works too hard in summer and not enough in winter.

The chief ideal of the farmer is to retire to an easier mode of existence.

With little labor, and less capital, the American farmer has never had the chance to become a manager.

The farmer has given too much attention to restricting his outlay and too little to increasing his income. To which type does this apply?

With too little knowledge of his own, the farmer spurns advice from others.

To the farmer, book learning is a dangerous thing; and it is, in the absence of sufficient education to apply it.

Tenancy is much dreaded by farmers who do not want to be efficient.

Dairying teaches the farmer to become used to a money income, to husband his resources, and above all to cater to the market.

The contrast between the large well-managed farm and the small poorly equipped holding is as great as between the big factory and the miserable workshop housing one man in a shed.

The farmer can gauge the weather pretty well, but the market is beyond him.

In years of crop failures the farmer would like to have the truth known; in years of bumper crops the fact should be kept in the dark.

For further references, see the notes below.

106. Notes to Chapter XIV

1. E. E. Dale, The Ranchman's Last Frontier, *The Mississippi Valley Historical Review*, vol. X (1923), pp. 41–46.

2. See B. Youngblood and A. B. Cox, *An Economic Study of a Typical Ranching Area* (1922).

3. See Elwood Mead, Rise and Future of Irrigation in the

RURAL TYPES HISTORICALLY CONSIDERED

United States, *Yearbook of the United States Department of Agriculture, 1899* (1900), pp. 591 f.

4. Notable projects in view are the reclamation of over four million of acres by water from the Columbia River and seven million by means of the Colorado River.

5. See above, ch. II, sect. 10, p. 31.

6. A. E. Cance, Immigrant Rural Communities, *Annals of the American Academy of Political and Social Science*, vol. XLI (1912), p. 73.

7. *A Documentary History of American Industrial Society*, vol. I, *Plantation and Frontier* (ed. by U. B. Phillips, 1910), pp. 166.

8. Frances A. Kemble, *Journal of a Residence on a Georgian Plantation in 1838–1839* (1863), pp. 140–147. A brilliant though prejudiced description.

9. *A Documentary History of American Industrial Society*, vol. I, *Plantation and Frontier* (ed. by U. B. Phillips, 1910), pp. 245–246.

10. U. B. Phillips, *American Negro Slavery* (1918), pp. 230–232.

11. *Ibid.*, pp. 251–253.

12. *Ibid.*, pp. 234–239.

13. *Ibid.*, pp. 242–243.

14. See above, ch. I, sect. 4, p. 19.

15. See Frances A. Kemble's *Journal of a Residence on a Georgian Plantation in 1838–1839* (1863), pp. 26 f., *et passim*. The description, though obviously prejudiced, is vivid and effective. The authoress failed to distinguish between the conditions that arose out of slavery and those that came from the low order of negro society existing at that time.

16. Compare the opinions of Dwight and Flint in G. S. Callender, *Economic History of the United States, Select Documents* (1909), pp. 604–608, 609–610.

17. See *The American Farmer*, vol. II (1821), p. 130.

18. For a study of the frontier, see the *Report on Population of the United States at the Eleventh Census, 1890*, pt. I (1895), pp. XVIII–XXXII; F. J. Turner, *The Frontier in American History* (1920); F. L. Paxson, *The Last American Frontier* (1910, 1911); A. M. Schlesinger, *New Viewpoints in American History* (1922), chs. II, III, VIII.

19. For an illustration of a southern pioneer, see *A Documentary History of American Industrial Society*, vol. II, *Plantation and Frontier* (ed. by U. B. Phillips, 1910), pp. 184–196; for a northern pioneer, see the *Minnesota History Bulletin*, vol. IV (1921), pp. 130–151.

20. *The Minneapolis Tribune,* 27 July, 1924.
21. A treatise on "Hints to Emigrants," approved by an American reviewer in *The Cultivator,* N. S., vol. V (1848), p. 311.
22. See above, ch. XII, sect. 87, pp. 294 f.
23. See above, chs. IV. VII, IX, and XI.

CHAPTER XV

FACTORS IN AGRICULTURAL DEVELOPMENT

107. GENERAL FARM CONDITIONS. The type of farm de- **Complex** pends in part upon natural resources which are beyond the **and simple** power of man in any very large way to change. The type of **factors** farmer is determined by both psychic and external material conditions. The farmer is a complex, the result of accumulated inherited characteristics and habits acquired from the environment from which he has come or in which he finds himself. Both farm and farmer are large factors in the agricultural situation, not entirely independent factors, but still at any particular time decisive and independent enough to be determining elements. In the very complicated agricultural situation they must as such receive considerable attention, as in the preceding chapter. Other factors, independent or derived, must also be taken into account in any attempt to explain situations and changes. While the farm and the farmer may be regarded as large summary factors, there are others, more simple, which require analytic rather than synthetic treatment. Most of them, perhaps all, have helped determine either the nature of the farm or the make-up of the farmer, but they may be separately considered as elements in the larger situation.

The rural districts of America, like those of Europe, have **Rural** witnessed a continuous exodus to the towns. Children are **exodus** born in agony and reared in care. Before they have been of much assistance, they go off to the urban centers. Those left are generally the slow and unambitious; while those who go away are industrious and enterprising. What the country loses, the town gains. Much of the educational work of the countryside is a free gift to the town, like that made by Europe and Canada when they send their emigrants to the United States. Although the farm keeps its care-free sons and

365

daughters in great plenty, as it seems, it loses many of those who would put agriculture on a more business-like basis.

Ownership of land

Most men like to own land, to have it to use as they will. And it has long been the ideal of statesmen to give farmers the ownership they crave. The thought is that they will be better citizens (tax-payers and soldiers), if they are not simply dwellers but part owners in the country they inhabit. And some agriculturists have believed that ownership turns sand into gold: so industrious is the owner in plowing and fertilizing that the barren soil is transmuted into golden harvests, while the mere tenant has no such power of alchemy. If the farmer is capable, ambitious, and industrious, the land may be made to yield large returns, but if he is none of these, ownership will simply enable him, or his family, to hold on to the land a little longer, keeping it out of the possession of the more capable. Many of the unfit have owned agricultural land in America, and many do so to-day, who would have been better as tenants of landlords who would force them to be efficient. Such landlords could have written into the leases, as do the Scullys of the middle west, conditions which are of the greatest value to agriculture. The tenants would be compelled to diversify their crops and to keep livestock. In this way they would not only have a money income (with which to pay their rent), but would keep up the fertility of the soil. On the other hand, if tenancy instead of ownership had been the prospect ahead of the emigrant, he would have hesitated to undertake the hardships and hazards involved. It has really been the gain from the gradual increase in the value of his farm, that has been the mainstay of many a farmer who could earn neither a good wage nor a profit from his own holding. It seems true to say that in America the ownership of land has had more favorable influence upon settlement and citizenship than it has had upon agricultural methods.

Size of farm

1862

The ideal of the American farmer has long been, not simply to own a farm but to own a big one. The Homestead Act gave him 160 acres, and he often purchased an equivalent amount. His adult sons also took up quarter sections for themselves. And to this day the sizeable farm of a quarter section has remained about the average for the country as a whole. But it would seem that this is too large, if we judge by the careless use of the soil and by the fact that only about 52% of the land has been improved.[1] However, it is hazardous to argue from a few facts. We cannot safely consider the condition of the soil to the exclusion of the general economic situation; and we cannot emphasise economic advantage and forget non-economic situations. The farmer has derived psychic satisfaction in viewing his broad acres which were visible evidence to his neighbors of his importance. Such satisfaction might constitute a greater real income than money from a smaller farm. There are two prominent forces at work in the determination of the size [2] of the farm. On the one hand there is the tendency for the farm to become smaller so as to facilitate more intensive cultivation. On the other hand, there is a slowly growing class of experts coming from our agricultural colleges capable of managing, or advising in the management of, large estates. Just which way the business farmer will go cannot now be judged, whether toward a small holding better equipped and managed, or toward a large holding directed by hired experts. Both developments may, of course, occur side by side. The bonanza farm, on which cultivation of one or two simple crops took place, still exists, but it is surely passing with the years. Sooner or later it is broken up into smaller units. Where there had been a few temporary laborers, there soon appear numerous permanent cultivators; and where there had been but one or two large dwellings, sometimes barracks, there appear many scattered homesteads. The general reason for this is the fact that, as the original productivity is impaired, and as special attention is required for various crops and expensive livestock, the small farmer can make larger returns than the bonanza farmer who has to depend upon hired laborers.[3]

One of the best established facts in American economic history is the depletion of the soil. As early as the seventeenth century [4] this took place in the east, and as late as our day it is a real fact in the Red River Valley of the west. This does not mean that the chemical constituents have been exhausted in

Soil depletion 1923

367

many districts, but that the growing quality of the soil has been impaired by biological or physical deterioration. Weeds, parasites, and the washing away of surface soil sum up a great deal. At first the abundance of growing power led to careless cultivation; as this exuberance of fertility has changed to niggardliness, better methods have come in. This change in conditions has already been traced in considering the stages through which American agriculture has passed.

Accessibility

108. MARKET DEVELOPMENT. Let the farmer own his own land, let him keep his most promising children at home, let him secure the proper size of holding, let the fertility of his land be adequately maintained, and he still has the problem of general accessibility and market connection. Just as Russia for centuries has striven for an outlet to the western world— ports on the Baltic and the Black Seas, so has the American farmer struggled for a market, outlets for his products, sources of supplies, and avenues of cultural well-being. To secure free land has been easy in America; to prepare it for cultivation has been laborious but immediately practicable. To establish economic and other relationships, however, with the old world left behind, has been a difficult and comparatively slow task. The river steamboat, the canal, the railroad, the telegraph and telephone, the rural postal service, the automobile, and the raido have all played a part. For large sections of the country —but not for parts of some states, such as Kentucky and Arkansas—the problem has been solved, except for a few adjustments which presumably will always have to be made and remade.

Market stages

The farmer on the very frontier of society in America for a year or longer had no market at all for the products of the field. He could sell the furs of animals which he might trap, by carrying them to the nearest trading post of some company. From such a trading post these furs would go to a central point, it might be Winnipeg or St. Louis, and then to London or New York, as the case might be. Gradually, however, sweeping westward from the Atlantic to the great desert, the town has sprung up, partly based on European models but largely molded by American needs. It has provided the farmer with a ray of hope, a place to sell his products and to buy supplies, a meeting spot for neighbors, and a source of news from the world beyond. The town in America had a two-fold relationship. It was a focusing point for the countryside and at the same time it was a permanent commercial colony dependent on some larger center. At first the larger center was some metropolis in Europe—London, Paris, or Amsterdam. Later it was a purely American city, such as New York or New Orleans, both pregnant with possibility, but only the former reaching full metropolitan proportions. The town might be solely commercial or it might become industrial, as well as commercial. In the southland, at least in many parts, it remained a market center where tobacco and rice, later cotton and other wares, were sold, and where a few goods, not manufactured on the plantation or farm, were purchased. Generally these manufactured goods came from Europe in early times and later more and more from the north. It has been the misfortune of the south not to develop many towns and not to develop industrial centers. Conditions are changing now, and in some places, notably in Birmingham (Alabama), very rapidly. In the northland commercial towns, or at least one here and there, early added manufacturing to their accomplishments. At first such goods as were locally made—wagons, plows, shoes, overalls, and the like—were sold exclusively to the neighboring farmers, who themselves ceased to make the goods they could buy so conveniently near at hand. As opportunity served, some towns developed skill and prestige in the manufacture of this or that article—Lynn in the making of women's shoes, Moline in the manufacture of plows, and Milwaukee in the brewing of beer. Some towns went so far, grew so large, traded in so many wares, and served so vast a district, that they ceased to be towns of the old type. They may be called metropolitan centers, as we have already seen. We may speak of the change as one from town to metropolitan economy.[5]

The metropolitan unit is made up of a large city and a considerable hinterland. The two exchange goods and services. As we approach the central city from the outskirts of the

What metropolitan economy is

hinterland, we find that the dependence on the metropolitan city becomes greater, not only for goods produced within the area but for wares from other metropolitan districts. The hinterland is made up not only of farms, mines, forests, and fisheries, but of towns subordinate to the great center. With these towns the farms and other productive agencies are in close and even immediate dependence. Metropolitan economy is the result of many factors, but chiefly of the need for a wide exchange group to bring about specialization by individuals and localities. Once formed, it becomes a cause of many developments. Primarily a result of an economic and social need, it is secondarily a cause of many realignments.

American peculiarities in metropolitan development

The growth of metropolitan units in America has differed from that in the old world. In America there was the great example of European models. In America the areas have been vast and quite undeveloped. Center and hinterland have grown up together. Political influence has been slight either to help or hinder. America has missed the political centralizing influence enjoyed by London and Paris, and has escaped the decentralizing effect of German local principalities. The local American political unit, the state, has commonly preferred a smaller city as capital, and where metropolitan centers have also been state capitals the political influence has been slight and in no case decisive. In America there has been much more rivalry for metropolitan position within the nation than in European countries, because of the fact that many towns were growing up together without any tradition of subordination, all with the rich hope of pre-eminence, and because the greater area of America has room for more metropolitan units.

Metropolitan rivalry

Although metropolitan rivalry in America has not had the political backing of national states, as has been the case in European countries, it has been no less keen in its economic aspects.[6] Promising centers have competed for trade and territory. New York has been the London; and first Montreal, then New Orleans, the Paris of America. New York had to struggle with its neighbors, Boston, Montreal, Philadelphia, and Baltimore for influence in western New York State, and then with victory behind it in New York State, it contested the position of New Orleans in the Ohio and Mississippi Valleys. The construction of the Erie Canal gave New York victory over its eastern rivals and was to help in the contest with New Orleans, as transportation on the Great Lakes with their connecting canals was developed and improved. A farmer in Ohio in 1830, in Illinois in 1850, in Minnesota in 1860 might look to either the Atlantic or the Gulf city. A decade later in each case his face was more commonly turned to the city on the Hudson. The construction of railroads strengthened the draw of New York City, and reduced relatively the flow of trade to New Orleans. When the east-west trade became dominant, rivalry sprang up between Cleveland and Cincinnati, Chicago and St. Louis, and the Twin Cities and Kansas City, not at once but gradually as the country was developed. In all of these cases both rival cities became metropolitan centers, though not of equal strength or promise. Local struggles took place, as between Buffalo and Cleveland, Milwaukee and Chicago, and Duluth and the Twin Cities, in which the first mentioned of each pair lost and, for the time at least, lost decisively. Rivalry, intensified in spirit and magnified by local enthusiasm, has absorbed the Pacific Coast and at the same time amused the rest of the country. San Francisco sees its aggressive rival in Los Angeles to the south and in Seattle to the north. They are all competing for the producing areas of wheat fields, stock farms, fruit gardens, and forests that lie near at hand.

In a district of no agricultural resources, a metropolis cannot develop at all, or grows up very slowly. Denver and Salt Lake City struggle along, but have little more than promise of success and only in case irrigation is extended on a large scale. Dallas has a large but relatively infertile territory to which it can look for support. Ranges, ranches, and dry farms are not the stuff of which rich metropolitan units are made. A weak agricultural hinterland can not entirely impair metropolitan development in case there are other rich resources. Boston was not prevented from becoming a metropolitan center, though it was held back by its rocky farms. It had forests, fisheries, a thrifty and industrious population, and ocean transportation

1825

Importance of agriculture for metropolitan development

facilities. In the south, where the soil is indeed fertile enough, there is no large measure of promise of a vigorous metropolitan growth, because of the debilitating climate which keeps back both agriculture and manufacture. In early days the plantation system, itself not independent of climate, contributed to the same end. At the present time, local self-satisfaction, refusal to learn either from Europe or the north, accentuates climatic influences. Atlanta has recent promise, but Baltimore, Cincinnati, St. Louis, and New Orleans are far from the strength of northern centers.

Importance of metropolitan development for agriculture

As generally, if not always, in social organization, the relationship is reciprocal. Agriculture does not simply support or help determine metropolitan growth, but is in turn profoundly influenced by it. As we have seen, agriculture is more intensive near to great central markets and is graded off to the most extensive system of the outer fringes of the hinterland. The central market makes it profitable to construct a great transportation system of railroads and waterways. It thereby enables the farmer, who had been compelled to sell his grain in the form of whisky and later in the form of pork, to market it as such in the grain exchanges of the metropolitan center. The metropolitan millers advertise the grain of their hinterland. Those of the Twin Cities have pushed forward to a national position the flour made of the hard spring wheat of the northwest in rivalry with the flour of St. Louis made of the soft winter wheat of the southwest.[7] And to-day the Twin Cities with their hinterland of hard spring wheat are rivals of Kansas City with its supply of hard winter wheat. This hard winter wheat is more rust resistant and therefore more dependable. At least partly for this reason, flour-milling is growing more rapidly at Kansas City than in the Twin Cities, and capital has actually left the latter to develop industry in the former. The metropolis of each district is doing what it can to further the sale of its agricultural products, but it cannot overcome, at least not at once, difficulties that arise from natural causes. The metropolitan center looks after the agricultural credit needs of its district. These vary much from one part of the country to another, though, other things being equal, they tend to be the same at the same stage of metropolitan maturity. Sometimes metropolitan agencies, for example the Chamber of Commerce at St. Louis, try to influence directly the course of agricultural practices in their hinterland. The business men of St. Louis realize that they are handicapped by the backwardness of agriculture in their district. If the farmers of Missouri, Arkansas, and Texas do not have a large surplus at the end of the year, they cannot purchase many wares from St. Louis. Accordingly they are urged to diversify their crops and balance animal and plant cultivation. They are told that they can grow their own foodstuffs and thereby emancipate themselves from northern dependence, keep more of the money coming from the sale of the cotton crop, and preserve the producing powers of their soil.

109. CYCLES IN CROPS AND BUSINESS. Most of the life of the farmer is taken up with growing and marketing, with crops and business. The growing of crops obviously depends on weather conditions. It is the weather that makes one district a garden, another a desert. We are told that the weather causes over 75% of the cultivated land of the south to be intertilled and over 90% of the cultivated land of the northwest to be broadcast; that it makes the harvest of the valleys of the Mississippi and the Missouri worth from ten to twenty dollars an acre and that of large sections of the far southwest even less than ten cents an acre.[8] The weather also makes the crops vary from time to time in the same district. The enormous differences from year to year are realized only by a study of the records. In Nebraska, to take but one illustration, in a period of sixty-five years the annual rainfall was away below the normal in 1859, 1860, 1863, 1864, 1890, 1893, 1894, and far above the normal in 1853, 1858, 1869, 1875, 1881, 1883, and 1915.[9] Such changes are of vast import to the cultivator. But it is obvious that what is most effective is not the rainfall of the year but of the critical growing season, not the temperature of the year but of the short period of growing and ripening. It has been estimated that what counts most in the yield of corn is the rainfall in July, in the yield of spring wheat in North Dakota the rainfall of May and June, in the yield of

Importance of the weather

1850–1915

potatoes in Ohio and New Jersey the temperature of July.[10] Knowing the weather conditions, the experts in grain marketing and in agriculture, estimate from week to week how much the farmer is going to lose or gain this year, as compared with the past. Once the farmer has done his part, he is like the pilot of a rudderless ship; he must yield to nature's mood.

Rainfall data

Since the fortune of the farmer is so largely dependent upon the weather, the statistics of natural conditions, especially rainfall, are of great value in tracing the ups and downs of agriculture. For a study of rainfall we have records in North Dakota since 1882, in Illinois since 1870, in the Ohio Valley since 1839, in London since 1726, in Padua since 1725, in Paris since 1690; the measuring of the rings of the pines of Arizona enables us to push back to the year A. D., 1392, and the rings of the sequoia of California take us back to at least 1306 B. C. We are told that the fossil trees may some day give us a record for millions of years.[11] Bulky as this evidence is, much of it has more value for the study of weather cycles than for a study of crop yields.

Weather cycles

The cycle, or periodic recurrence of a run of weather, has been the subject of speculation and study. The rain fell heavily in America, generally or in important growing districts, in 1843, 1850, 1858, 1865, 1873, 1882, 1890, 1898, 1906, and 1914. For at least the last five years similar conditions were found in Great Britain and in France. This suggests a cycle of eight years, more or less.[12] A study of the records of tree rings and solar conditions, however, indicates varying cyclic periods, as follows:

Period of years	Cycle [13]
1595–1661	11 + years
1661–1677	16 + years
1677–1770	10 + years
1770–1793	9 + years
1793–1817	14 + (?) years
1817–1910	11 + years

It thus appears that if there is a generating cycle, it has wide variations. So far, no one has discovered the key to the rhythm of the weather, even though some scholars, perhaps many, think there is such a regular sequence.

Hand in hand with the quest for the cyclic period has gone speculation about the *causes* of the cyclic recurrence. Long ago Sir William Herschel, the astronomer, sought to connect the price of grain with sun-spot variation, and Jevons associated the weather and crop yield on the one hand with sun-spots on the other.[14]   Venus has been thought to be the possible cause of a cycle of eight years.   The argument is that Venus, coming near to the direct path of radiation from the sun to the earth every eighth year, affects the terrestial climate.   Although the planet is small, it is near to the earth and is believed to be constantly harried by violent winds blowing from one hemisphere to the other.[15]   Recently the sun-spot theory has had a revival.[16]   The sun-spots are held to recur in a period of a little over eleven years, and to affect the temperature on this earth and even more the velocity of the wind. The cause of the recurrence of the sun-spots may possibly be ultimately traced to the influence of Jupiter on the sun.[17] Because of all the divergence and uncertainty, the farmer had better be careful when he blames weather conditions on any one of the gods or planets.

Causes of weather cycles
1801
1875

1921

The results of weather cycles, especially cycles of weather conditions during the critical period of crop growth, are for the farmer translated into dollars and cents, success or failure in the year's work.   Some, notably Jevons and Moore, have gone beyond this.   They have regarded the yield of the crops as the cause of general business cycles.   According to this view, the periodic sequence of prosperity, boom, crisis,[18] and depression in production is fundamentally the result of crop conditions; the crops have a cycle which in turn produces a cycle in industry, commerce, transportation, storage, and mining.   When the crops are good, the farmer's purchasing power is considerable and his demand for manufactured wares great.   When the crops are poor, the farmer's demand is slight and business falls off.   What a fine chain of causation we have: Jupiter causes sun-spots; these affect the rainfall, temperature, and prevalence of storms on the earth; these

Results of weather cycles

1875,
1914

determine the yield of crops; this causes the farmer's demands for the products of the towns to increase or decrease; this means general economic prosperity or depression. That there is some validity to this general sequence is very likely. But there are at least two weak links in the chain. There is no proof that generating or crop cycles coincide with general business cycles. The evidence, indeed, is against this view. So far there has been no convincing demonstration of a general cycle of crop yields following a cycle of weather conditions in the growing periods. Also, correlations of crops and annual rainfall have been attempted, but correlations of crops and general weather conditions at critical periods still need to be made —on a large scale. We may summarize by saying that while crop conditions affect business conditions, there is no evidence that a cycle of crops determines the cycle of business.

Causes and results of business cycles

If weather and crop conditions do not cause business to go through the cycle already indicated, we may well seek the explanation. This, of course, lies beyond the scope of the subject at hand. In a general way we may say that the cause of the rhythm in business is to be found in the habits of business men and the mechanism of production. It is rooted in human demand for wares [19] and in business machinery.[20] In the demand for goods the farmer plays his part, and an important one, but not demonstrated to be cyclic. The effect of the business cycle on the farmer is more likely to produce a rhythm of rural well-being, than is any cycle of crops (so far discovered) likely to determine a cycle of general production. In other words, the farmer has become part of the cash nexus of society. He is part and parcel of the exchange mechanism by which human wants are satisfied. Demand for his goods fluctuates with business conditions. If Germany cannot afford to buy American cereals and meat products, the American farmer suffers. If prices fall for any general reason, the farmer loses, unless the price of the goods he purchases falls in precisely the same way. Wars and recurrent credit disorders have affected the farmer, as they have affected the manufacturer or railroad man, though not necessarily to the same degree or at the same moment. They have elminated the unfit and the unlucky producer in both town and country. One of the most significant of farmer's demands in this connection is that there should be a dirt farmer appointed to the Federal Reserve Board. The demand has been acceded to: agricultural interests are now represented.[21] A farmer has been appointed a member of the United States Shipping Board and another a member of the Federal Trade Board. Accordingly, public recognition has been given to the farmer's position in our modern capitalistic and bureaucratic system. **1922**

The successful farmer must be an adjuster of conditions. **Farmers' adjustments** He must have one eye on the weather and the other on the market. To get best results he should study the day's weather forecasts. In parts of the United States infested with cyclones and hurricanes this is already a common practice. He should also give some attention to weather variations. Though there be no reliable rhythm of rainfall or the like, there are unquestionably changes which are suggestive. After a year, especially after two years, of excessive rainfall, there is likely to be much less precipitation. In certain dry parts of the country especially, use of this fact might be made to plant more drought-resisting crops. Adjustment to general business conditions is equally important. There are helpful business barometers which forecast future conditions and which the farmer should follow (critically), if he is to get the most out of the business of farming. All this presupposes, however, that the farmer has become a business man with the aptitudes and training of business. So far in America this development has not taken place to any great extent.

110. CAPITAL AND LABOR IN AGRICULTURE. Part of the **Capital** general adjustment that the farmer must make in the business side of agriculture is in the use of capital and labor. As the market develops and agriculture becomes more intensive, additional capital is required. That farmer succeeds best who applies the factors of production most effectively, that is, capital, labor, and management in proper proportion. Throughout American history there has been a scarcity of capital. Some of it was brought in ships from Europe and across country from the east to the west, but most of it was amassed right

on the farm, growing out of the business it was to serve. From the surplus of the fields and stables, the pig-sty and the hen-house, has come the money for current use and for investment in farm equipment. This is in the form of drainage tiles and ditches, fences, barns, machinery, fertilizer, livestock, and seed. In the aggregate the amount of this capital is colossal, and its increase in the last forty years beyond belief [22]— a tribute to the activity of farmers and to the fertility of the soil.[23] And yet it is true that even to-day one of the most frequent causes of failures among both tenants and owners is lack of capital sufficient for current business and permanent improvements needed in progressive agriculture.

Machinery constitutes one of the most significant items of agricultural capital in America. It has been estimated that the value of farm implements and machinery combined amounted in 1900 to three-quarters of a billion dollars, and in 1912 to one and one-third billions.[24] In about a century, machinery has grown from almost nothing to constitute, shall we say, about ten per cent of the total farm capital (excluding land). Although the variety of machines driven by horses, steam, or gasoline power is considerable,[25] the reaper and thresher are the most significant. Alongside of the reaper, which cuts grain, should be put the mower, which cuts hay. The reaper has now taken on the form and name of binder, because it binds the grain into sheaves after cutting it. For about one generation, efforts were made in the middle Atlantic states to invent reapers and other machines. Then in the short period of three years McCormick of [West] Virginia and Hussey of Baltimore invented and patented their machines. For a while these men were rivals in perfecting and marketing reapers. But there was relatively slight adoption during this period, because the machines had to be made largely by hand in small shops, were as yet far from perfect, and the prairies, where they were to be most useful, had hardly been opened up. But during the next generation the reaper came into its own. While only about 3,000 were manufactured in 1850, about 60,000 were made in 1880.[26] Gradually the McCormick reaper made headway, till it became *the* Amer-

Sidenotes:

1924

Machinery

1800–31
1831–34

1834–50

1850–80

378

ican reaper, now known everywhere at home and in a dozen
other countries.[27] The reaper, and to a less extent other machines, was brought to the front by the increased demand for
labor-saving devices. This demand arose out of the increase
in the production of grain for use at home and sale abroad.
The demand for cheap American grain could be rapidly met
by extending the farm area over the prairies—with the help
of machinery. The Civil War was a factor in so far as it
accentuated the need for machines to take the place of laborers
who served in the armies of the north, but the development
would have gone on, had there been no war. Not only did
these machines aid American agriculture, but they were the
occasion for the establishment of a great American industry [28]
which is personified to-day under the name of the International
Harvester Company. This industry supplies not only American needs but exports its products abroad.[29] Although
America had long looked to England for ideas in the manufacture of machines, it finally came to supply that land, the About
1800–60
mother of both the reaper and the thresher, with many of its
best machines. When the McCormick reaper competed with 1862
six English machines and won, it was claimed that 3,000 of
the McCormick instruments had already been manufactured
in England and 45,000 had been imported from America.[30]
Wherever the machines are used, whether in America or England, labor has been made more effective, and accordingly the
cost of production has been reduced. It has been reckoned
that, while one bushel of wheat was taken from the standing
grain in a little over three hours in 1830 and at a cost of almost eighteen cents, by 1896, this could be done in ten minutes
at a cost of three cents and a half. And it has been concluded
that the effectiveness of farm labor was increased 86% within 1870–
1900
the life of one generation.[31] But while machinery has done
much for farming generally, it has not been equally beneficial.
The saving for corn and cotton has not been so great as for
barley, oats, potatoes, and wheat. And it has been computed
that machinery is actually more expensive than hand labor for
peas and especially tobacco.[32] Since cotton and tobacco are
two important southern crops, we can see that on the whole the

Credit

north has been the chief beneficiary of agricultural machinery. The average farmer has had to struggle hard for his capital gains. He has been greatly handicapped in securing loans of capital with which to improve his farm and undertakings. He has been obliged to compete with the large farmer who has had greater command of credit. The large farmer frequently has established close business connections in towns and metropolitan centers; often indeed he has lived in one or the other. He is more of a manager, and bankers and mortgage houses have more confidence in his ability and willingness to meet his obligations. The small or average farmer has not competed successfully with the commercial group in getting credit, because the latter has appealed more to money lenders. The merchants, retailers, and even speculators, have been more business-like in their management. They plan carefully to meet their obligations, while the small farmer, knowing that he himself is both honest and solvent, is careless in paying back a loan. He has commonly expected an extension or continuation of his obligation. Another fact is that the urban commercial group has seemed to have even greater *capacity* to repay than the farmer. Their turn-over has been more frequent, the risk from weather and over-production has been less, because they have dealt in the products, not only of agriculture, but of mining, manufacturing, fisheries, and lumbering. The commercial metropolitan organization has been growing very efficient, while most of the farmers remained relatively inefficient. The average farmer likewise has failed in a general way to compete successfully with the urban group, whether for production or consumption, partly because the urban group has been on a firmer money basis and partly because it has been resident in the town, the seat of the loanable surplus, and therefore well-known and trusted.

Farmer's credit improving

But times are changing. The farmer is beginning to get his share of credit on terms commensurate with the risk involved. This may be due in part to the fact that the non-agricultural productive agencies have approached an equilibrium in their development. The private merchant has organized metropolitan economy and made a success. He has reaped his reward. Much of his constructive work, however, is done. It is now possible for the farmer, and for small people generally, to enter into co-operative associations to reap some of the advantages of commercial control, not feasible when the development of the market was under way. Another reason for the new condition is the changing nature of the farmer's own affairs. The system of natural husbandry is declining in the south and the west. In its stead comes a safer technique, one that promises a larger and steadier income. And the type of farmer is changing, as we have seen. The new business farmer is capable of entering into successful co-operative arrangements with his fellows for securing credit. He demands and secures government aid. The semi-official Federal Reserve System helps him indirectly through the local **1914 f.** banks, in so far as it rediscounts short-time agricultural paper for current dealings. The Federal Farm Loan System provides the farmer, large or small, with low-priced loans for long **1916 f.** periods on the security of farm mortgages. With these loans the farmer repays the old mortgage which bore a high rate of interest, adds a little land where that is necessary, or per- **1923 f.** fects his general equipment. The Intermediate Rural Credits System loans the farmer indirectly through the local banks or co-operative associations, such sums as are necessary to carry on his business, usually for the purchase of livestock to be fed for a year or two or for the holding of his crops till a favorable time for sale arrives. At last, we may say, the farmer has come into his own, as far as credit is concerned. Some bankers have maintained that the farmer already has too much credit and that the facilities for securing it are too facile. Certainly some farmers have received too much credit at very high rates, that is, loans secured when business has been brisk and rates high. Such loans have proved hard to pay back later when prices of farm products have declined. It is true that, for some farmers, the securing of credit is too easy. It is too easy for the old type who cannot make good use of it. Indeed the new mechanism of agricultural credit will probably be a potent instrument for weeding out the unfit and bringing in the fit. It gives the farmer credit—at low rates withal—so that he will have either to become a business man and make good or get off the land. This conclusion is, of course, based on the assumption that the credit agencies will be managed in an economic and not political fashion.

Farm labor

In the absence of careful studies of farm labor,[33] it is difficult to deal here with the subject. Some facts, however, seem fairly well established. From first to last the chief labor power has been supplied by the occupier of the farm himself. Next in importance comes his family, his wife and children. Only third do we find hired laborers.[34] There are two classes of these, those who are all-round agricultural laborers with some skill and who hire by the year or season, and those who come into the harvest fields to help with the peak of the labor load. Some of the last-named are amateurs, looking for a combination of profit and adventure; others are out-and-out laborers who shift from place to place, agricultural rounders, who follow a seasonal trail. For instance, some laborers migrate at the end of their period of work from California, to Washington, to Idaho, to the Dakotas, and back to California again.[35] While the regular agricultural laborers are quite commonly on the way to become tenants and finally owners, the rounders are of a permanent laboring class, often members of the Industrial Workers of the World, and holding a class-conscious attitude of antagonism to their employers. Apart from the organization of some of the hired laborers, it seems that the chief change in the history of farm labor since the Civil War is the development of the cropper class in the southland.

1920

These number over half a million.[36] They are nominally tenants but in many cases only laborers or at most manager-laborers. They rent a small holding from a landowner, who not only provides the land but the machinery, implements, and seed, and who often specifies the way in which the agriculture shall be carried on. In many cases the agents of the landowners supervise the daily routine of the cropper. In short, these people, many of them once negro slaves or rather the descendants of slaves, are still essentially laborers with only a slight measure of independence, all that it would be safe to entrust to them in many instances. The future

382

would seem to have in store for the agricultural laboring class some changes of moment. The southern cropper, if he is susceptible to education, may develop out of his class into a good tenant or into the position of owner. The northern laborer promises to be in greater demand as agriculture changes. Ultimately, both large farms extensively cultivated and small ones intensively operated will probably require more labor, though in both cases there are forces operating to restrict the use of hired labor, in the first case the greater use of machinery, in the second the greater use of family labor. With this greater demand will come better treatment which is sorely needed, especially for the regular farmhand. An increase in the number of laborers means in part the training of more men to become independent farmers on smaller holdings carved out of the large estates of the present. As in retrospect we look back over the generations during which labor has been performed on the farm, we conclude that it has been probably unusually efficient, because so much of it has been performed by the farmer or his family and by laborers about to become farmers in their own right. From the standpoint of labor alone, it is a matter of congratulation that America can look forward to the continuation, at least for a time, of a system which provides an opportunity for the capable industrious agricultural laborer to become a tenant on a fair-sized farm and finally even an owner.

III. NATIONAL AND RACIAL INFLUENCES. In the application of capital and in the use of labor, in fact all along the line of American agricultural experience, Europe has exerted an influence that has been at once wholesome and lasting, unless we except some recent developments to be considered later. Europe provided the enterprising peoples who have made the plans and done the work of agriculture. Europe has maintained a continuous demand for American products, though with many variations. An illusion that has played a vital part in rural America came from Europe. In the old world land in itself was desirable, because it would produce a revenue and give the owner a life of leisure. Land was rented to the farmer or the peasant cultivator who paid a rental that enabled

General
influences
of Europe

the landlord to live comfortably in the town or the metropolis. In America this was not the case, at least not at first when free land was plentiful. Only gradually, first in the east then in the west, has it been possible to find a tenant. Accordingly, the immigrant, peasant or artisan, coming to get rich, remained to labor. A landlord he was but also a laborer. A mistake had been made, but America was settled.

English contributions

Until at least the Civil War, Americans looked to England for educational guidance in things agricultural. English books on agriculture were read by Jared Eliot (about 1750), John Taylor (about 1800), and Thomas Jefferson. English methods were preached in American agricultural journals. English horticultural literature was in vogue in America before national efforts were made to develop garden culture suitable to American conditions. The English practice of

1803

holding sheep-shearings was adopted, apparently first on the Potomac and later elsewhere to some extent. In the first of these, toasts were drunk, speeches made, and prizes given for wool, sheep, and domestic manufactures.[37] The import of these gatherings, however, was not the same in America as in England. They were not so much to improve agriculture as to further home manufactures and industrial independence. This national aspect is not surprising, when we remember the circumstances of their origin, which, while individually quite unimportant, were collectively very significant. These meetings were begun by the ward and heir of Washington; they took place on an estate bequeathed by the General; and they were held in the great war tent of Revolutionary days. In addition, English agricultural chemistry made headway along the Atlantic coast. But emancipation came in time, though not complete, because interest shifted in part from English to German methods. It was at Yale that this study first flour-

1846-52

ished in America. While J. P. Norton, the first professor of agricultural chemistry at that university, had obtained much of his preparation in England and Scotland, S. W. Johnson,

1856-74

a successor in the same chair, studied in Germany.[38] Subsequent developments of the subject in many American uni-

384

versities have brought about relative if not complete independence.

The English also contributed much to American animal husbandry, as we have seen. While the English, and we may add the Scotch, are good all-round livestock people, the Danes and Swiss are excellent dairymen, the Danes taking to butter making, the Swiss to cheese. The Danes are the best livestock farmers among the Scandinavians, the Norwegians the worst. Generally, Scandinavians are progressive, with high ideals for improving their houses as well as their barns. They readily adapt themselves to their environment and see to it that their children obtain an education so that they will not all have to remain on the farm. The Germans are industrious, inclined to save, with a propensity to field gardening and land ownership. Their barns are likely to be better than their houses. In one community of Yankee farmers along the upper Mississippi, the Germans came in and gradually bought up the farms. The Yankee women did not labor in the fields, as German women did. The Yankees sold what they did not eat, while the Germans ate what they could not sell. The Yankees lived for the present, while the Germans saved for the future. Accordingly, the Germans crowded the Yankees out, and still hold their land. The Germans have a capacity for taking pains. They care for their cattle and their machinery. They use all the soil available and get the last grain from the harvest. The French have never been progressive in America, though in their homeland they cannot be called poor farmers. They are in some parts more inclined to horticulture than to agriculture, and have more children than cattle.[39] The Irish are shiftless farmers, unprogressive like the French, careless of detail, and unsuccessful with livestock. On the other hand they are often outstanding in local political and administrative work and in the social life of their community. The Poles have large families and work long hours. They have ousted many American onion and tobacco growers in New England. In Wisconsin they have taken left-over farms in the sandy regions of the center and the north. The

Continental European influence

Poles seem to be making good in American agriculture, but their progress is not striking and their numbers not large. The Finns in many parts have poor land, but by industry and skill in dairying, they have attained some material success. They are a suspicious people, clannish, and unsanitary. Like the Germans, they are musical, a rather uncommon trait in rural America. Italians have settled in New Jersey, New York, the coastal plain of the Gulf, and in Wisconsin. They do best in communities of their own people. Loving agriculture, they are successful in maintaining fertility or even improving it. Usually their farms are small and carefully worked by hand tools.[40]

The Jews

1880's f.

The Jews have established small colonies, in New York very early (1837–42), and later in Louisiana, South and North Dakota, Colorado, Oregon, Kansas, Michigan, California, Connecticut, and New Jersey. Most success has come in the last-named state. The Jews tend to develop a highly commercialized agriculture, such as dairying, poultry raising, or gardening,[41] in which there is a good deal of selling. They have had the aid of the Jewish Colonizing Society and the special assistance of benevolent compatriots who have gained wealth in towns. On the whole, however, the Jews are not successful farmers in America. They have frequently had poor land and little capital. They do not like the physical drudgery. Agriculture does not utilize their business ability to its fullest extent. In their ranks generally the cultivation of the soil is not held in high esteem. The success of individual Jews is promise of what is attainable, but the failure of the many is evidence of what is really practicable.

The negro

After emancipation the negro had to shift for himself.[42] At first, when not engaged in religious exercises or politics, he idled away much of his time and moved about a good deal. He has indeed become an agricultural laborer or a tenant, and has had some measure of success. So far, the negro has suffered from the enervating effect of the climate, the degradation of his social ostracism, and the excesses of a newly won freedom. Everything conspires to keep him a laborer or a tenant. His own thriftlessness, his ignorance, and the cupid-

386

ity of his white neighbors, all tend in this direction. The negroes are most numerous in Mississippi, Georgia, and South Carolina. Their localization in certain counties, in these and other southern states, deprives them of the educational influence of more advanced white neighbors. When the negro moves north, he becomes a town laborer. In his cultivation in the south he takes to cotton and neglects animal husbandry. He has little system in his cropping, except the most elementary. The future will doubtless see him slowly emerge from peonage. Cropper tenancy will probably be supplanted by more cash tenancy. Ownership and good technique are a long way ahead.

Some of the groups already mentioned have been characterized by their low standard of living, such as the negroes, the Italians, the Finns, and, we may add, the Portuguese, Mexicans, and Japanese. When these peoples are hard working and intelligent, they compete with already established groups possessing higher standards. The struggle then becomes one of standards of consumption and living in general.[43] Those who are thrifty, willing to eat simple food and live in poor dwellings, and not opposed to woman and child labor in the fields, can outrun native Americans with higher standards. Such persons can take small bits of the large farms of old-stock Americans. It pays the owner of 160 acres to sell out to the newcomers, and it pays the newcomers to buy. Thus have the nationalities competed freely in America in a way that is denied them in international trade. But already laws are preventing the Japanese from owning land in California, and many European peoples from immigrating in such large numbers as in the past. As long as the national groups were about equal to the Anglo-Teutonic or so-called Nordic peoples in their plane of living, there was but little question of restricted immigration of peoples or of their habits of living; but when those of southern and eastern Europe began to come in with a threatening standard of living, agitation arose. It is a serious question, however, whether existing tendencies towards smaller holdings, more intensive agriculture, and less gain from unearned increment, will not go on unchecked. The added cultivators of the future, coming in to

Standards of living

About 1890 f.

supplant the old ones, may be the hardest pressed laborers and tradesmen from American towns and cities. If so, the battle of standards of living will continue in the country as at present.

Conclusions concerning national influences

It has been fortunate for America to be able to take advantage of the special aptitudes of diverse national groups. These have lent variety and provided models of excellence. The agricultural habits acquired in the old land, however, are not inherited instincts or tendencies. Environment produced these habits in the old world and is quickly making them over in the new, except in isolated communities. The danger lies solely in the apparent fact that some peoples, below the general American level, have nothing to add. Absorption in their case means not so much a levelling off as a levelling downward.

Propagandist societies

112. ORGANIZED ACTIVITIES AS FACTORS. Before the problem of diversity of national strain had become an issue, the influence of organization began to be exerted. American agricultural societies early sprang up to propagate the best

1 Mar., 1785

known doctrines of cultivation. The first of them (still in existence) was set up in Philadelphia, not by farmers but by public-spirited townsmen eager to promote agriculture. The

19 Dec., 1785

second was established in South Carolina and still operates under the original charter. Other states followed fast, New York (1791), Massachusetts (1792), and Connecticut[44] (1794). About one generation later, as we have seen, came the state horticultural societies.[45]

Agricultural literature

While Americans long continued partly dependent on foreign treatises, English, French, and German, they early developed a literature of their own.[46] Jared Eliot, we have already

1760

met with, and have noted that his essays had but little influence.[47] Barring a few unimportant writers,[48] Samuel Deane

1790

was next with his *New England Farmer*. John Taylor was

1813 f.

probably the most influential of them all, for his treatise went through several editions. But the complaint has long been that farmers as a class do not read books on agriculture,[49] and

1867

later it was lamented that few of them really know how plants grow, and that there are ten farmers who consider book farm-

388

ing nonsense to the one who reads either agricultural treatises or journals.[50]   But manuals helping the farmer, continued to be printed, advertised by journals, and peddled by agents. They doubtless had some influence though not much.   The farmer, not being a bookish man, has to get his lessons otherwise.   Agricultural journals doubtless have come as near to providing serious study as the farmer could stand.   Probably **1819–** the first of these journals was *The American Farmer* published **about** at Baltimore.   Among the most distinguished have been the **1862** *American Cultivator* (Boston, 1839–1915), the *Genesee Farmer* (Rochester, N. Y., 1840–1865), the *Prairie Farmer* (Chicago, 1841–present), and the *Country Gentleman* (Albany, 1853–1911; Philadelphia, 1911–present).   By 1853 there were said to be about 40 or 50 agricultural journals in America;[51] recently the number has been placed at 500, more **1912** or less.[52]

Formal instruction in agriculture developed very slowly dur- **Agricul-** ing the first century of effort (1751–1857).   Courses on sun- **tural** dry subjects were offered in various educational institutions.[53] **colleges** Some insignificant special schools, such as the Derby Agricultural School, Connecticut, were established to aid the farmer, **1826** but they were generally short lived and distinguished chiefly by their good intentions.   With the opening of the Michigan **1857** Agricultural College, however, a new era in agricultural education began; but even after several had been established, it **1876** was said, the farmer's lack of interest in them had kept them from success.[54]   After the Morrill Act giving the states fed- **1862** eral aid, there could, however, be no question that the agricultural college had come to stay.   At least one has been set up **1920** in every state (sixty-nine in all), and the curriculum has been extended and amplified till it includes many subjects of use to farmers and others.   One of the latest and most significant additions is agricultural economics which will probably do much to aid in the development of farming as a business. Still there is much criticism of these colleges.   Some think that in America they have neglected research in the demand for instruction; while in Canada the contrary complaint has been made.   It is said that the graduate in the United States is such an expert that he cannot afford to throw away his skill and knowledge on a small farm of 160 acres. He is equipped to manage a much larger estate, but one which is not forthcoming. In fact, he most commonly becomes a county agent advising farmers, a teacher of agriculture, or a government official.

Agricultural education in secondary and primary schools

1890's

1917

The schools of agriculture set up on a basis of about high school grade have been of more immediate service to the farmer. And the spread of agricultural education to rural primary and secondary schools [55] is very hopeful. So close has instruction come to the farmer, that only those in pocket farms can wholly escape it. A generation ago New York State carried on itinerant experiments as a means of teaching, issued expository bulletins, conducted itinerant school work, and gave instruction by correspondence and reading courses.[56] And recently the federal government has inaugurated a policy of making grants up to three millions of dollars a year to states for carrying on educational work in agriculture, trades, industries, and home economics. The effect of all this effort is at times hard to see, but the faith in it is probably not misplaced. There are few things so slow and undramatic in their effect on a nation as education, and few so far-reaching when absorbed and applied.

1875

1893

Experimental stations

Closely connected with the agricultural colleges in most states is the experimental station. The first was started in Connecticut, then in North Carolina, New York (Cornell), New Jersey, and so on till there came to be at least one station in each state, and fifty-six in all. Later the number was sixty-six. To the credit of these stations is to be put a great number of inventions and discoveries, to the Wisconsin station, for example, an apparatus for determining the fat content of milk, a new variety of barley, and information about the nutrition of dairy cows and the ripening of cheese.[57]

Associations

1785

While the public educational and experimental institutions were generally the work of urban as well as rural groups, the agricultural associations have much more commonly been purely rural in origin, objects, and psychology. As we have seen,[58] such societies have existed since the eighteenth century.

By the middle of the nineteenth century, it was said, there **1853** were about three hundred of them.[59] The number of such societies has gone on, until they are to be counted only in thousands. Their purpose has been widened. They have been formed to conduct fairs, to hold meetings, to publish bulletins, to assist in popular education, to further social life, to improve crops, to help animal husbandry,[60] to sell products, to test cows, to furnish telephones, to buy supplies, to provide credit, and to insure their members against fire, hail, sickness, and death. How a twentieth century American farmer can escape some kind of association is hard to discover.

The society which just now seems to promise most for the **Farm** future is the Farm Bureau Association. In the individual **Bureau** county there is a farm bureau or association or club, the first **association** of which was established in New York State. This bureau is **1911** made up of actual farmers who are anxious to make practical local improvements. Their most important work, perhaps, is to employ a county agent, whose business it is to demonstrate ways and means of improving agriculture, and to give advice on all kinds of farmers' problems, such as the purchase and sale of goods. Although the earliest county agents, employed **1906** in the south, actually antedate the farm bureaus, they have had their most distinctive development since the farm bureau came into existence. The county farm bureaus come together, like **1917** the local trade unions, to form state federations, and the state federations to form the American Farm Bureau Federation. **1919** Although the usual weakness, brewed by dissensions, has already appeared, there seem to be so many merits that success is deserved, if not assured. It is purely a farmer movement for self-help, rather than a grafted governmental device. It makes use, however, of governmental agencies established for agricultural experiment and instruction. It adopts a new plan of influencing the farmer, not by precept but by actual demonstration. Some farmers agree to try an experiment under the county agent's direction. The success of this is observed and the plan adopted by others. Thus the farmer's conservatism and his impatience with theory are largely overcome. The emphasis of the farm bureau is upon good agricultural technique and profitable marketing. Where possible, co-operative marketing is to be developed; where not, the cost of distribution is to be reduced. Attention is to be given to world conditions so as to prevent or lessen overproduction; and means are to be adopted to reduce sharp price fluctuations.[61] Such is the program of the business farmer, and whether it fails or wins in the hands of this particular association, it necessarily points the way to permanent changes of great moment. But the farmer must change his attitude to such associations. The cultivator has been willing to join; the business farmer will be willing to stick. The cultivator has been anxious for quick returns; the business farmer will patiently await his gains. The association of cultivators has been generally ephemeral; that of business farmers must be long-lived.

Government assistance

We have noted the influence of the government in giving assistance to agricultural education. Aid in irrigation has been very great and promises much for the future. Assistance in rural credit is now a very real part of governmental bureaucracy, but the story belongs elsewhere. The granting of land in large units on easy conditions, has had its effect on agriculture, as has already been observed. The official co-operation of the federal government for the improvement of agriculture has had a noteworthy historical development. At

1839

first an appropriation was made for a few agricultural purposes under the ægis of the Patent Office. Then there was

1862

established a bureau which finally grew into a full-fledged executive department which now receives a large appropriation

1889

of funds and employs an army of officials. This organization not only helps co-ordinate the work of states, but in many ways helps the farmer directly. A study of the department's complicated organization makes one wonder whether there is anything that can be left out. New varieties of seed have been brought from many lands (such as durum wheat from Russia), plant diseases have been studied and fought (notably the cotton weevil of the south), and the economic problems of farmers have been investigated in a very helpful fashion. State departments of agriculture, it should be noted, were established first in the south—in Georgia in 1874, Tennessee in 1875, North Carolina in 1877, Virginia and Alabama in 1888—later in the north, in New York not till 1893 and in Pennsylvania not till 1895.[62] All in all, we may say that, between private associations and government agencies, there is sufficient organization in America to make agriculture flourish, if organization can do it.

The government may assist the farmer directly by provid- **Tariff** ing seeds, fighting plant and animal diseases, and broadcasting information about weather, crop, and market conditions; it may conceivably assist him indirectly by protecting farm products from foreign competition. From the first national tariff **1789 f.** to the latest, such products as come from American farms have borne a customs duty when imported. When there has been a general change in tariff, the number of farm products has been increased or the rate has gone up (or down). Apart from wool growing, sugar planting, and perhaps dairying, the tariffs have had but little effect on agriculture. Canadian imports may have been somewhat affected, but no general change in the prices of agricultural products has been brought about. It is said that the purpose in raising the nominal protection has been to deceive the farmer, to throw dust into his eyes.[63] In other words the political parties, in order to win the rural vote, have given a sop to the farmer, while they handed out substantial viands to the manufacturer. Many, perhaps most, of the farmers were really deceived, but some at least accepted the protection of manufacture as of indirect benefit to themselves in so far as it seemed to make American manufactures prosperous and therefore maintained a brisk demand for farm products, such as wool, cotton, hides, wheat, barley, meat, and dairy products. Before the Civil War the south emphasised a low tariff, because it expected that manufactured wares, imported or domestic, would be cheaper. At various times this idea of aiding the farmer as a consumer has been strong, as in the election of 1912 and the tariff of the following year. It is doubtful whether the farmer has emphasised the policy of low import duties simply on the ground that foreign countries sending in their manufactured goods would be the better able to purchase American farm products.[64]   In the period since the Great War this possibility has certainly been discussed, but it must seem to farmers rather impracticable to try to deprive American manufacturers of their favored position.   The latter have behind them a host of voters, laboring men who believe that tariff protection tends to maintain the high level of wages in America.   It is not our task to pronounce judgment on a controversial issue, but it seems logical to conclude that the farmer can receive no benefit from a tariff on imported wheat,[65] cotton, corn, meat, or tobacco.   In the production of these commodities America is either pre-eminent or stands high. Few countries could afford to send such goods to America. It happens that for these wares there is a "world" market, that is, a brisk inter-metropolitan trade, and that accordingly there is an inter-metropolitan price.   The price is fixed according to the ratio of supply to demand in the most highly commercialized consuming and producing areas in the world. Thus the price of wheat in Chicago is the price in Liverpool, less the costs of transportation to Liverpool.   The amount of wheat available in Winnipeg affects the price in Liverpool and Chicago, but whether the Winnipeg wheat is sold in Liverpool or Chicago matters not, as far as the price in either Chicago or Liverpool is concerned.   And yet the American farmer, fearing the free importation of Canadian wheat, was alarmed when reciprocity with Canada became an issue some years ago.

1911

Direct subsidy

In recent years there has been a wide-spread recognition of the farmer's position.   It is perceived that, while the manufacturer has received the assistance of the tariff since the Civil War, the farmer has had no real help from that source, with a few exceptions.   Moreover, it is clear to many farmers and their leaders that nothing much can be expected from a tariff. Hope springs from another source.   The farmer must be put in the favorable position of the manufacturer by another device.   There must be established both a domestic and a foreign price for wheat.   According to a measure (the Haugan-McNary bill), recently before Congress, a price was to be fixed for agricultural products from month to month accord-

1924

394

ing to the rise or fall of prices of goods in general. The basis was to be the average of the period 1905–14. This price was to be paid by American consumers. All the agricultural products that could not be consumed in America at this price were to be exported and sold at world or inter-metropolitan levels.[66] Elaborate machinery was to be set up to bring about the desired result. A corporation with a capital of $200,000-000 was to purchase all commodities that it was ordered to purchase and at the fixed price. It was to sell within the country what was required and to export the balance. The farmer was to receive from this corporation a price which at the time would be much higher than the competitive one. American consumers were to pay this price for all the agricultural commodities they used, while the corporation, that is, the American government, was to stand any loss on exports. Two prices were, in short, to prevail. The domestic was a political price sufficient to hold the farmers loyal to the party enforcing the scheme. The foreign was an economic price, governed by the equilibrium of supply and demand.

Economic reasoning indicates that this measure is unsound. At any rate the proposal would set up for agriculture a consumption, instead of a production, standard; what the farmer needs for what he can actually get under a "free" competitive system. A similar policy *seems* to succeed in the case of organized labor. Those open-minded persons who are not held back by the teaching of experts may make the experiment and learn by experience what others think they know by logic. We would hardly be justified in dwelling so at length upon this scheme were it not for the fact that it very clearly calls attention to the new policy of demanding for agriculture similar treatment to that meted out to manufacture. Agricultural producers, being at last fairly well organized, are insisting upon equal favors. Now this might not have much chance of receiving serious attention in the country at large, were it not for the rather wide feeling that the balance between agriculture and manufacture should be maintained.[67] According to this view, agriculture is going behind relatively—certainly this is true of the *number* of farmers—and therefore the nation

A balanced state

395

is in danger of being weakened. The awful example of England, the industrialized state, is one that can be effectively held up. What a long way we have come, from an agricultural country alarmed, in the time of Hamilton, because it had few manufactures, to a great industrial state somewhat disturbed because it may lose its agriculture and its rural virtues! The mercantile-protectionist will welcome the new argument, because it points to more government aid and more control over production. The free trader will welcome it, because to him it seems to bring out clearly both the fallacy of granting public assistance to any group of producers and the need for returning to free trade. If the proposed policy were carried out to its logical conclusion, after assistance to the farmers would come aid for the transporters (railways and steamships), then perhaps for the public warehousemen, till finally everybody would be getting a subsidy from everybody else. At any rate, it is historically significant that the new mercantilists are farmers, whom List, Hamilton, and others of the old school never dreamed of helping by tariff protection. From protection for infant industries we have come to assistance for senescent agriculture. Whether all this is just an after-war ripple on the surface of things, or actually the beginning of the pressure of population on subsistence, is not yet clear. At a time of overproduction or great plenty, it would be hard to persuade a farmer that there is any shortage of raw materials on foodstuffs. But beneath the surfeiting plenty of America may be concealed a growing shortage, now a reality for Europe, ultimately for America also.

113. SUGGESTIONS FOR FURTHER STUDY

1. Read the statistical summary entitled Agricultural Progress in Fifty Years, *Twelfth Census of the United States,* vol. V, *Agriculture,* pt. I (1902), pp. XVI–XXXV.

2. From the United States census volumes on agriculture, study the changes in the average size of holding. Compare especially the changes in different parts of the country.

3. Make a chronological list of the most important happenings in the history of American agriculture, using the following broad periods: (a) 1607–1785, when settlement, and not technique,

counted, (b) 1785–1862, when the problem of improved cultivation arose, and (c) 1862–present, when the problem of cultivation passes westward and is joined by the problem of organized marketing.

4. Is it not true that the wide-spread ownership of land in America has prevented free economic competition for a time, by keeping the inefficient farmer unduly long on his estate? What compensation has there been for this situation?

5. Would the growth of subsidiary industrial occupations be favorable to American agriculture? Consider especially the districts in which the soil is barren, ownership widespread, and the population large. What has been the experience of the Jews in America in this respect?

6. Which impresses you the more, the desire of men to avoid the towns and metropolitan centers, or the tendency to leave the farms? Which farmers remain, which leave?

7. Enumerate the factors that determine the technique of agriculture in America to-day.

8. Which seems to be more periodic, the weather or business condition?

9. In what ways does the farm influence the metropolis, and in what ways the metropolis the farm?

10. In which metropolitan area are you located? Characterize its agricultural variations.

11. Has America ever gone very far in the use of commercial fertilizers? Are there available domestic supplies? Consider the Muscle Shoals project.

12. Comment: further irrigation projects would increase acreage but would not help the farmer.

13. Comment: the liberal extension of agricultural credit is better for farming than for farmers.

14. Comment: some European nationals make the farmstead flourish like the baytree; others reproduce the unkempt establishment that they left at home.

15. What is to be said for the view that the year 1862–63 was the greatest one in the history of American agriculture?

16. Study the important federal laws giving aid to agricultural education, such as the Morrill acts, the Hatch act (1887), the Smith-Lever act (1914), and the Smith-Hughes act (1917).

17. Study the work of the International Institute of Rome. Who was responsible for its establishment? What criticism is there of its labor?

18. Consider the contributions to American agriculture of the following: S. W. Johnson, Cyrus McCormick, James Wilson, Luther Burbank, H. C. Taylor, L. H. Bailey. For short biogra-

phies of other men who have made contributions to American
agriculture, see L. H. Bailey, *Cyclopedia of American Agriculture,* vol. IV (1909), pp. 547–628.

19. Comment: it has been maintained (by Professor J. M.
Gillette, 1912) that the need of the south for improved technique
is not so general as for a "new outlook on life, its meaning, its
possibilities of enjoyment," and for a class consciousness that
will rebel against politicians, trusts, railroads and middlemen.

20. Which seem to you the more potent general factors in the
farmer's existence, the economic machinery to which he must to
some extent conform, or the ideals of consumption and well-
being that he develops?

For further references, see the notes below.

114. NOTES TO CHAPTER XV

1. The average total acreage per farm in 1910 was 138, and in
1920, 148. The average improved acreage per farm in 1910 was
75, and in 1920, 78.

2. The average size of farms (in acres), as recorded by the
Census, is as follows:

1850	202.6	1890	136.5
1860	199.2	1900	146.6
1870	153.3	1910	138.1
1880	133.7	1920	148.2

3. Following are some examples of large farms in America:
George Washington's Mount Vernon estate in Virginia (3,260
acres); Colonel Lloyd's farm in Maryland, about 1852, with its
400 servants and 30,000–40,000 bushels of wheat (6,000 acres in
all); a Solano County farm in California, costing $10,000 in 1851,
with 1,700 acres broken, employing 20 people (40,000 acres);
Dalrymple farm in Minnesota, 1867 f. (2,000 acres, later holdings,
100,000 acres); Sullivant farm in Illinois, extensive agriculture
and low unit costs (30,000–40,000 acres); Grandin farm in North
Dakota, 1878 f., with 300 men, 300 horses, 100 plows, 50 seeders,
75 binders, 10 engines (38,000 acres); farm of Chas. W. Cass of
New York City, in Minnesota, about 1880 (6,355 acres); Smith-
sonia, farm in Georgia, beginning 1866, earnings over $100,000 a
year in 1905, great variety of crops (23,000 acres); Texas farm
of Green and Taft, a highly organized commercial undertaking,
8,000 acres of cotton, many hogs, cattle, sheep, industries connected (100,000 acres in 1913); White Face ranch in North
Dakota, sold in 1921 for $225,000, 1,000 acres farmed (total acre-
age 6,500). Near Lethbridge, Alberta, Canada, is a very large

grain farm, 18,287 acres in crops worth about $1,000,000 a year in 1920, 60 binders, 240 horses used in harvest (33,000 acres); Campbell farm in Montana, using only machinery (110,000 acres cultivated, over 40,000 in wheat 1919–23). See *The Cultivator and Country Gentleman*, vol. XXXVII (1872), p. 500; the Bonanza Farms of the West, *Atlantic Monthly*, vol. XLV (1880), pp. 33–44; H. Hodgson, A Great Farmer at Work, *World's Work*, vol. X (1905), pp. 5723–5733; T. H. Price, A 100,000 Acre Business, *World's Work*, vol. XXV (1913), pp. 271–275; S. Mackenzie, The Greatest Wheat Farm in the World, *The American* (Oct., 1923), pp. 37–39, 166, 168; J. U. Terrell, The World's Largest Wheat Farm, *The Field Illustrated*, vol. XXXIV (1924), no. 5, pp. 28–29.

4. *A Documentary History of American Industrial Society*, vol. II, *Plantation and Frontier* (ed. by U. B. Phillips, 1910), pp. 169–170.

5. See above, ch. VI, sect. 40, pp. 128 f.

6. Much of the rest of this section is based on N. S. B. Gras, *An Introduction to Economic History* (1922), ch. VI.

7. I am here drawing upon the doctoral dissertation of Professor C. B. Kuhlmann, *The Development of Flour-Milling in the United States with Special Emphasis on the Industry in the Twin Cities* (University of Minnesota, 1924).

8. J. Warren Smith, Speaking of the Weather, *United States Department of Agriculture Yearbook, 1920* (1921); pp. 198–199.

9. R. R. Spafford, The Effect of Climate and Soil upon Agriculture, *The University Studies of the University of Nebraska*, vol. XVI (1916), p. 95.

10. J. Warren Smith, Speaking of the Weather, *United States Department of Agriculture Yearbook, 1920* (1921), pp. 199–201.

11. See H. L. Moore, *Economic Cycles: Their Law and Cause* (1914), pp. 32, 34; A. E. Douglass, *Climatic Cycles and Tree-Growth: A Study of the Annual Rings of Trees in Relation to Climate and Solar Activity* (1919), pp. 84, 85, 113, 117.

12. H. L. Moore, Generating Cycles Reflected in a Century of Prices, *Quarterly Journal of Economics*, vol. XXXV (1921), p. 516. Sir William Beveridge suggests a cycle of 15.3 years. See the *Economic Journal*, vol. XXXI (1921), pp. 429–452; and *The Journal of the Royal Statistical Society*, vol. LXXXV (1922), pp. 412–478.

13. A. E. Douglass, *Climatic Cycles and Tree-Growth: A Study of the Annual Rings of Trees in Relation to Climatic and Solar Activity* (1919), p. 108.

14. *The Scientific Papers of Sir William Herschel*, vol. II

(1912), pp. 177–178; and W. S. Jevons, The Solar Period and the Price of Corn (1875), in *Investigations in Currency and Finance* (1909), p. 185. Cf. pp. 176 and 187.

15. H. L. Moore, The Origin of the Eight-Year Generating Cycle, *Quarterly Journal of Economics,* vol. XXXVI (1921), p. 29.

16. For example, by H. S. Jevons in 1909 and Ellesworth Huntington in 1923.

17. Ellesworth Huntington, *Earth and Sun: An Hypothesis of Weather and Sunspots* (1923), pp. 75, 101, 125, 261, 263, 287.

18. The outstanding crisis years in American history have been 1837, 1857, 1873, 1893, and 1920.

19. See A. H. Hansen, *Cycles of Prosperity and Depression in the United States, Great Britain and Germany: A Study of Monthly Data, 1902–1908* (University of Wisconsin Studies, 1921), pp. 81–89.

20. W. C. Mitchell, *Business Cycles* (Memoirs of the University of California, 1913), pp. 502–511, *et passim.*

21. 67 Cong., sess. II, ch. 205, sect. 10, *United States Statutes at Large,* vol. XLII, pt. I (1923), p. 620.

22. Livestock and farm implements and machinery were valued (in dollars) as follows:

1880	2,406,000,000 (livestock on or off farms)
1890	2,703,015,040
1900	4,056,249,248
1904	4,918,781,599
1912	7,606,613,533
1920	11,608,097,736

Taken from *Estimated Valuation of National Wealth, 1850–1912,* Bureau of the Census (1915), p. 15; and *Fourteenth Census of the United States, Agriculture* (1922), p. 6.

23. In 1905 James Wilson, Secretary of Agriculture (*The Making of America,* vol. V, table following p. 14), gave figures indicating that the aggregate agricultural capital of America was the greatest in the world, and that when reckoned per capita of population it stood fifth.

24. *Estimated Valuation of National Wealth, 1850–1912,* Bureau of the Census (1915), p. 15.

25. For pictures of agricultural machines in use by 1846 see *The Farmer's Dictionary* (ed. by D. P. Gardner, 1846), pp. 80, 120, *et passim;* for later machines, see the catalogues of the various companies, especially *The International Harvester Company.*

26. M. F. Miller, *The Evolution of Reaping Machines* (1902), p. 39.

27. Statistics of the sale of McCormick reapers (*Illustrated Annual Catalogue, McCormick Machines,* Chicago, 1885):

1841	2	1864	6,090
1844	50	1874	10,114
1854	1,558	1884	54,841

28. Statistics of the manufacture of agricultural implements and machines (*Ninth Census of the United States, 1870, The Statistics of Manufacture* (n. d.), pp. 399, 406; *Census of Manufactures, 1914,* vol. II (1919), p. 291; and *Fourteenth Census, Manufactures, Agricultural Implements* (1922), p. 4:

Census year	No. of Establishments	Laborers	Val. of Products (1000 dollars)	Capital (1000 dollars)
1850	1,333	7,220	6,843	3,564
1860	1,982	14,814	17,598	11,477
1870	2,076	25,249	52,067	34,835
1880	1,943	39,580	68,640	62,110
1890	910	38,827	81,272	145,314
1900	715	46,582	101,207	157,708
1905	648	47,394	112,007	196,741
1910	640	50,551	146,329	256,281
1915	601	48,495	164,087	338,532
1920	521	54,368	304,961	366,962

29. Exports of Mowers and Reapers (Commerce and Navigation Reports, for the years in question, U. S. Treasury Department and U. S. Department of Commerce):

Year	Value (1000 dollars)
1870	66
1874	1,797
1881	654
1885	1,348
1890	2,093
1895	3,660
1900	11,244
1906	12,150
1910	11,282
1916	6,247
1920	10,166

30. *M'Cormick Reaping and Mowing Machines* (pamphlet, Chicago, 1863).

31. *Twelfth United States Census,* vol. X, pt. IV, p. 352.

32. T. N. Carver, *Selected Readings in Rural Economics* (1916), p. 49.

33. The following may be consulted on the agricultural laborer: *Report of the Industrial Commission on Agriculture and*

Agricultural Labor, vol. X of the Committee's Report (1901), especially pp. XVIII–XXIII; D. D. Lescohier, *The Labor Market* (1919), pp. 276–306; C. H. Parker, *The Casual Laborer* (1920), ch. II; V. B. Turner, Industrial Relations and Labor Conditions, *Monthly Labor Review* (Bureau of Labor Statistics), vol. XV (1922), pp. 22–40; Condition of Harvest Labor in the Wheat Belt, 1920 and 1921, *ibid.,* vol. XVI (1923), pp. 44–50.

34. Farm Population in the United States, 1920:

Total number of farmers	6,448,343
Male laborers on home farm (sons, etc.) [1]	1,273,477
Hired male laborers [2]	[2,200,000]
Female workers on home farm (daughters, etc.) [1]	576,643
Female workers hired out [2]	[350,000]
Others (mothers, small children, etc.)	[20,765,806]
Total	31,614,269

(1. Unusually small because the census was taken in winter, Jan. 1st.

2. Estimates).

35. *Report of the Industrial Commission on Agriculture,* vol. XI (1891), p. 108.

36. Table showing number of croppers, 1920 (*Fourteenth Census of the United States, Agriculture Summary* (1922), p. 26:

State	Number
Georgia	97,497
Mississippi	86,859
Texas	68,381
Arkansas	47,665
South Carolina	43,789
North Carolina	39,939
Tennessee	38,078
Louisiana	31,309
Kentucky	29,450
Others	78,124
Total	561,091

37. *Recollections and Private Memoirs of Washington by his Adopted Son George Washington Parke Custis* (1860), pp. 65, 583 n.

38. See the book entitled *From the Letter-Files of S. W. Johnson* (1913), pp. 38, 49, 80, 81.

39. L. A. Chase, *Rural Michigan* (1922), pp. 156–157.

40. See A. E. Cance, Immigrant Rural Communities, *Annals of the American Academy of Political and Social Science,* vol. XL (1912), p. 76; *Agricultural Economics* (ed. by E. G. Nourse, 1916), pp. 228–232.

41. Cf. L. G. Robinson, *The Agricultural Activities of the Jews in America* (1912), pp. 62 f.

42. For important data and commentaries on the negro, see the following: Carl Kelsey, *The Negro Farmer* (1903); Economic Co-operation among Negro Americans, *Atlanta University Publications,* no. 12 (ed. by W. E. B. Du Bois, 1907) ; A. H. Stone, *Studies in the American Race Problem* (1908), chs. III, IV, V; The Negro's Progress in Fifty Years, *Annals of the American Academy of Political and Social Science,* vol. XLIX, no. 139 (1913).

43. T. N. Carver, Economic Significance of Changes in Country Population, *Annals of the American Academy of Political and Social Science,* vol. XL (1912), pp. 21–24.

44. A. C. True, Education and Research in Agriculture in The United States, *Yearbook of the United States Department of Agriculture, 1894* (1895), pp. 81–82.

45. See above, ch. XII, sect. 88, pp. 302–303.

46. See the list of books on agriculture published in the United States before 1815, in P. W. Bidwell, *Rural Economy in New England at the Beginning of the Nineteenth Century,* Transactions of the Connecticut Academy of Arts and Sciences, vol. XX (1916), pp. 392–393.

47. See above, ch. XII, sect. 87, p. 295.

48. Cf. J. B. Bordley, *A Summary View of the Courses of Crops in the Husbandry of England and Maryland* (1784). 22 pages.

49. *The Plough, the Loom and the Anvil,* vol. III (July, 1850), p. 59.

50. J. R. Commons, *Documentary History of American Industrial Society,* vol. X (1911), p. 71.

51. *The Genesee Farmer,* vol. XIV (1853). p 208.

52. J. C. Marquis, Social Significance of the Agricultural Press, *Annals of the American Academy of Political and Social Science,* vol. XL (1912), p. 160.

53. See Agricultural Education in *The New International Encyclopædia,* vol. I (2nd ed., 1914), pp. 245–246.

54. J. R. Commons, *Documentary History of American Industrial Society,* vol. X (1911), p. 121.

55. See C. H. Robinson, *Agricultural Instruction in the Public High Schools of the United States* (1911), p. 23.

56. A. C. True, Popular Education for the Farmer, *Yearbook of the United States Department of Agriculture, 1897* (1898), p. 283.

57. A. C. True, Agricultural Experiment Stations in the United States, *ibid., 1899* (1900), pp. 516–517, 542–543.

58. See above, ch. XV, sect. 112, p. 390.

59. *The Genesee Farmer*, vol. XIV (1853), p. 265.

60. In 1920, the number of livestock associations was as follows (*Yearbook of the United States Department of Agriculture, 1920* (1921), pp. 510–533):

National	133
Inter-state	56
State	551

Of the state associations, about two-fifths were in the south; Missouri ranked first, Minnesota second; Delaware and Wyoming came last with two each; Rhode Island was the only state with none.

61. See O. M. Kile, *The Farm Bureau Movement* (1921), pp. 73, 77, 81, 82, 97, 99, 112, 113, 121, 130.

62. E. Wiest, *Agricultural Organization in the United States* (1923), p. 296.

63. See F. W. Taussig, *The Tariff History of the United States* (1888, 6th ed., 1914), pp. 249, 274, 367, 443.

64. Cf. D. Strange, *The Farmers' Tariff Manual* (1892), pp. 356–357.

65. Except perhaps the higher grades of hard spring wheat grown in the northwest.

66. Both Senator S. W. Brookhart of Iowa (Governmental Aid for Co-operative Marketing. *Proceedings of the Academy of Political Science,* vol. X, 1924, p. 39), and Governor C. W. Bryan of Nebraska (acceptance speech of 18 August, 1924) object to the determination of the price of American farm products by "world," or general marketing, conditions.

67. A. Capper, *The Agricultural Bloc* (1922), pp. 11, 107–108.

CHAPTER XVI

RESULTS OF AGRICULTURAL DEVELOPMENT

115. AGRICULTURAL SECTIONALISM. In the preceding chapter causes of agricultural development were considered. Some of the causes there set forth were quite independent of American agriculture in their origin and influence. This is true of the weather but less true of European guidance and even less of business conditions. These shade off into market developments and organized activities which are not only causes of agricultural change but also results. In this present chapter nearly every result of agricultural development is in itself also a cause of further progress. It is obvious, therefore, that it is in large part emphasis of treatment rather than logical or sequential relationship that distinguishes this chapter from the preceding one. Causes and results in social history

America is so large and natural resources so various that we often raise the question whether it will one day split into its component parts like the empires of the past.[1] A study of American agriculture throws some light on this subject. For convenience and effectiveness of tabulation the Bureau of the Census at Washington has divided the whole country into large sections, before the Civil War five and now nine. These districts are about as homogeneous as such rough divisions could be. Three of them are along the Atlantic—New England, the Middle Atlantic States, and the South Atlantic. The Mississippi valley is cut up into four sections, two on each side of the Mississippi River. They may be called the Northeastern Central with Chicago as a central focus; the Northwestern Central, including the Twin Cities, Kansas City, and St. Louis; the Southeastern Central south of the Ohio River, and the Southwestern Central in which New Orleans, Dallas, and Galveston are the chief commercial centers. Then there Census divisions

is the dry part, called the Mountain section, extending from
Canada to Mexico. And finally there is the Pacific Coast area.

The Federal Farm Loan System creates twelve regions, no
one of which closely resembles any of the Census districts,
though in both cases whole states are taken and grouped together. Although there were many weighty considerations
taken into account in mapping out these regions, they were
largely administrative and fiscal. In some cases, states that
were unlike in agricultural development seem to have been pur-
posely lumped together so as to add variety and thereby give
the region such strength as may come from diversity of production.

Besides these divisions there are the Federal Reserve and
the metropolitan areas, ostensibly not agricultural in design.
Some areas are rather loosely marked off by national groups.
Around New Orleans there are the French, as also in the
northern part of New England. In the southwest there are
many people of Spanish speech and some Spanish blood. In
the northwest there is a solid Scandinavian group. And in
the south generally there are the negroes. Although each of
these national or racial groups may have certain agricultural
preferences and traditions, the influence of their present environment is probably in the long run a more determining
factor. Moreover the process of the dispersion of these groups
is constantly a factor in dissipating their influence. Education and the infiltration of other strains will in the long run
level off the national peculiarities.

While administrative devices and temporary national influences have little or no permanent agricultural significance,
it may be that local natural environment will develop and
perpetuate agricultural sectionalism. It has been the practice
to speak of the cotton belt, the corn belt,[2] the spring-wheat
belt, and the winter-wheat belt. Although there is much
overlapping, nevertheless, these areas are fairly well marked
off. The crops in one may fail, while those of the other
regions remain in normal condition. Accordingly, one area
may demand political relief, while another may not need any
assistance.

1916

Federal
Farm loan
divisions

National
areas

Crop areas

Different areas have different periods of ripening. Southern crops are ready much earlier than northern. Accordingly, some southern products receive higher prices in the northern market than the northern products maturing later. Further, some districts have elaborate irrigating systems, as we have seen. For them the chances of crop failure, through irregular moisture, are practically eliminated. They have a more or less certain supply of water, but with it goes the necessity of paying high charges. Since much of the irrigation is done by government plants, there is a close relationship between the government and the farmer, the relationship of creditor and debtor. The government is liable to be importuned for easy terms, in case of crop failures through pests, or in case of low prices. If the irrigated regions receive such special treatment, why not other areas? A farmer psychology is thus created by irrigation that many would consider dangerous. *Climatic divisions*

Considerable differences occur in the emphasis on plant and animal culture. New England, once raising its share of wheat, has for nearly a century been giving up cereal crops. It has in the present century devoted about one-half of all its improved farm acreage to hay and forage crops. The south, for nearly a century emphasising cotton to an increasing extent and neglecting wheat and cattle, has begun to make some progress toward greater variety, notably in the direction of animal husbandry. The increase in the amount of hay and forage raised during the present century indicates that clearly.[3] *Divisions according to emphasis on cereals and fodder*

Closely bound up with the specialization in crops is the question of self-sufficiency. At first the Pacific Coast was unable to grow enough cereals for its own support, but within a decade it had at least enough for its own use and has gradually developed a considerable surplus. The North and South Atlantic and the South Central states, throughout the period for which we have statistics, have had to depend upon the North Central states, especially for wheat. In recent years the dependence of the south has become somewhat less. Other crops might be considered also, but only the two tendencies would be shown, on the one hand a development towards specialization as in the fruit section of southern California and in *1850* *Areas of surplus and deficit 1850 f.*

New England, and on the other hand a development toward relative self-sufficiency as in the case of the south. In the future, it seems, the south will put its fertile soil to better uses. It will emphasise cotton less, and hogs and cattle more. It will raise much, if not all, of its staple foodstuffs. And then, when pests come, only a few crops will be hit, and at a time of low prices there will be plenty of cheap products for local use. It is more economical for a southern farmer to grow his own corn, raise his own hogs, and have a few cattle than to buy hogs and cattle in the north out of the money he receives for his cotton crop which has become more and more uncertain as the boll-weevil has ravaged his fields.

On the whole it seems that agricultural sectionalism has less of a foothold than it had one generation ago. The ranching district has dry-farming. The Pacific coast has not only fruit but wheat and cattle. The south is developing away from cotton, and all parts of the northwest are gradually balancing wheat with other crops. New England is an instance of specialization, but it is based on the fundamental fact that its soil is best used for animal husbandry. In all probability there will develop plenty of localism in America, but it will probably be metropolitan: rooted in considerations of marketing within a restricted area. Agricultural variations there will doubtless be within the metropolitan district, depending on soil and climate and distance from the central market. Out of a welter of conditions resulting from a maze of factors, of which marketing is becoming increasingly important, there seems to be developing, with some exceptions, a local balance in agriculture, a self-sufficiency in the chief essentials of life. Of course, this means much for both economic and political developments. It means that bulky foodstuffs will be hauled shorter distances and it means that each district will be on a more business-like and stable basis, less subject to violent fluctuations of weather or market.

Trend in localism

116. SLAVERY AND ITS AFTERMATH. Before the Civil War the outstanding instance of sectionalism in America was the south, with its predominence of agriculture, its free trade policy, and its substratum of slavery. It was the Black Belt

Rise and development of slavery, 1619–1793

of America. Servitude arose out of the production of staple crops for sale in the great consuming and manufacturing markets of the world. The first of these crops was tobacco **1612** which was grown in Virginia soon after the first settlement. It is significant that the first importation of slaves on record **1619** took place a few years later. Tobacco spread to Maryland, North Carolina, and elsewhere. With it went slavery. Tobacco requires a great deal of patient work in planting, tending, and preparing for market. Until recently tobacco culture has been little affected by machinery and even now only on certain soils and on large farms. After tobacco came rice, first in Carolina and then in adjoining states. This staple also re- **1694** quired much hard work, and, on irrigated rice plantations, work under the most trying conditions of humidity and malaria. Indigo followed rice, but it was an important crop for only a few years preceding the American Revolution.[4] Sea-island cotton was introduced into Georgia and South Carolina, and being of a long, fine, and strong fibre, it rapidly rose in favor **1780's** in both English and America markets. Cotton is another crop which requires a great deal of hand labor, especially in the picking. For this work there seems to be no possibility of inventing a machine to take the place of the human hand and eye.

In spite of the strong economic need for slaves, there arose a popular feeling that slavery should and would soon be abol- **Slavery** ished. The thought inevitably came before the public when **in the** freedom from England became an issue. To deny freedom **balance,** to the black man seemed to rob it of some of its beauty and **1776–93** holiness. But southern planters needed the slaves and northern slave dealers enjoyed the profits of importing black people. Declarations by individuals were made on behalf of abolishing negro slavery, both in the north and in the south. Virginia and North Carolina were ready to prohibit further importation of slaves. Behind this sentiment was a new situation: the production of the staple crops was no longer so profitable. The price of tobacco was low, indigo had lost the British subsidies, and rice had not developed into an irrigated crop, requiring the more exacting labor in mud and water.[5] The most important result of the new situation was the prohibition of the importation of slaves, made in the constitution of 1789 and effective in 1808. Henceforth slaves must be smuggled into the country or bred on the plantations. Both means were relied upon throughout the next period.

Revival of slavery, 1793–1861

The slump in the cultivation of tobacco, indigo, and rice threatened the existence of slavery. The development of sea-island cotton had not gone far enough to have much effect one way or another. But two other crops turned the tide of events toward slavery again. These were upland cotton and sugar cane. It is an oft-told story, but one that bears repetition, how the invention of a simple machine changed the face of the south, heightened slavery, and sent thousands scurrying off westward for new land. That machine is the cotton gin, simple in construction but effective in execution. Worked by manual labor, it separates the cotton seed from the cotton fibre. To do this by hand is a slow and extraordinarily tedious business. It had been easy to grow cotton, somewhat harder to pick it, but impracticable to gin it. A northerner, Eli Whitney, when on a visit to the south, was requested to use his ingenuity to invent a machine to do the required work.

1793

He soon produced the thing that planters so sorely needed, and the very next year adoption started on a large scale. In 1797, 275 bales of cotton were exported, but by 1800 the amount was nearly 36,000 bales. The gin could be used either for the sea-island or the upland cotton, that is, either for the long fibre or the short fibre. The production of the former, however, was confined to the islands and coasts, chiefly of South Carolina and Georgia. The short-staple cotton, on the other hand, could be grown on the uplands of these states, and inland as far as the imagination could reach. A new situation prevailed in the south. There was a new money crop which could be produced in the inland districts from the Piedmont to Texas, with black or white labor. Soon there was a movement westward. Soon there was new life in the plantation. Virgin lands and negro slaves were the prospective sources of great wealth. To some the movement meant an effective quest for newer and larger farms and plantations.

To others it involved just an imitative restlessness set off by the general movement westward.[6] Driving the same way as the invention of the cotton gin was the acquisition of Louisiana, with its sugar plantations and prospects of profits from the exploitation of negro labor. The harvesting of the sugar cane is heavy work; and labor in the sugar mills, located on the plantations, is required for a period both day and night. Accordingly the sugar plantations created a demand for ablebodied slaves, that was perhaps beyond all precedent. Labor on the delta and banks of the Mississippi involved harder treatment than the negro had known in the Atlantic coast states.

Slavery was at its height in America during the period 1793–1861. It also came at that time to be analysed as never before, in both its social and economic aspects. Contemporaries saw that it tied up enormous sums of capital which might have been used to drain swamps, purchase machinery, and improve roads as well as public buildings and private dwellings. Slavery put a stigma upon labor, as we have seen, and thereby tended to keep Europeans from emigrating to the south. In other words negro slavery kept population sparse. It compelled southerners to adopt and maintain a routine type of agriculture that allowed for neither experiments nor improvements. An effect not so often considered but one no less real and far-reaching is the fact that slavery, being an inefficient labor system, compelled the plantation owners and overseers to accept poor work. A northerner going south preferred to do the work himself and have it well done. This preference wore off, as the climate began to have its effect and as the scale of field operations enlarged to the point of employing gangs of laborers who by force of circumstances must be negroes. In short, the slaves helped pull down the masters. Slavery grew upon what it fed—free land. A time must have come, when the free lands, even the Indian lands of Oklahoma, were all settled, and when the institution of slavery would again be questioned by the slave owners, as had been the case during the American Revolution. When it was no longer possible, say after about 1890, to secure public

1803

Economic aspects of slavery

lands at low prices, the profit from slave labor would have declined. A movement to withdraw some of the capital invested in slaves would have set in, so that mechanical and other improvements might be instituted for the working of the plantations. It seems probable that something like a system of serfdom would have supplanted slavery. The plantation might have given way to the manor, in modern America as in medieval Europe and the ancient Mediterranean world. But the time for such a change was unfavorable in other respects. A storm was brewing in the north which gave the south no time to make its own adjustments. The southerner had been trying to educate the negro in habits of discipline and regular effort under the lash of the driver and with the sanction of law. He might have continued the process under serfdom—something like legalized peonage—with more chance of success. Indeed serfdom would have offered the opportunity of the self-interest of the black to develop under the guidance of a white master.

Negroes in turmoil, 1861 to 1880's The Civil War and following years [7] saw the negro turned from one situation to another. The intentions of the north were good, but the immediate and perhaps the ultimate effects of its action bad. One of the clearest ringing notes in economic history is that a period of great change is fraught with many evils and much suffering. The institution of slavery may have been unfortunate; its abolition was for a period disastrous. The north had sold slaves to the south, and collected freight, insurance, and cost on them. Then it took these slaves away without compensation. The north left the south with its problem of readjustment. The plantation owners in some cases kept the black men as free laborers; in other instances, the plantations were rented out to the negroes. Often the negroes moved from place to place to prove to themselves that they were really free. Generally there was idleness when compulsion had been withdrawn. The period was characterized by lack of law and settled custom, by lack of guidance and tradition. Regardless of the cost, the *big* thing had been overturned. The slave plantation was destroyed as later the range was overthrown and corporation curbed.

412

RESULTS OF AGRICULTURAL DEVELOPMENT

The negro population has experienced some of the changes that America generally has been undergoing. The blacks numbered 4,880,000 in 1870, 8,581,000 in 1880, and 10,463,000 in 1920. Negro schools are playing an important rôle; negro leaders have sprung up in place of the colored preachers of the preceding period. Negroes have come to own more and more land and even banks and insurance companies. Discontent with economic, political, and social conditions, a superlatively hopeful sign, has grown with the years. It has helped to induce many negroes to go north to labor in the cities. The friends of black folks say that this will force the southern whites to appreciate the economic value of the negroes and yield them better treatment. From submergence in a slave gang and immersion in a plantation system, many negroes have risen to be individuals, improvident and slothful, but still individuals. They have even made some progress in co-operation [8] to help themselves, a clear indication of a rising spirit of initiative and self-control. *(Development of the free negro, 1880's f.)*

117. INDIVIDUALISM AND CO-OPERATION. When some of the negroes had passed from subjection (slavery) to individualism and then to co-operation, they had, at least formally, completed a development that has taken Europeans hundreds of years to go through. Here, as so often in American history, we find the experience of Europe compressed into a short period, epitomized in remarkably small compass. The whites of America have had to go through only one of the developments, from unorganized individualism to co-operation. The pioneer was a rank individualist, often by choice, nearly always also by necessity. The cultivator was a transition type. He tried co-operation with a little success, but left the more enduring work to be done by the business farmer. The farmer is, in general, noted as an individualist. This is his reputation, and it is founded on current fact. Nevertheless, to go back into history, many centuries ago a kind of compulsory co-operation existed on the European manor, as it probably had in the earlier free village. Then came the period of individualism in the enclosure movements and in the agricultural revolutions. Here the farmer gained his individualism and his *(Individualism precedes co-operation)*

413

reputation for it. But first in Europe,[9] then in America, this has had to bow before co-operation. Individualism is for the strong or those favored by circumstances. The small must join one with another in order to survive. In America to-day it is a common thought that the small farmer must either co-operate or go under. Either a factory organization of agriculture (something like the bonanza farm), or small farms united in co-operative associations are held up as the alternatives.[10] The large factory-like farm would employ experts in cultivation, machine work, and marketing. They would have capital to buy and sell in the most favorable markets. The small farmer could obviously meet such competition only by co-operation.

Beginning of the agricultural co-operative movement 1869

Agricultural co-operation in America began as a movement [11] when the Patrons of Husbandry, otherwise known as the Grange, organized in 1867, began to make their influence felt. Apparently the first local co-operative activity of the Grange occurred in St. Paul (Minnesota), when an agent for the purchasing of supplies was appointed. Three years later co-operation rapidly became a part of the work of almost every Grange.[12] The earliest state co-operation, fostered by the

1872

Grange, took place in Iowa, and within the next two years spread to twenty-five other states.[13] The movement extended rapidly till there was co-operation north and south, east and west, from boundary to boundary. The intensity and the success of the efforts were various. An agent was appointed for the general purchase and sale of goods. His work was made possible by capital provided by the farmers either in the form of a subscription loan or shares of stocks. Such an agent might buy machinery or barbed wire; he might sell livestock, grain, provisions, or grass seed.[14] He either gave the farmer information as to sale or purchase or he handled the transactions himself. His success depended on his ability and honesty, which were in some cases conspicuous, but the combination was on the whole very rare. Farmer members of the Grange were commonly appointed, with too little reference, however, to their business capacity. Co-operative cheese factories were

established and with considerable success. In Ohio they were 1874 f.
the most prosperous co-operative associations.[15] Co-operative
creameries got a start, for example, in Springfield (Massa- 1884
chusetts) and attained considerable local importance,[16] though
their most distinguished service was to come later. Co-
operative fire-insurance companies—farmers' mutual associations—were set up in Iowa and elsewhere,[17] some of them 1874 f.
having a long and successful career.

Although the English co-operative movement was well known Origin and
to American leaders, it is questionable whether the farmers failure
themselves were influenced very much by it at first. In America co-operation arose out of the rural conditions of the times,
as had the German credit banks, already referred to. The
farmers faced a diminished income. The price of their products was falling, and they accused the middlemen of unfair
practices. They thought that they could obtain a greater income by banding together for sale and purchase, for credit
and goods. They had success in cheese factories, creameries,
and fire insurance. They experienced failures in life insurance, implement factories, and stores. In the last-named type
of activity some reform was attained through reorganization
on the Rochdale plan of northern England. The general
failure of co-operation under the suspices of the Grange was
due to lack of business farmers, the scarcity of capital among
rural producers, and the complexity of the metropolitan marketing system. The metropolitan organization could be mastered by the more capable specialized middlemen; it was beyond
most of the cultivators of the day. The series of efforts, however, gave the people an interest in the details of marketing,
which, when sufficiently developed, might lead to success.
The farmer must learn the intricacies of a central marketing
system—as the townsman had learned them—by experience.

How long the first period of Grange influence lasted is Periods
difficult to determine. Failures began to be conspicuous as in the
early as 1875, but the decline of early co-operative efforts history
may be spread over about a generation. Probably prolonged of co-
investigation would set the first period within the years 1869 operation
and 1902. The second period, one of revival, took about a 1902–12

1902

1919

decade to get a good start. In one year, the first state farmers' grain dealers association (in Illinois), the Farmers' Educational and Co-operative Union,[18] and the American Society of Equity, were established. Three years later the California Fruit Growers Exchange began its victorious career.[19] This association, which has stimulated endeavor in many parts of the country, now has 11,000 members, and handles 75% of the product which amounts to $54,628,000 a year. After the first decade of revival, co-operation developed with more rapid pace. The problems of co-operation have been carefully studied, books and especially articles and bulletins, appearing in great numbers. Financing[20] and accounting methods are now becoming standardized. Favorable laws are being passed. Experts, local and national, have come into existence. Principles of successful co-operation have been carefully drawn up and widely disseminated. According to one of these principles, organization must henceforth be on a commodity not a community basis. In California alone we have specialization in citrus fruits, raisins, peaches, prunes and apricots, walnuts, almonds, lima beans, apples, berries, poultry, and milk. Another principle is that no association should be started unless it controls a large part of the local supply of its commodity. Experts should be employed, men who study and follow the market. The competitive system of the central market is largely accepted. The effort is not so much to reform the existing situation as to take advantage of it.

Agricultural co-operation in 1919

A sign of the progress attained is the fact that the census of 1920 took cognizance of co-operation for the first time. Although its statistics are probably under rather than over the mark, we at last have an approximation to real knowledge of existing conditions. The chief co-operating states, in the order of declining importance, are California, Minnesota, Iowa, Illinois, New York, Nebraska, Kansas, South Dakota, Wisconsin, North Dakota, Michigan, Ohio, Washington, Missouri, Indiana, Virginia, Louisiana, Pennsylvania, Colorado, and Oklahoma. We observe that New England is not included, and that the south is represented by only four states, all low in the list. There were 511,383 farms reporting participation in co-operative selling, only 329,449 in co-operative buying. The average for the former was $1412, for the latter $257 per farm. Together the farms engaging in some kind of co-operative marketing made up nearly 10% of the total in the United States. Although the total amount of yearly sales and purchases is put down as $807,000,000 by the census[21] other estimates put it at $1,500,000,000.[22]

Agricultural co-operation educates the farmer in the business side of farming. That is probably its greatest single accomplishment up to date. The fact that nearly 10% of the farms are operated by persons co-operating with their fellows is significant. Possibly one-half are small business farmers, the rest cultivators who merely take advantage of, or are forced into, the co-operative associations. Even allowing for the existence of well-to-do business farmers outside the associations, we probably would not find that 10% of the total are business farmers. Perhaps we may continue this guessing by putting down the pioneers at 5% of the number of farmers, the rest being the cultivators. Co-operation has a long way yet to go, then, to bring in the possible 85% of cultivators. A second advantage is that co-operation gives the farmer a larger return from his products through orderly marketing. This result probably comes only after years of effort. A dozen or more years of experience do not seem to have been enough to make the gains exceed the losses in the co-operative marketing of potatoes in Minnesota.[23] A third result is the saving in purchases of supplies. Here again the gains of many years must be set against the losses of a few. But notice has been served on private dealers that if they go too far in their selfish enterprises, they may have to face competition with co-operative societies.

Advantages of co-operation

1911

Agricultural co-operation is not co-operative agriculture. Indeed it is not agriculture at all in the narrow sense, except for cow-testing associations, threshing associations, and the like. In America it has actually taken capital and enterprise from the cultivation of the fields. Some would put this down as a loss; and loss it is in technical matters, but it is probably

Disadvantages of co-operation

more than offset by the gains already indicated. Co-operation often helps the inefficient producer to continue, at least for a time, while private enterprise would help to get rid of him. Credit co-operative agencies probably are a case in point. Some creameries in the northwest are said to have held up such standards to the farmer as give him the greatest return for the poorest cream. Being owned by the farmer, the creamery has not forced him to bring in clean sweet cream. One creamery official said that it would not pay the farmer to be a little cleaner just to get a cent per pound more for his product. Some private creameries put a premium on good sweet cream and accordingly manufacture a higher grade of butter than their co-operative neighbors. In the effort made by some associations to market high-grade commodities, it is interesting to note, we find some waste of product. California citrus growers will not ship co-operatively an inferior orange or lemon. They must find a local market for subnormal but still good fruit, or let it perish. Also, local instances have occurred, of coercion of neighbors who have been forced either to join associations or to curb their crop so as to put into operation the policies of the associations. It is very difficult to balance the advantages and disadvantages. Popular judgment is in favor of co-operation. As we have seen, there is much to be said for it, but it is a serious question whether up to date, all instances being considered, co-operation has brought great economic gains to American farmers generally. It has increased self-respect and taught habits of business-like dealings. Perhaps we might discover, if we had all the facts, that while in the future direct economic gains would greatly exceed losses, in the past they have not done so. So far a system of education, agricultural co-operation promises to become an efficient agency in production.

Two periods in farmers' movements in America

118. FARMERS' MOVEMENTS. Earlier in this book[24] we have noted some of the outstanding peasant revolts in medieval and modern history. They were, of course, the farmers' movements of the time and place in which they occurred. We have just considered the growth of co-operation which is one of the chief memorials to farmers' movements in America.

RESULTS OF AGRICULTURAL DEVELOPMENT

These movements have not prevailed throughout American history. They began shortly after the Civil War, but have not been continuous in their operation. The first period in which farmers were active in organizing associations and parties is 1867–1896,[25] the second since 1915.

The first association of farmers that gained national position was the Patrons of Husbandry, otherwise called the Grange. The latter term means, of course, barn or granary and was applied more particularly to the local societies. This association, formed shortly after the Civil War, had great influence on farmers' action and provided a prototype for succeeding organizations. It was a secret order made up of both men and women, whether in the north or the south. Like many lodges, it put its members through various degrees, seven in all. To some democratic adherents, this seemed like the inequality which they had hoped to combat. Their program of reform, as expressed in a convention at St. Louis, indicated their ambitions. They sought to eliminate middlemen, reduce interest and profits, lower railroad rates, and further agricultural and industrial education. They declared their intention to remain a non-political association.[26] Although the Grange still exists with organizations in about thirty-three states, it early began to decline. Indeed it may be said to have reached its height one year after the St. Louis convention. The causes of its decline are rooted in the make-up of its members. Individualism, localism, particularism, and poor business judgment go a long way in explaining the decline. But in giving agricultural cooperation a start, as we have seen, the Grange had not lived in vain.

The second movement, unlike the first, was political. A Greenback Party was formed and for a while played a part in state and national politics. The party took its name from the currency, greenbacks, issued by the federal government during the Civil War. These greenbacks were treasury notes unsecured by specie. They depreciated from one dollar to 38.7 cents, rising to a point nearer par when the movement began. The party was made up of farmers, laborers, and debtors generally. The farmers owed for machinery and other

The Granger movement

1867

1874

The Greenback movement, 1876–84
1862

18 Nov., 1864

419

supplies. Many had not paid for the land they held. Accordingly they did not welcome the proposed abolition of greenbacks and the return to specie payment, which would mean that they would have to pay their debts in dollars worth 100 cents rather than 80 or 90 cents. Formed in 1876, the party was able two years later to poll a vote of over a million in the national congressional elections. Its strength, however, was

1884

soon spent, many of its members joining another movement recently set on foot.

The Alliance movement

None of the movements in America is so hard to characterize as the Farmers' Alliance. The reason lies in the heterogeneity of the groups that composed it. It arose in no one year and developed in no particular state. It was made up of two main associations, the one secret and southern (1889), the other open and northwestern (1880). The former was composed of elements that went back to 1873. The two associations never came together to form a strong national society.

1890

When the movement was at its height, it enjoyed a membership of some four million individuals. The outstanding characteristic was faith in legislation to remove the farmers' handicap. The old policy of the Greenback Party in favor of cheap, soft, or fiat money was one of the planks of the platform. In the north the railroads were to be curbed; in the south the position of the mortgagor was to be modified. In short, the members sought economic advantages for themselves. Some of their plans have been embodied in later reform, the federal regulation of railroads, the restriction of the liquor business, woman suffrage, and the eight-hour day. Resembling its predecessors, the movement, wave-like, gave way to a new party which embodied much of its policy.

The Populist movement, 1890–96

The Populist (or People's) Party was not an aggregation of local associations but a national party formed to fight political campaigns and put through laws favorable to its members. It was made up of the discontented elements of society, generally speaking of debtors, whether farmers or laborers. Its

1892

entry into politics gave victory to the Democrats who later took over so much of its platform that it ceased to have any influence and disappeared.

The farmer was suffering from hard times, and he struck out to save himself. He was the victim of at least three circumstances.[27] One was the failure of crops through unfavorable weather. The most noteworthy cases of this occurred in the western parts of the Dakotas, in Nebraska, and in Kansas, and indeed southward to Texas. The district in question was on the fringes of the dry section, where rainfall was just enough in the most favorable years. Bad crops led to suffering, enlistment in whatever political party promised relief, and even in abandonment of farms and migration elsewhere.

Crop failure as a cause of these movements

The second circumstance unfavorable to the farmer was his technique. It was natural husbandry, or some other extensive system that prevailed, with its tendency to soil exhaustion or impoverishment and crop failures. The technique prevailing in the period 1867–96 has now largely changed, though here and there are to be found whole sections still operating under an extensive system of agriculture.

Farming methods as a cause

Marketing conditions constitute the third cause to be considered. At the time in question the farmer was largely of the cultivator type. The business farmer was still very much in the future. Partly because of the lack of skill in buying and selling goods, securing loans, and obtaining other favorable conditions, and partly because the farmer was trying almost desperately to develop at a rapid pace, he was commonly a debtor. And like debtors generally, when a period of economic stress arrived, he was hard put to it to pay his obligations and retain his farm. Complaints were raised in plenty. Transportation charges were held to be excessive. Storage rates were too high. The profits of town middlemen were unreasonable. Money was scarce and rising in value, as the production of gold failed to keep pace with current needs. Two great crises almost finished many who had weathered the difficult preceding years. The farmer, like many a townsman, has not learned to reckon in terms of business cycles. When the price of his products is high and he is prospering, he buys machinery and other equipment, often on credit. Then comes the period of depression when he must pay for his purchases with goods sold at a reduced price. The story is the same when

Marketing as a cause

1883 f.

1873, 1893

he borrows money. He secures a loan when rates are high and has to repay it when prices are low. In a period of four or five years he found that a debt which would have originally been satisfied by the yield of a ten-acre field would be paid off only by the products of twenty acres.

Farmers' demands

Out of this general situation arose the parties and movements already enumerated, and concrete demands of reforms in great numbers. Townspeople were to be taxed more heavily. Railroads were to stop discriminating against the farmer. Cheap money, first irredeemable paper money (greenbacks) and then silver coins, were demanded. As these increased, prices would go up, and old debts could be paid off at the new price level. Some of the demands were partly met, but the monetary situation righted itself with the increase in the production of gold.

1895 f.

No movements, 1896–1915

After thirty years of organizing effort, the farmers remained for twenty years politically inactive, at least as far as separate parties were concerned. This was a period of rising prices. The old political parties enacted legislation to meet the farmers' demands, especially to check monopoly. A better technique of agriculture aided a great deal and co-operative societies were pointing the way to self-help as an alternative to government assistance.

Non-Partisan League

1915

1915–20

In spite of general prosperity and the continuation of price increases, the National Non-Partisan League came into existance as a farmers' party.[28] Rising in North Dakota, it spread over thirteen or fourteen states. In the state of its birth it actually captured the government and proceeded to put its program of reform into execution, but it fell foul of wartime patriotism that protested against its socialistic tinge, of capitalist objectors who refused loans for the new enterprises, of the panic of 1920, and of dissensions within its own ranks. Never before, however, had a farmers' party gone so far in politics. The plan was to capture one state after another, and then to hold the balance of power at Washington, or possibly actually to dominate the federal government. How far this party arose as a protest against the political machines that persisted in ignoring the farmers' demands, how far it was

422

based on real agricultural grievances, and how far it was owing to diminished rainfall in the drier parts, is hard to say.[29] Certainly when in power, the farmer government proceeded to enact a program of agricultural relief,[30] including a heavier tax burden for public utilities and for the well-to-do, state-owned elevators and packing plants, a state hail-insurance company, and a state bank. The way of farmers' parties is hard, and this one has proved no exception. The farmers' movement is not dead, but it goes on under different leaders and with different plans.

Following the crisis of 1920 came an almost national demand for aiding the farmer. The old story after 1873 and 1893 was repeated. The farmer was caught napping. He could not just write down his inventory and then pass on. His position was difficult and complicated. He could burn his corn for fuel and feed potatoes and wheat to his hogs; but doing those things would still not pay his debts. In some cases the trouble arose out of unwarranted expenditures, in others out of efforts to raise more wheat to help win the European war. For many tenant farmers and others, it was sheer misfortune, that they had started on their agricultural career when prices were rising. Land and equipment had been purchased at the peak of the market; they had to be paid for under the most unfavorable market conditions. Accordingly we have not only the fragments of the National Non-Partisan League Party but the agricultural bloc in Congress and the Farmer-Labor Party formed in Chicago.

The agricultural bloc is a congressional group, not a party. In fact, it is made up of both Republicans and Democrats, from both north and south, and members from both Senate and House of Representatives. It is a handful of men who must effect certain laws favorable to agriculture, if they are to remain in Congress. Laws have been sponsored or enacted providing the farmer with credit, assisting co-operation, improving highways, and aiding agriculture locally—whether in the boll-weevil district of the south, the drought area of the west and northwest, or the irrigated part of the far west where farmers have been unable to pay their water dues. In spite of

Marginal notes:
1916–20

Recent troubles, 1920 f.

1921 f.
1923 f.

The agricultural bloc, 1921 f.

all declarations to the contrary, this group is formed to secure class legislation after the fashion of the labor associations. So long as it continues to work with the Farm Bureau Federation, we may expect it to remain helpful to agriculture and fairly moderate in its demands. In seeking to maintain a balance between agriculture and manufacture, however, it, or a section of it, has championed a plan for a gigantic marketing mechanism, politically controlled, which is alarming to all lovers of the old order of doing business.[31]

Summary of attainment In a relatively few years American farmers have made many efforts, directly as farmers and indirectly as citizens, to improve their position. They have developed co-operation, formed political agencies (temporary but helpful), and developed leaders. Some of these leaders have shown power and skill, and their supporters are perhaps displaying somewhat more steadiness in maintaining them in their positions. Farmers have a mighty brotherhood, and power will doubtless be theirs, if they stand together and avoid extreme measures. Whether most good for agriculture would result from a nonpartisan congressional bloc, or the formation of an avowedly agricultural party, or the genuine participation in a farmer-labor party will provide the leaders with plenty of opportunity for exercising their imagination and displaying their skill.

Class reputations 119. CHARGES AGAINST THE FARMERS. Even in America scholars and some of the public are becoming accustomed to think in terms of social classes. A great struggle has prevailed in America to maintain the republic as a one big family of common men. This has never succeeded, least of all in our day. We must accept social classes as the expression largely of economic conditions. With each of these classes we associate certain traits. The landed aristocracy of the south, like that of Europe, was noted for its generosity and refinement as well as its extravagance and tendency to degenerate. The middle class of rich capitalists, successful professional men, and tradesmen generally has stood for thrift and careful management, leading to self-satisfaction and materialism. The laboring class has its cultural rough edges and destructive habits, but also a buoyancy and lightheartedness that are the despair and envy of all other classes. A little reflection has taught us all that there are many exceptions to such class characterizations. Many individuals stand above or below the class to which they belong. There are types within each class that make generalization difficult. Accordingly, in considering the farmers, we may well be on guard against accepting sweeping characterizations.

There is "no more grasping, selfish and dishonest mammal" than the farmer. His only political principle is "direct loot." The patron of mountebank politicians, he is the "prince of political nuisances." He uses his monopoly of food to blackmail consumers, and is himself the worst of the speculators whom he denounces. In championing prohibition he has committed an offence against the American commonwealth.[32] The clever author of this diatribe has spoken in hyperbole. There is something in all his statements, but not so much as he puts into them. The farmer has been selfish like other classes; when he has formed parties, they have stood for his interests. He has held up prices, when he could, and speculated to the extent of keeping his products for a more favorable market. He has always been a Puritan, whether in early Massachusetts or recent Kansas. He has been too hard a drinker of ardent spirits not to be keenly aware of the value of abstinence. For him there is no practical distinction between abstinence and prohibition. *Recent charges*

120. RURAL CULTURE. It would hardly be gainsaid that the test of agricultural production and rural life is the culture to which it has given rise.[33] Man does not live by bread alone, and living is broader than working. The traditional seat of the highest rural civilization in America is in the old south, among the planters of colonial and early national days. There it was that leisure for reflection and for entertainment were found. Young men went abroad, especially to England, for an education. In the spacious homes to which they returned, books were to be found and musical instruments. Guests from far and near arrived often and stayed long. Sports were the order of the day. All of these were the advantages of the rich plantation owners and their families, who scorned labor *Culture in the old south*

and those condemned to toil. If such a social condition had been put to the best uses, it might have found public justification, and, conceivably, might have persisted. But it led to no creative art or science. It gave rise to no useful idealism. It is true that it bred a type of political leader of poise and charm, but that is about all. Perhaps we may say that southern culture was at best a good imitation of English rural life, an exotic plant that struck no very deep root in America.

In New England It is specially difficult in the case of New England to separate rural from urban cultural influences and attainments. Certainly the country shares in the establishment and maintenance of popular education and government. The Puritan's ideal of strict accountability for one's conduct was deeply rooted and has spread, as New England's farmers have migrated westward. The practice of careful husbanding of this world's goods was a characteristic of the Yankee; and his propensity to drive a hard bargain has stuck with him to this day. The substantial residences, the ample orchards, and the well-stocked larders are the material evidence of the generally high plane of living enjoyed by the New England farmer. But standing high above all else, like a tower on a hill, was the intellectual life based on the reading of books, particularly the Bible. All standards, like altitudes, however, are relative, and so the rural Puritan's position would be regarded as low enough in comparison with the attainable to-day in natural and social sciences. His was a middle-class status and his ideas were bounded by his social limitations. Coupled with his narrow middle-class point of view has been his satisfaction with himself and his culture. To his thinking the rest of America has been a poor patch as compared with New England cloth.

Labor conditions Apart from the old south and New England one is inclined to say that the culture of rural districts has been of the fields rather than of the mind and body. It has been so much a life of hard work that the higher aspects have suffered. The family has had to join in the common tasks. Probably not **1921** over one farm in sixteen has a household servant, and not one in sixty has two. And in the North Central and Rocky Mountain states very few domestic servants of any kind, working

426

by day or by week, are employed. Most of them, indeed, are found in the south and east.[34] This lack of assistance in the home means that the mother is tired out at the end of the day and cannot effectively read or talk to friends or children. The farmer has seldom a laborer to assist him,[35] and, except in the winter, is daily wearied by his work, so that nothing more serious than a newspaper can be read. Such laborers as are employed are indifferently treated. It is true that they usually sit at the table with the family, and this gives them psychic satisfaction, but their wages are relatively low and the conditions of employment bad. The hours are necessarily long and the housing is frequently inadequate. Seldom is there a separate dwelling in which a laborer could rear a family.

In some parts of America, remarkable changes have taken place in the material comforts of the farmer's home. By means of the telephone the farmer, who lives near a town, informs a near-by grocery store of his wants which are promptly supplied by means of the grocer's light truck. In New England and elsewhere he requests the town implement dealer to send him needed parts of a mower or reaper by the next trolley car; or he arranges to have his order telegraphed to headquarters, if the parts are not at hand. In case of fire or sickness of man or beast, he summons speedy assistance.[36] The telephone and now the radio break the monotony of an isolated existence, especially in bad weather. Electric or acetylene gas light makes the home brighter and more cheerful. Bathrooms make healthful living easier. Washing-machines and running water lighten the drudgery of the kitchen. Pianos add to the social prestige of the owners. Nevertheless what is most appreciated is the motor car which takes the farmer off and away from this improved dwelling. It takes him to church, to picnics, to political meetings, and on the slightest provocation to the hardware or grocery store. In many outlying parts of America there is a dearth of physicians; in almost all parts a lack of medical specialists and trained nurses. The farmer does not enjoy the urban advantages of health inspection of his children or sanitary inspection of his meat and

Material comforts

milk.[37] For the pioneer these things had no existence; for the cultivator they have been remote luxuries; but for the business farmer they are beginning to develop into necessities.

Effect of restlessness

Throughout American history, the farmer has been regarded as restless, always moving. This is probably much less true to-day than formerly, and yet it prevails to such an extent that it somewhat colors rural life. Many will not make improvements because they are going west or north, or are soon going to retire to the near-by town. In any case they need every penny for the project at hand. It is the more unnecessary but still important things that suffer. The front yard will not be improved, flowers will not be set out, and unsightly or unsanitary buildings will not be removed.

Ugliness

Indeed one of the greatest of all faults of farm life is its ugliness. Hardly anything that the eye sees close up fails to repel. And worse than this is the blissful satisfaction with the unsightly. The nearest approach to beauty is in the lines of the pure-bred cows, but there seems no immediate danger that the appreciation of the beautiful will spread to the landscape or the personal costume of the farmer. This is America as a whole. It does not apply so much to New England or to the plantation homes of the south. A lover of the open life of the country may well dream of a day when farms will be the object of pilgrimage and study. Townsmen will talk of the beauties of the Valley Farm and the Arden Homestead. Here, they have seen a combination that has made them long to possess such a farm. There, artists have gone to paint a sloping hill, and old orchard in bloom, a rose garden, and the evening glow of a day that is spent. Of course no reasonable person could expect that a few generations of farmers could both clear the wilderness and beautify the landscape. The evidence, however, that something can be done without waiting for the mellowing effect of moss and ivy, is found in the attractive homesteads and granges that probably every state can here and there exhibit.

Farmer's food

The farmer's food is abundant and generally wholesome, though rarely tastily cooked. Quantity, not quality, is appreciated. Of course, this would be stoutly denied by many farmers, the same who tell you that a clay road is a good one. On the American farm it is literally true that hunger is the best cook. If the food is not much improved in the cooking, it is unquestionably in considerable variety and generally fresh, except in winter when the townsman is more favored. In recent years there is a pronounced tendency for the farmer to buy much at the town store—his bread, breakfast food, and dried fruits. Gardens are neglected by some; orchards, it would seem, by most general farmers. In parts of the northwest there are many farmers who do not supply themselves with eggs or meat. Milk, once so plentiful when there were but few cows, has now become scarce in some districts as the cows increase in number, every possible pint of it being sent to the creamery.

The farmer has demanded education, both technical and cultural, and he is getting it, though groaning under the cost. **Lack of a high indigenous culture** And many are the signs of the school's influence, as son or daughter comes home. But even yet the farmer has not developed a rural culture of which he is proud. He feels ill at ease in homes of townsmen and is conscious of his shortcomings. With one breath he laughs at the city fellows; with another he speaks with envy of their advantages and accomplishments. The farmer reads newspapers and journals, but very few books. He has not progressed so far. Of course, he has the chest of books that his ancestors brought from Norway or Germany, but these are in a tongue that he does not understand and of which he is significantly not proud. He reads the Bible but uncritically. There are a few school texts so torn that they could not be sold to the neighbors' children. Some volumes expressing religious prejudice are with the others. There is a medical or veterinary dictionary purchased from a travelling agent. The rest are pamphlets, patent-medicine almanacs, and catalogues of mail-order houses. The most serious cultural shortcoming of rural life in America is that it has developed no high ideals that are independent of the town, no culture to be set against that of the town, no attractiveness that will be clung to in youth and old age in preference to what the town has to offer. In material aspects, American agriculture has been a success, though not an unqualified success; in higher things, it has been a failure, and an almost unqualified failure. Its traditional showing is the little red schoolhouse, wretched in equipment and attainment; the old swimming hole, often as disgusting to taste as threatening to health; and the tear-raising thought of mother, worked out during life and honored only in death. The future clearly rests with the new business type of farmer who may emancipate the countryside from its parasitic dependence on the town and give it pride in its own inherent wealth and beauty. There is no thought that the new farmer is the architect of his own fortunes and as such the savior of rural culture. He is truly the child of the new circumstances which arise out of recent mechanical inventions and economic reorganization.

121. Suggestions for Further Study

1. Enumerate the instances of sectionalism in American history and those existing at the present time.

2. On the subject of slavery in America, see G. S. Callender, *Selections from the Economic History of the United States, 1765–1860* (1909), ch. XV; and U. B. Phillips, *American Negro Slavery* (1918), ch. XIX.

3. Comment: in village economy (free and manorial villages) we find *co-operative agriculture,* while in well developed metropolitan economy it is chiefly *agricultural co-operation.*

4. Illustrate from American agricultural history (a) agricultural co-operation, and (b) co-operative agriculture.

5. Which is the older in America, (a) co-operation among farmers or among town laborers, and (b) co-operation for purchase and sale or for obtaining credit?

6. Why was there little or no agricultural co-operation in America before the Civil War?

7. On early farmers' co-operation, see S. J. Buck, *The Granger Movement,* ch. VII, Business Co-operation (pp. 238–278).

8. Comment: the success of the farmer since the Civil War is due to private effort, co-operation, and legislation. Illustrate.

9. Study the co-operative features of the Federal Farm Loan System.

10. Compare for likeness and differences the peasant revolts

described in chapter V with the farmer movements in American history.

11. What economic reforms have resulted from farmers' movements?

12. Compare the proposed American plan of a single marketing mechanism for agricultural products with Brazil's coffee valorization.

13. The western farmer has been accused of socialistic tendencies. Is this just?

14. For a study of general cultural conditions on American farms, see the *Proceedings of the National Country Life Conference* (1919 f.).

15. Compare the rural culture of (a) southern California and eastern Kentucky, (b) Minnesota and Mississippi, and (c) Wisconsin and Montana. Whence come the differences?

16. Contrast the culture and general position of the farmers of the north with those of the south. Explain the differences.

17. How do you explain the existence of social cleavage among farmers, such as is lamented by rural sociologists? Consider color, nationality, and the position of tenant farmers.

18. Comment: the American farmer "is a shrewd observer, a ready innovator" (F. W. Taussig, 1915).

19. Enumerate the mechanical conveniences and instruments that are useful on the farm (a) that were invented by farmers, and (b) that were invented by townsmen.

20. Indicate the arguments in favor of the view that production determines the consumptive habits of farmers, and in favor of the complimentary position that consumption greatly influences production.

21. Comment: "The farm is pre-eminently, (1) the creator of material wealth, (2) the breeding-place of the race, (3) the source of virility, (4) the fountain of reserve force, (5) the school of morality and religion" (C. Ager, *The Farmer and the Interests: A Study in Parasitism*, 1916, p. 152).

For further references, see the notes below.

122. NOTES TO CHAPTER XVI

1. See on this subject F. J. Turner, Sections and Nation, *Yale Review*, vol. XII (1922), pp. 1–21. The author argues for American unity.

2. See *Statistical Atlas of the United States, Bureau of the Census* (1914), plates, 365, 366, 383.

3. Table showing percentage of improved land devoted to wheat and hay and forage.

	Wheat					Hay and Forage				
	1880	1890	1900	1910	1920	1880	1890	1900	1910	1920
U. S.	12.4	9.4	12.7	9.3	14.6	10.8	14.8	14.9	15.1	19.2
N. Eng.	0.6	0.1	0.1	0.1	0.5	32.4	38.9	49.8	52.3	58.4
Mid. Atl.	7.0	6.0	7.2	5.5	7.0	23.4	28.6	28.8	29.1	36.3
E. No. Cent.	16.1	11.8	12.0	7.9	13.0	11.5	16.6	15.6	16.6	23.1
W. No. Cent.	19.2	12.6	18.5	15.7	22.4	11.1	18.1	16.3	16.7	19.4
S. Atl.	9.0	6.4	7.3	4.6	6.0	3.1	3.6	4.7	5.9	13.5
E. So. Cent.	8.6	5.1	7.4	3.0	3.5	1.7	3.7	3.8	5.7	11.3
W. So. Cent.	3.1	1.6	7.4	2.7	11.5	0.6	1.9	6.0	5.6	8.8
Mountain	10.9	6.0	11.2	8.1	16.0	16.7	27.7	42.6	31.2	24.7
Pacific	17.7	21.5	24.8	15.2	19.5	7.3	12.4	18.5	19.1	18.8

4. U. B. Phillips, *American Negro Slavery* (1918), pp. 92–93.

5. Cf. *Ibid.*, p. 150.

6. Cf. *A Documentary History of American Industrial Society,* vol. II *Plantation and Frontier* (ed. by U. B. Phillips, 1910), pp. 185–196.

7. A great deal of illustrative material is to be found in Booker T. Washington, *The Story of the Negro,* vol. II (1909). See also R. P. Brooks, *The Agrarian Revolution in Georgia, 1865–1912,* Bulletin of the University of Wisconsin, History Series, vol. III (1914), pp. 393–524.

8. Economic Co-operation among Negro Americans, *Atlantic University Publications,* no. 12 (ed. by W. E. B. DuBois, 1907).

9. The Raiffeisen co-operative credit banks (1849 f.) had made local headway among cultivators in Germany before there was any movement in America. Rural co-operation in Britain, Denmark, Ireland, and France developed somewhat later than in America.

10. E. G. Nourse, Revolution in Farming, *Yale Review,* vol. VIII (1918), pp. 90–105.

11. Isolated cases of co-operation might be discovered at an earlier date, but their significance would be local and limited.

12. S. J. Buck, *The Granger Movement* (1913), pp. 46–53.

13. *Ibid.,* pp. 241, 243.

14. Cf. A. G. Warner, Three Phases of Co-operation in the West, *Johns Hopkins University Studies in Historical and Political Science* (ed. by H. B. Adams), vol. VI (1888), p. 371.

15. *Ibid.,* p. 381.

16. E. W. Bemis, Co-operation in New England, *ibid.,* p. 85.

17. Albert Shaw, Co-operation in the Northwest, *ibid.,* pp. 341–342.

18. The Farmers' Educational and Co-operative Union of America, started in Texas in 1902, has remained local. Its strength lay at first in the south, later in the west. It has remained a loose farmers' organization, the chief activities of which have

been to stimulate co-operative marketing. It arose out of the farmers' suffering at the hands of middlemen and money lenders. It has sought a minimum sale price for cotton and wheat. Although it has been regarded as the successor to the Farmers' Alliance because of its personnel and ritual, it has never been a political organization. See Commodore B. Fisher, *The Farmers' Union,* University of Kentucky Studies in Economics and Sociology (1920).

19. W. W. Cumberland, *Co-operative Marketing* (1917), p. 57.

20. See Ivan Wright, *Farm Mortgage Financing* (1923); J. B. Morman, *Farm Credits in the United States and Canada* (1924).

21. *Fourteenth Census of the United States, 1920,* vol. V, *Agriculture* (1922), p. 510.

22. O. B. Jesness, *The Co-operative Marketing of Farm Products* (1923), pp. 20–21.

23. J. D. Black and others, *Local Co-operative Potato Marketing in Minnesota,* Bulletin 195, University of Minnesota (1921), p. 73. It should be noted that the marketing of potatoes is a very difficult business.

24. See above, ch. V.

25. S. J. Buck, *The Granger Movement* (1913), and *The Agrarian Crusade* (1921). Bibliographies are to be found in both. *The Populist Movement in Georgia* (1922) by A. M. Arnett has appeared since their publication; also an article by H. C. Nixon, The Economic Basis of the Populist Movement in Iowa. *Iowa Journal of History and Politics,* vol. XXI (1923), pp. 373–396.

26. S. J. Buck, *The Granger Movement* (1913), p. 64.

27. These three factors, and possibly others, have never been fully or adequately worked out, though a mass of details is available in local sources.

28. I have used an honor bachelor's thesis written on the subject of the *National Non-Partisan League* at the University of Minnesota by M. L. Hartsough (83 pages, 1919).

29. Crop failures in western North Dakota and in Montana, partly due to climate and partly to faulty technique, greatly aided the movement.

30. See the pamphlet, *The New Day in North Dakota: Some of the Principle Laws enacted by the Sixteenth Legislative Assembly* (Bismarck, N. D., 1919).

31. See above, ch. XV, sect. 112, pp. 394–395.

32. H. L. M [encken], in an editorial, *The American Mercury,* vol. I (1924), pp. 292–296.

33. See treatises on rural sociology; also the *Report of the Country Life Commission,* 60th Congress, 2d session, Senate Document no. 705 (1909), pp. 41–65.

34. *Employment Hours and Earnings in Prosperity and Depression, United States, 1920–1922* (National Bureau of Economic Research, 1923), p. 39.

35. In the slack season (1 Jan., 1920), 1,843,307 male agricultural laborers were returned by the Census enumerators.

36. H. E. Van Norman, Rural Convenience, *Annals of the Academy of Political and Social Science,* vol. XL (1912), p. 162.

37. W. H. Swift, Social Life and Social Standards in Agricultural Communities, *Proceedings of the Academy of Political Science,* vol. X (1924), p. 30.

INDEX

Africa, North, 6, 7, 40, 60, 67.
Agrarian revolution, 162, 172, 177.
Agricultural and industrial state, 395-6, 424.
Agricultural aphorisms, 361-2.
Agricultural bloc, 251, 423-4.
Agricultural chemistry, 384-5.
Agricultural college, 299, 333, 357, 367, 389-90.
Agricultural economics, 354.
Agricultural factors, 365-404.
Agricultural journals, 227, 247, 308, 317, 319, 384, 389.
Agricultural policy, 153-4, 246. (See government influence.)
Agricultural revolution, 163, 172, 173, 177, 184, 201, 208-32, 233, 299, 413.
Agricultural societies, 227, 246, 293, 341, 388, 390-1. (See co-operation.)
Agricultural treatises, 32-35, 41, 46, 215, 289, 297, 309, 319, 388-9.
Agriculture, attitudes toward, 22-23, 227, 243, 247, 424-5, 431.
Agriculture, Board of, 170, 214, 216, 222.
Agriculture, commercial, 72, 147, 202-3.
Agriculture, Department of, 392.
Agriculture, Ministry of, 170.
Agriculture, stages of, 22-42, 181-203, 284-311.
Agriculture, types of, 146. (See technique.)
Agromania, 240.
Alfalfa, 37, 270, 309, 342.
Allod, 254-5, 263, 267.
Allodial tenure, 254-5, 260.
Alternate husbandry, 203.
America, 7, 20, 21, 23, 24, 47, 57, 124, 136, 138, 139, 142, 148, 152, 154, 167, 172, 175, 176, 183, 185, 193, 198, 200, 210, 211, 214, 224, 233, 242, 247, 255, 258, 259, 261, 266, 284f.
Amsterdam, 133, 369.
Animal breeding, 7, 15, 314-15.
Animal diseases, 322, 326, 332.

Animal feeding, nutrition, 319, 321, 330, 332, 337, 390.
Animal husbandry, 171, 188, 194, 200, 312-37, 387. (See livestock.)
Argentina, 139, 193, 327.
Australia, 7, 8, 139, 327.
Auto-truck, car, 330, 427.
Avolution, 209.
Ayrshire cattle, 317, 318.

Babcock test, 329, 336.
Babylon, Babylonia, 3, 9, 191.
Bailiff, 27, 33, 50, 56, 59, 62, 63, 83, 84, 86, 89, 349.
Bailiff farming, 69, 92, 94, 95, 96, 173, 235.
Bakewell, Robert, 214-15, 314-15.
Ball, John, 110, 114.
Baltimore, 303, 318, 370, 372, 378.
Banks, 141, 143-4, 304, 357, 358, 381, 406, 415, 432.
Barbed wire, 175.
Barley, 12, 25, 29, 31, 33, 37, 39, 88, 89, 90, 183, 186, 188, 193, 194, 195, 291, 294, 298, 379, 390, 393.
Beans, 12, 29, 31, 35, 37, 49, 88, 89, 188, 194, 289.
Beauty, rural, 428, 430.
Bedford, Duke of, 215.
Beef belt, 321.
Beer, 17, 84, 89, 90, 113.
Belgium, 147, 194, 246.
Berewick, 100.
Bertin, 236, 246.
Big business, 128, 131, 157.
Bill of exchange, 141, 142.
Birds, 5, 8, 23.
Black Death, 113, 126.
Blythe, 210.
Bonanza farm, farmer, 99, 359, 367, 414.
Boston, 20, 303, 318, 370.
Bounty, 220-1, 222, 229.
Bovate, 102.
Broker, 142.
Buckwheat, 290.
Buffaloes, 313.
Burghley, Lord, 149.

435

INDEX

436

INDEX

Crop areas, 406.
Crop cycles, 373-7.
Crop failures, 116, 162, 195-7, 421, 433.
Cropper, 383, 387, 402.
Cultivators, 52, 53, 55, 65, 66, 70, 72, 104, 148, 150, 151, 165, 183, 224, 233, 241, 242, 247, 284, 353-6, 392, 413, 417, 428.
Cultural nomadic economy, 5-9, 11, 40, 262.
Culture of the country, 22-23, 42-44, 267, 348-9, 424-30.
Culture of the town, 20. (See town economy and towns.)
Customary tenants, tenure, 224, 226, 228, 257, 261.
Czecho-Slovakia, 9, 80, 175, 272.

Dairy associations, 328-9.
Dairy belt, 330.
Dairy, dairying, 138, 188, 191, 193, 194, 299, 314, 319, 320-1, 327-31, 359, 362.
Danes, Denmark, 152, 188, 193, 385, 432.
Deane, Samuel, 295, 388.
Dearth, 234, 236, 239.
Demesne, 27, 79, 80, 85, 92, 113, 118, 121, 163, 165, 173, 174, .258, 263, 268.
Depopulation, 165, 170, 172.
Diminishing productivity, 292.
Diminishing returns, 192-3, 198, 201.
Distribution, sharing, 241, 246.
Diversified agriculture, 203, 366. (See scientific rotation.)
Domesticated animals, 5-8. (See cattle, chickens, cows, goats, horses, livestock, pigs, and poultry.)
Drage, 89.
Drainage, 41, 218, 244, 246, 378, 411.
Drill, 211, 212, 219.
Drought, 195-6. (See weather.)
Dry farm, 342-3, 371.
Duhamel du Monceau, 240, 245.
Du Pont de Nemours, 238-9.
Duroc-Jersey hogs, 318, 332.

Economic interest, 128.
Economists, commercial, 236.
Economists, financial, 236.
Economy, meaning of, 3-4.
Education, agricultural, 226, 390, 392, 417. (See agricultural college.)

Education, rural, 44, 432.
Efficiency, 30-31. (See management.)
Eggs, 88, 93, 138, 140, 193, 325, 429.
Egypt, 3, 10, 23, 40, 60, 70, 191, 192, 196, 203, 205, 257.
Elevators, grain, 134, 423. (Cf. storage.)
Eliot, Jared, 289, 295, 384, 388.
Enclosures, 38, 47, 95, 150, 157-80, 187, 212, 226, 228, 229, 235, 243, 244, 245, 261, 264, 413.
England, English, 14, 32, 38, 42, 45, 47, 50, 78, 93, 96, 105, 109, 119, 139, 150, 151, 152, 154, 157f., 171, 172, 177, 183, 184, 186, 193, 195, 198, 199, 200, 202, 208-28, 234, 238, 240, 241, 243, 246, 248, 255, 258, 259, 261, 280, 284, 297-8, 299, 300, 314-15, 317, 318, 332, 334, 354-5, 374, 379, 384, 388, 425, 432. (See London.)
Ensilage, 295. (See silo.)
Erie Canal, 300, 371.
Escheat, 255, 256, 257, 259, 281.
Estates, large, 242, 269. (See plantation, ranch, and range.)
Exchanges, 131.
Exodus, rural, 356, 365-6.
Experimental stations, 390.
Export of farm products, 332, 335, 336, 410.
Export of grain, 134-5, 150-3, 231, 234, 239, 241.
Express cos., 139.

Fairs, 91, 92, 142, 318.
Fallow, 23, 35, 45, 48, 50, 90, 95, 118, 188, 234, 235, 244, 245, 284, 301. (See naked-fallow system.)
Family, 53, 54, 253, 254, 255, 260, 264, 267, 268, 275, 330, 426.
Famine, 41, 187, 189, 195-7, 199, 206.
Farm accounts, 86, 357.
Farm Bureau Association, 391-2, 424.
Farmer, 21, 41, 42, 129, 139, 140, 142, 144, 174, 177, 223-5, 231, 235-6, 243, 245, 268, 328, 349f., 365, 419. (See cultivators, business farmer, metayer, and pioneer.)
Farmer, French, 16. (See metayer.)
Farmer-Labor Party, 423.
Farmer leaders, 424.
Farmers' Alliance, 420, 433.
Farmers' movements, 418-24.

INDEX

Farmers' policies, 277, 359.
Farmers, types of, 350-9, 381.
Farm population, 402, 411.
Farm, size of, 52, 58-59, 62, 74, 78, 154, 158, 165, 189, 194, 206, 223, 310, 366-7, 398.
Farm, types of, 338-44.
Federal Farm Loan System, 381, 406.
Federal Reserve System, 377, 381, 406.
Fence, 158, 175, 176, 218, 270, 339, 340, 378. (See hedge.)
Fermiers, 235. (See farmer.)
Fertilizer, 191, 192, 201, 205, 218, 292-3, 303, 323, 347, 359, 378, 397. (See manure.)
Feudalism, 92, 93, 95, 98, 103, 104, 112, 117, 148, 166.
Field-grass husbandry, 23, 36-42, 46, 162, 172, 187, 188, 208, 226, 244, 289-92, 295, 299, 301, 339, 340.
Fields, 28. (See two- and three-field systems.)
Fines for entry, 164, 168.
Finns, 386, 387.
Flail, 218, 219.
Flanders, Flemings, 35, 49, 104-5, 119, 183, 187, 202, 204, 209, 213.
Flax, 30, 35.
Fodder, 15, 34, 35, 88, 182, 191, 193, 291, 296, 297, 327, 329, 330. (See corn (Indian), hay, and turnips.)
Food, farmers', 428-9.
Food farms, 84.
Forest, 7, 160, 216, 272, 275, 323, 340, 371.
Four-field system, 32.
France, French, 12, 13, 23, 45, 50, 78, 94, 96, 105, 112, 116, 120, 121, 122, 142, 147, 150, 151, 153, 175, 177, 183, 184, 190, 200, 201, 202, 212, 213, 217, 226, 233f., 258, 260, 300, 309, 360, 361, 374, 385, 388, 432.
Franklin, Benjamin, 247.
Free alms, 256.
Freedmen, 11, 55.
Freeholder, 163, 165, 173, 174.
Free land, 276, 411-12.
Freemen, 11, 256, 261, 267.
Free ownership, 254, 259-67, 272, 278, 300, 387, 397.
Free trade, 141, 151-3, 245, 246.
Frisia, 81, 103-4, 260.
Frisian cattle, 313, 315. (See Holstein cattle.)

Frontier, 193, 313, 352, 360, 368.
Fruit, 3, 140, 147, 416, 418.

Gaismayr, Michael, 21.
Garden, 12, 27, 29, 52, 64, 118, 172, 349, 359, 384, 429.
Gardener, 5, 147, 148, 194.
Gaul, 12, 34. (See France.)
Gavelkind, 280.
Genesee Valley, 146, 269.
Gentleman farmer, 33, 43, 57, 224-5, 228.
George, Henry, 242.
Georgia, 286, 306, 344, 347, 351, 387, 392, 398, 409, 410.
German Revolt of, 1524-25, 115-20.
Germans, Germany, 4, 9, 13, 14, 21, 24, 26-27, 32, 38, 47, 78, 80, 81, 95, 97, 100, 119, 120, 122, 139, 153-4, 175, 183, 184, 193, 200, 202, 246, 247, 266, 285, 300, 309, 361, 370, 384, 385, 388, 415, 432.
Goats, 43, 56, 159, 322, 323, 343.
Gournay, 236, 248.
Government, influence, aid, 222, 226, 332, 382-8, 392-3, 406. (See agricultural policy, bounty, mercantilism, and national economy.)
Gracchus, Tiberius, 58.
Grain, 17, 231, 234. (See barley, buckwheat, millet, oats, rye, spelt, and wheat.)
Grain elevators, 304.
Grain policy, 149-54.
Grange, 27.
Grange, National, 298, 313, 419.
Grass, artificial, 37, 209, 323, 340.
Grass, true, 37.
Grazing, 270, 295. (See pasture, ranch, range, and stubble.)
Greece, Greeks, 26, 32, 129, 205.
Greenback Party, 419-20.
Guano, 218, 293, 309, 347. (See fertilizer.)

Hacienda, 272. (See manor.)
Hamilton, Alexander, 216, 396.
Harrow, 34, 42.
Haugan-McNary bill, 394.
Hay, 40, 90, 235, 270, 289, 290, 291, 294, 295, 298, 310, 328, 348, 407. (See fodder.)
Hedge, 158, 162, 174. (See fence.)
Hemp, 30.
Herdbook, 317, 318, 319, 332.
Hereford cattle, 314, 318, 319, 321.
Heriot, 118, 257, 281.

438

INDEX

439

INDEX

440

INDEX

441

INDEX

INDEX

443

INDEX

Village economy, settled, 9-16, 26, 32, 38, 41, 129, 130, 145, 252-3, 430.
Villeins, 86-87, 113, 158, 173, 224, 256, 349.
Villein tenure, 257.
Virgate, 90, 102.
Virgil, 34-35, 45.
Virginia, 132, 202, 262, 285, 286, 290, 292, 293, 297, 302, 312, 318, 344, 346, 351, 378, 393, 398, 409, 416.

Wages, 113, 119, 174, 200-1.
Wales, 9, 12.
Walter of Henley, 48.
Wandering (human), 5-9, 193. (See migration.)
War, 13-14, 57, 63, 70-71, 82, 94, 148, 193, 199, 234, 376.
Washington, George, 213, 217, 268, 290, 291, 296-7, 313, 340, 398.
Waste land, 158, 159, 160, 163, 165, 171, 172, 173, 226, 244, 254, 262, 313.
Weather, 373-6, 377.
Weeds, 5, 8, 12, 25, 47, 90, 182, 186, 194, 212, 286, 288, 289, 295, 299.
Well-being, 148, 150, 228.
Weston, 210.

Wheat, 12, 27, 29, 31, 33, 35, 37, 39, 49, 56, 61, 88, 89, 90, 181, 182, 183, 185, 194, 198, 200, 210, 235, 245, 270, 288, 289, 290, 291, 293, 294, 295, 298, 299, 300-1, 311, 320, 342, 346, 347, 359, 379, 392, 393, 398, 404, 406, 407, 432, 433.
Wholesalers, 130-1, 133.
Wine, 33, 51, 70, 84, 234.
Winnipeg, 368, 394.
Wisconsin, 328, 329, 330, 334, 360, 385, 386, 390.
Women, 8, 9, 12, 15, 23, 94, 194, 200, 244, 253, 323, 357, 382, 385, 387, 420.
Wood, 27, 51, 118, 172, 339, 346.
Woodland farm, 338-9.
Wool, 166, 172, 201, 221, 314, 322, 352, 393.
Wraw, John, 110-11.

Yardland, 90. (See virgate.)
Yield, 31, 90, 173, 192, 211, 292-4, 299, 303, 307.
Yeomanry, 172, 224, 226, 228.
Young, Arthur, 185, 187, 213-14, 244-5, 295, 296.

Zannekin, Clais, 104.

444